STUDIA FENNICA
LINGUISTICA 6

Anu Klippi

CONVERSATION
AS AN
ACHIEVEMENT
IN APHASICS

SUOMALAISEN KIRJALLISUUDEN SEURA • HELSINKI

ISBN 951-717-915-4
ISSN 1235-1938
UDK 800.316
      801.4
Ykkös-Offset Oy, Vaasa 1996

Table of contents

Acknowledgements

This study was carried out as part of a project called *Communication and Speech Processing in Aphasia*, which was funded by the Academy of Finland. Above all, I owe my thanks to the other members of the project for their scientific co-operation, inspiring discussions and friendship over the years of this project: Professor Matti Leiwo, the director of the project, Minna Laakso, Phil.Lic., and Inga-Britt Persson Ph.D. I am also indebted to the members of the project, especially Professor Matti Leiwo, for their constructive criticism and numerous comments during the different stages of the manuscript. The financial support of the Academy of Finland is gratefully acknowledged.

I wish to express my gratitude to Professor Antti Iivonen for his support and his collaboration and for providing the facilities at the Department of Phonetics of the University of Helsinki. During the project I had the opportunity to work for a short period at the University of Arizona with Professor Audrey Holland whose ideas and approach to the study of aphasics have had a major influence on my work. My sincere thanks go to her.

My dear colleagues and friends have encouraged me throughout the study. The numerous discussions from the very beginning of the study with Professor Matti Lehtihalmes and Reijo Aulanko, Phil.Lic., were invaluable. They both also provided constant advice and patient support with the computer facilities. The close and inspiring collaboration of Anna-Maija Korpijaakko-Huuhka, Phil.Lic. and Eila Lonka, Phil.Lic. was very important for me. The ever-stimulating thoughts of Leena Salonen, M.A., have been a great contribution to the research of logopedics, from which the present study also benefited. All these colleagues provided stimulating companionship at all times. For this and for their warm friendship I wish to express my sincere thanks.

Professor Auli Hakulinen and Professor Charles Goodwin inevitably spent a lot of time in the process of pre-examination of the dissertation and both offered many valuable comments. These comments were extremely beneficial for the study. I am greatly indebted to them. Moreover, I owe my thanks to the researchers of conversation at the Department of Finnish, amongst others to Marja-Leena Sorjonen, M. A., Liisa Raevaara, Phil.Lic., Liisa Tainio, Phil. Lic., Eeva-Leena Seppänen, Phil.Lic., Sara Routarinne, M.A., who were always helpful during the course of the study.

The process of writing the thesis in English was not easy. Several people assisted me in the process of writing: Kate Moore, M.A. and Anthony Shaw, B.Sc. corrected and edited the text with patience. Andrew Chesterman, Ph.D. provided consultative help with the translation of the examples and Terry Schulz, B.A. provided the finishing touches of the final text. Samuli Jokipaltio made the lay-out. I want to express my gratitude to all of them. I am also grateful to the publisher, Suomalaisen Kirjallisuuden Seura, for publishing this thesis in the Studia Fennica series.

My husband, Yrjö Klippi, has been great support during these busy years. Without him my scientific work would never have succeeded. My warmest thanks go to him for his understanding and encouraging attitude to my work and for his good sense of humour, which were often indispensable. My warmest thanks also go to our children, Pyry and Suvi, for their love. I also wish to thank my dear mother, Lempi Walta, my sisters and my brother, and my friends for their understanding support during these years.

Finally, my deep thanks are due to the aphasics whose permission to videotape the group sessions and to use the material made this study possible.

Suomenlinna, 20 March 1996

Anu Klippi

Abstract

Conversation as an Achievement in Aphasics
Anu Klippi
University of Helsinki, 1996, 214 p.
(Studia Fennica,
ISSN 1235-1938)
ISBN 951-717-915-4
UDK 800:316
     801.4
Diss.

The purpose of this study was to investigate aphasic conversation, and the means of interaction within a group of aphasics. The main database consists of four group conversations between five aphasics and a speech therapist. The conversational sequences in them were investigated applying an analysis based on methodology of conversation analysis. The recurrent characteristics studied were nonverbal behaviour, writing and drawing, the use of humour, the use of aphasic speakers' initiated repair and the use of single words in conversation. Furthermore, the consequences of the use of these means in interaction were studied.

The results show some conversational resources and means which are initiated by aphasics when recurrent troubles arise. Aphasic speakers are able to deal with many types of troubles. With expressive problems, when unable to access her/his verbal resources, an aphasic speaker may utilize contextual resources in communication, for instance by using writing or drawing, or by using gestures referring to the physical context so as to provide additive information. At times, an aphasic may only contribute to the conversation with a very minimal verbal resource, such as an uninflected single word. In receptive problems, when an aphasic is unable to understand the previous turn, or when the earlier conversation is unclear, s/he may use various verbal other-repair initiations. However, the examples in this material revealed that many occurrences utilizing these resources offered only an initiation for a longer collaborative repair sequence in which all interlocutors participated. The function of conversation is not only information transmission, but it is a complex, shared activity with several social and emotional functions. Laughter and humour in conversation served as social resources used to strengthen the group's intersubjectivity.

The methodological approach of this study turned out to be extremely relevant in investigating aphasia and its consequences for conversation. It is evident that this approach can be applied to the study of other speech- and communication-disordered groups, too, when the aim is to get more knowledge of deviant conversation and interaction and to develop new therapy methods.

Key words: aphasia, aphasia group, conversation analysis, nonverbal behaviour, writing, drawing, laughter, repair, uninflected single-words

Transcript notation

The transcription symbols used are principally the same as in conversation analytic transcriptions (e.g. Levinson 1983, Atkinson & Heritage 1984, Button & Lee 1987, also the Finnish versions Hakulinen 1989, Tainio et al. 1991).

1. OVERLAP AND PAUSES

[ ]	beginning and end of overlap
(.)	micropause (less than 0.2 seconds)
(1.2)	measured pause (1.2 seconds)
=	two turns connected to each other without any pause

2. INTONATION CONTOUR

.	falling
,	slightly falling
,.	steady
?	rising
↓	falling shift in intonation
↑	rising shift in intonation

3. LAUGHTER

he he	transcribed from particle to particle if possible
$ $	laughing voice

4. BREATHING

.hhh	discernible inhalation
hhh.	discernible exhalation
.yes	inspiratory articulation

5. SPEECH RATE AND EMPHASIS

we::l	prolongation of part of a word
JUST	emphasized word or emphasized part of one
° °	silent voice

6. OTHERS

+	legato articulation (siel+on)
(--)	inaudible word
(---)	inaudible longer segment
# #	creaky voice
ʔ	glottal stop
puo-	incomplete word
sirontaa	inaccurately articulated word or unrecognized word
{*follow up*}	hypothesized target of the word in English translation
{?}	unrecognized word

7. GESTURES

* *	beginning and end of gestures in conversational turns
O	refers to the movement of head, e.g.shake/nod
H	refers to the movement of hand
RH	refers to the movement of right hand
LH	refers to the movement of left hand
B	refers to the movement of body
E	ear
¤	mouth (facial area)
EYB	eyebrows
↓	gesture downward
↑	gesture upward
->	forward
<-	backward
D	point to
DR	point to the right
DL	point to the left
T	turn to

8. GAZE

GJ	gaze towards J
GJ...	gaze towards J
G,,,J	speaker turns her/his gaze to J
GxxJ	mutual gaze between speaker and J

Additional:

A	all speakers (e.g. laugh)
Y	unrecognized speaker
X	speaker throws a pencil on the table.

Glossing symbols

(Modified from M.-L.Sorjonen, forthcoming)

The morphemes have been separated from each other with a vertical line. The following forms have been treated as unmarked forms, not indicated in the glossing:
- nominative case
- singular
- 3rd person singular (except when there are special reasons for indicating it)
- active voice
- present tense
- 2nd person singular imperative

Different infinitives and participal forms have not been specified.

Abbreviations being used in glossing are:
1   1st person ending
2   2nd person ending
3   3rd person ending
4   passive person ending

Case endings:

Case	Abbreviation	Approximate meaning
nominative	NOM	subject
accusative	ACC	object
genitive	GEN	possession
partitive	PAR	partitiveness
inessive	INE	"in"
elative	ELA	"out of"
illative	ILL	"into"
adessive	ADE	"at, on"
ablative	ABL	"from"
allative	ALL	"to"
essive	ESS	"as"
translative	TRA	"to","becoming"
abessive	ABE	"without"
instructive	INS	(various)
comitative	COM	"with"

Other Abbreviations:

CLI	clitic	PPPC	passive past participle
COM	comparative	PRT	particle
CON	conditional	PST	past tense
CNJ	conjunction	Q	interrogative
FRE	frequentative	REF	reflexive
IMP	imperative	SG	singular
INF	infinitive	SUP	superlative
NEG	negation	1nameF	1st name, female
ORD	ordinal number morpheme	1nameM	1st name, male
PASS	passive		
PC	participle		
PL	plural		
POS	possessive suffix		
PPC	past participle		

1. Introduction

1.1 Background of the study

The basis for the present study emerged from my empirical observation of aphasics' communication and interaction while working as a speech-language therapist. There are different grades of aphasia, from total speechlessness to only mild verbal disorders and the persistency of aphasic symptoms vary; some speakers remain globally aphasic whereas others recover totally. From the point of view of communication, an amazing discovery for me as a therapist was that while communication with a severely aphasic speaker could succeed moderately, sometimes a rather mild aphasic speaker could become frustrated with her/his aphasia so that s/he withdrew from communication. These observations led to a difficult problem: which features are crucial from the communicative point of view when conversing with an aphasic speaker, and which features – or the lack of them – cause trouble in aphasic conversation? This led to other questions: what is important in aphasia therapy, and what should be rehabilitated and in what ways?

In clinical work, traditional aphasia tests used to analyse the aphasic syndrome aim mainly to assess the loss of linguistic skills: speech comprehension and expression, repetition and naming skills. These tests have frustrated many clinicians who work with aphasia rehabilitation, mainly because these tests do not provide information concerning aphasic interaction or communication, nor do they recognize the basis for communicatively-oriented rehabilitation. In fact, this lack of information has led Claire Penn (1993:25) to state that many aphasia assessment procedures prove to be an end-point rather than a beginning for aphasia therapy.

Although the Functional Communication Profile was developed in 1969 by Martha Taylor Sarno for analysing some of the everyday language abilities of aphasic speakers, it was only during the 1980's that aphasiologists became more widely aware of the pragmatic and functional perspective in assessing aphasic speakers. These approaches pointed out the contextual, as well as nonverbal and prosodic factors in conversation. Although these perspectives incorporated the role of context in communication, they did not take into account the interactional characteristics of communication, and their methods were not sufficient for analysing the interaction between the interlocutors.

During my research I became acquainted with the approach and methodology of conversation analysis, which focuses on interaction and the coordination of interactants in the activity of conversation. I decided to work

Conversation as an
achievement in aphasics
Studia Fennica
Linguistica 6
1996.

in this framework, and to get acquainted with it. The purpose of this study, therefore, has been to examine aphasic conversation and interaction and the means of interaction within an aphasia group by applying the methodology of conversation analysis.

To my knowledge, there has been no previous research concerning conversation and interaction in an aphasia group. My interest in studying aphasia group interaction was based on my clinical observations that group conversation among aphasic speakers may reveal devices which are rarely found in aphasic-therapist dyads. I found support for this assumption from the results of studies concerning aphasic-therapist dyads which indicated asymmetry and limited variation of speech functions in these conversations (e.g. Gurland et al. 1982, Armstrong 1989, Laakso 1992). On the other hand, there are empirical observations, for instance of children with specific language impairment, that they show better symmetry in interaction in peer dyads than in child-adult (parent or professional) dyads (Nettelbladt & Hanson 1993).

The study of aphasic group interaction presupposed a different method from the traditional ones used in aphasia research. There were several reasons to apply the approach of conversation analysis for this study. According to Goodwin & Heritage (1990:286), conversation analysis seeks to provide a theoretical and empirical analysis of how human interaction is produced and organized. It seeks to characterize the underlying social organization and analyses the rules, procedures and conventions through which orderly and intelligible social interaction is made possible. The basic assumption in conversation analysis is that using language in conversation is a reciprocal social activity which is organized according to social conventions, and it is best studied using data drawn from real life situations.

Conversation analysis differs clearly from the traditional methods of investigating language and its use. In contrast to methods that analyse isolated words or sentences, conversation analysis studies language in its natural environment, in interaction, as one of the principle assumptions is that utterances are understood as forms of action situated within specific contexts and are designed with attention to these contexts (Goodwin & Heritage 1990).

Everyday interaction has several recurrent features which have not been systematically considered in the study of other pragmatic approaches. These features are, for instance, silent and filled pauses, hesitations, repetitions and overlaps. The rigorously empirical basis of conversation analysis also yields a possibility to take account of and analyse the nonverbal behaviour connected to utterances. The methodology of conversation analysis is the only approach to pragmatics which explicitly takes account of these interactional features (cf. Heritage 1989:23).

This study is part of a larger project, "Communication and speech processing in aphasia" supported by the Council of Humanities of the Academy of Finland. The principle aim of this project has been to elucidate both the communicative and the linguistic abilities of aphasic persons in natural settings. Professor Matti Leiwo has led a team of researchers including Minna Laakso, Inga-Britt Persson and Anu Klippi.

1.2. The pragmatic approach in speech-language pathology and aphasia research

The study of language in context within speech-language pathology arose as a result of the change of focus in linguistics to the pragmatic aspects of language. The term 'pragmatics' was introduced to the field of speech-language pathology in 1976 by Elizabeth Bates, and the first studies within the pragmatic approach concerned child language acquisition. Bates defined pragmatics as "rules governing the use of language in context" (e.g. Prutting 1982, Arwood 1983). Since then, there has been a growing interest in the new conceptual framework in speech-language pathology (Prutting 1982, Arwood 1983, Foldi et al. 1983, Prutting & Kirchner 1983, McTear 1985, Gallagher 1991, McTear & Conti-Ramsden 1992).

Current views in linguistic pragmatics have their origins in philosophy. Philosophers such as Charles Pierce in the early 1870's, and later Ludwig Wittgenstein in his work *Philosophical Investigations*, as well as John L. Austin in his work *How to Do Things with Words*, and John R. Searle in his work *Speech Acts*, all have shaped contemporary views of pragmatics by developing the philosophical notion of how language is used (e.g. Prutting 1982, Arwood 1983). Within the field of pragmatics the most essential insight is that language, action and knowledge are inseparable. This was the main idea of J. L. Austin in his speech act theory, according to which utterances are to be treated as actions (Austin 1962). Later, Searle (1969) developed a taxonomy of speech acts suggesting that the speech act should be treated as the basic unit of communication. In addition, a distinction between language and actual speech was re-emphasized. Since Ferdinand de Saussure, structural linguistics has made a distinction between the concepts of language (langue) and of its use (parole), and the discipline of linguistics has mainly focused on the study of language (langue). Within the pragmatic approach the focus of research has shifted from the abstract langue to actual speech, that is, to parole (e.g. Prutting 1982), and to its consequences for interaction. Speech act theory and a methodological shift to actual speech have had several implications for the research of speech-language pathology (see e.g. Gallagher 1991, McTear & Conti-Ramsden 1992).

Ludwig Wittgenstein proposed that words are like instruments and may be classified according to their method of operation and to their performed functions (Prutting 1982). The pragmatic view has likewise emphasized the use of language as an instrument for social interaction, and for this reason context has become central. The term 'context' has been understood in various ways, and it can refer to everything external to the utterance itself. In speech-language pathology research, the definition of context has been broad, including the participants, the setting and the topic of conversation.

Prutting (1982) for example, has a broad definition of context, and proposes several dimensions that are important in the study of communication: the cognitive and social context, the physical context, the linguistic context and the nonlinguistic context. Davis & Wilcox (1985:3-15) also share the broad definition and thus define their major contextual categories to include linguistic, paralinguistic and extralinguistic variables. For Davis & Wilcox, the linguistic context is the verbal behaviour that occurs before and after a given linguistic unit. In this framework, paralinguistic context accompanies an utterance and its linguistic context, and including suprasegmental features, intonation and prosody. For Davis & Wilcox, extralinguistic context involves a wide range of features; it covers *which, how* and *when* a message is communicated, for instance, including purposes, setting, participants, roles and movements. Lesser & Milroy (1993:110) link deixis and context, and regard the basic features of context such as speaker, place and time to be necessary for interpreting deictic expressions. Furthermore, within the approach of conversation analysis, Goodwin and Duranti (1992) emphasize the dynamic character of the context; participants become environments for each other, and they constantly reshape the context in interaction. The notion of context has greatly enriched the study of speech-language pathology because it has introduced several relevant aspects to the study of deviant communication.

The pragmatic approach and the notion of context have also led to an awakened interest in the interactional view, and this, in turn, has shed new light on the so-called 'speech chain' model (e.g. Denes & Pinson 1963) which has been widely used within speech and language sciences. From an interactive perspective, this model can be regarded as monological in character because it assigns the main importance to the speaker or the sender. This model assumes that a speaker produces utterances or speech acts all on her/his own, independently of context and of the interlocutor's reactions. This view has also been influential within aphasiology, and it has had major consequences for aphasiological research and therapy.

Linell (1991) argues against the speech chain model's operation in actual spoken interaction. First, there is clear evidence that before verbalization, the sender's communicative intentions are not complete or well-defined. In fact, speakers often modify their contributions in response to recipient reactions during the process, which is why the speaker can be regarded as a co-author of the utterances (see also Goodwin, 1979). Here co-authorship accounts for all listener behaviour that influences the speaker, including the rhythmic co-structuration of the speech flow, the verbal and nonverbal ways of giving feedback and acknowledgement, filling-in utterances, etc. Second, understanding is not just passive reception but rather an act of creative use of inference. Moreover, monological models do not properly analyze the role of context, the surrounding conversation, the settings and the cultural frames that influence conversation.

Studies that label themselves as pragmatic have different theoretical departure points. Lesser & Milroy (1993:107-108) state that there are two major approaches to the study of conversation, the 'top-down' linguistics/philosophy of language approach and the 'bottom-up' ethnomethodology/conversational analysis approach. The older and more traditional 'top-down' approach can be traced to Austin's speech act theory, and this approach has been influential in aphasiology. These studies employ deductive reasoning in which an abstract competence is modelled by idealized speakers in idealized situations. Unfortunately, clinical researchers who have applied this theoretical approach have ignored that its origins and development are in the abstract traditions of philosophy rather than in the descriptive needs of linguistics. The other perspective, conversation analysis, has only recently been applied within aphasiology. This tradition offers a contrasting 'bottom-up' orientation and inductively seeks patterns and structures in bodies of naturally occurring data.

1.3. Aphasiological research on conversational data

As the previous overview indicates, studies concerning conversation and interaction of aphasic individuals are still in early stages and come from a variety of theoretical backgrounds. It has only been since the late 1970's that aphasiology has slowly adopted a functional or a communicative perspective. At first, clinicians and then later researchers, began to look at aphasic individuals' communication in authentic speech situations. Martha Taylor Sarno was an early pioneer in this field and she developed the Functional Communication Profile (Sarno 1969, 1983) for analysing some of the everyday language abilities of aphasic speakers. In the late 70's, theoretical bases were derived from Austin's speech act theory (1962), and from Dell Hymes' (1972) notion of communicative competence. This latter notion focused on the relationship between context and the resources to perform a communicative act (e.g. Davis & Wilcox 1985). Audrey Holland (1977) pointed out that language and communication are not necessarily isomorphic, and suggested that "aphasics probably communicate better than they talk". Since then, this suggestion has served as a starting hypothesis for several aphasiological studies.

Another branch of investigations related to functional communication emerged that analysed the compensatory functions of aphasic speakers within interaction (Prinz 1980, Holland 1982, Green 1984, Glosser et al. 1986, Penn 1987 and 1988, Smith 1987a and b, Feyereisen et al. 1988, Le May et al. 1988, Herrmann et al. 1989, Klippi 1990, Ahlsén 1991, Hadar 1991). This branch has its roots in several disciplines such as psycholinguistics, as well as pragmatics and sociolinguistics. These studies used data from patients' conversational interactions but they primarily focused on the aphasic speakers' interactive and especially on their compensatory strategies, not on the collaborative work between the interlocutors. Holland (1982) reported a study of the functional communication of aphasic adults which was based on the observations of aphasic speakers in everyday interaction, and characterised some of the aphasic patients' compensatory strategies. Furthermore, Penn (1987) has described several compensatory strategies: linguistic, sociolinguistic, nonverbal and interlocutor's. In addition, an interest in studying nonverbal behaviour emerged, both as an interactional resource and as a compensatory strategy. In these studies, the data consisted of videotaped conversations in which nonverbal behaviour had been quantified; several researchers have reported that aphasic speakers use more nonverbal behaviour than their interlocutors in interaction (Larkins & Webster 1981, Feyereisen 1983, Ahlsén 1985, Smith 1987a, Le May et al. 1988, Herrmann et al. 1989, Hadar 1991). Some studies report that the type of aphasia may have an influence on the use of the gestural channel (Cicone et al. 1979; Behrmann & Penn 1984; Le May et al. 1988). Moreover, there is evidence of compensatory functions of nonverbal behaviour (Smith 1987a and b,

Feyereisen et al. 1988, Le May et al. 1988, Herrmann et al. 1989, Klippi 1990, Ahlsén 1991, Hadar 1991).

The research line that focused on the interactive aspects of conversation was developed parallel to the studies of communication strategies. The first reports which used transcribed data from aphasic conversations were published in 1980 (Lubinski et al. 1980, Schienberg & Holland 1980). The theoretical background of these reports referred clearly to the findings of conversation analysis, although this framework was not explicitly mentioned. Lubinski et al. (1980) compared the breakdowns and repairs of an aphasic conversation in three different speech contexts: conversations between an aphasic and a spouse and between an aphasic and a speech therapist, and a segment of a treatment session with a speech therapist. The results revealed differences in the different contexts with respect to repairs. One noteworthy finding was that in conversations between the aphasic and the speech therapist, the speech therapist did not respond to the difficulties of the aphasic speaker by doing repair work but instead glossed over the breakdowns, whereas in the conversation with the spouse, the interlocutors worked together to resolve the breakdowns. Schienberg & Holland (1980) analyzed conversational turn-taking in a conversation between two Wernicke aphasic individuals. They noticed that conversational turn-taking behaviour was intact in their subjects, and pointed out that aphasia does not impair a person's knowledge or use of the rules of conversation.

There are also aphasiological studies based on speech act theory that utilize conversational data. Prinz (1980) studied the requesting strategies and the propositional adequacy of aphasic speakers in situations where they were to request e.g. a light for a cigarette or a pencil for writing. Gurland et al. (1982) analysed the use of communicative acts in two speech contexts and in conversational sequences with a spouse and with a speech therapist, and their results indicated that therapy conversations contained the least amount of different speech acts. The results of Armstrong (1989) showed the same tendency; she analysed the speech acts used in aphasia therapy sessions and noticed that the variation of speech acts was very limited, consisting mainly of questions and requests.

There is yet another influential branch of aphasiological studies which I will briefly mention here because they utilize conversational data (spontaneous speech) as their data. These studies aim to compare, by various means, aphasic speakers' expressive language from one context to another (e.g. Easterbrook et al. 1982, Glosser et al. 1988, Roberts & Wertz 1989, Ulatowska et al. 1990). In these investigations the focus of the research has been to do linguistic analysis at different levels (sentence, clause, phrase and word). Here, patients' speech samples have been analyzed by, for instance Crystal et al's Language, Assessment, Remediation and Screening Procedure, LARSP (Easterbrook et al. 1982), by various verbal and verbal complexity indices (Glosser et al. 1988), by a T-unit analysis (a main clause with all the subordinate clauses or nonclausal structures attached to it), ratings of syntactic well-formedness and semantic accuracy (e.g. Roberts & Wertz 1989), and by measures of syntactic complexity, use of modifiers, grammatical correctness, etc. (Ulatowska et al. 1990). All these studies indicate some linguistic differences in various contexts. However, these works usually do not discuss what their results mean at the interactional level, nor do they propose a logical direction to remedy the problems they emphasize.

Furthermore, several studies cannot easily be identified with a certain theoretical background as they employ general pragmatic presuppositions and methods. For instance, Ahlsén (1985) studied word-finding problems, nonverbal communication and narration in the spoken interaction of aphasics. Matthews (1987) presented a case study involving a speaker before and after the onset of aphasia, attempting to determine the impact of aphasia – the nature of the deficits – in one individual's speech. There are also studies based on discourse analysis that have analysed the communicative burden and participation in aphasia conversation in terms of initiative and responsive turns in aphasic conversation (Linebaugh et al. 1982, Copeland 1989, Klippi 1991a). Linebaugh et al. indicated a strong positive relationship between the percentage of initiations by an aphasic individual and the level of functional communicative ability measured by Communicative Abilities of Daily Living, CADL (Holland 1980). Klippi (ibid.) did not find a clear relation between the type and severity of aphasia and the aphasic's participation in conversations. Edwards (1987) and Laakso (1992) studied the interaction between an aphasic speaker and a therapist, finding that the structure of the interaction between the aphasic and therapist resembled more a question-and-answer format than 'free' conversation.

Only recently has the method of conversation analysis begun to be applied in aphasiology (Klippi 1992, Milroy & Perkins 1992, Laakso 1993a and b, Perkins 1993, Ferguson 1994, Goodwin 1995, Wilkinson 1995). The majority of these studies focused on analysing the conversational repair of trouble in interaction, which seems to be an essential issue in aphasic conversation.

Milroy & Perkins (1992) have proposed a collaborative model of repair in aphasic conversation based on Clark & Schaefer's model of conversational contributions (1987, 1989; cf. also chapter 8). Milroy & Perkins applied this model to analyse aphasic conversational sequences and revealed the collaborative negotiation of repair in those sequences. Perkins (1993) enlarged the investigation with attempts to identify the impact on the conversation of impairments found in cognitive neuropsychological investigations. She analysed turn-taking, self-repairs and collaborative repairs in conversations of three aphasic speakers with two different interlocutors. In addition, Laakso (1993b) has studied self-initiation of repair of fluent posterior aphasic persons.

Ferguson (1994) studied the influence of aphasia, familiarity between speakers and activity on conversational repair in interactions between nine aphasic speakers and 18 normal subjects. Her results indicated that normal subjects increased their frequency of interactive trouble-indicating behaviour and used more interactive repair patterns when conversing with aphasic individuals than with normal partners. No significant differences were found in the frequency of interactive trouble-indicating behaviour used in conversations in which the partners differed in their degree of familiarity, although differences in the nature of repair patterns occurred depending on the familiarity of the participants. Conversational repair was found to differ across two activities, casual conversation and a semi-structured retelling event.

Goodwin (1995) has found very interesting interaction patterns in the conversation with a severely aphasic speaker. This aphasic person could speak only three words: "yes", "no" and "and". Goodwin analysed a conversational sequence between the aphasic person, his wife and a nurse, to examine the co-constructing of meaning in the conversation. The organizational principles of the sequence were clear; first, unlike many problematic negotiations, the interlocutors assumed that there was a correct answer to the word search and that the aphasic party knew that answer. Second, there was a strong division of labour in the conversation. The participants performed different kinds of action so that the interlocutors provided relevant guesses for the aphasic speaker who accepted or rejected proposals. Third, the interlocutors engaged in systematic work to formulate new guesses; and finally, the organization of the activity located the aphasic interactant as the central participant. Goodwin emphasises the collaborative process which emerges in the co-construction of meaning, and also, the importance of aphasic participant's ability to make full use of the expressive powers of his body (intonation, gesture, face, body) in this kind of conversation.

Wilkinson (1995) applied conversation analysis when assessing an aphasic patient's language abilities in conversation and discussed its relation to other assessment approaches as well as its implications for therapy. He analysed three repair sequences and emphasized conversation analysis as an ecologically valid approach which complements more 'decontextualized' methods of sampling language.

The use of conversational data in research has become increasingly important in aphasiology over the past ten years, but as was mentioned earlier, the theoretical background and focus of the studies vary greatly. However, the general idea of these studies is the same; there is a variety of aspects of interaction that cannot be grasped in formal test situations and there is a great need for that type of information. These studies have already shown their usefulness in providing knowledge that has been impossible to attain using other methods of investigation.

2. Aims of the research

2.1 Research questions

The traditional aphasia tests attempt to measure the linguistic limitations of an aphasic patient. Thus, these tests do not measure or evaluate the pragmatic strengths of an aphasic speaker, nor do they examine the compensatory means that an aphasic speaker uses in conversation. In addition, the interactive perspective that focuses on the cooperation of the interlocutors in communication and interaction is relatively unknown within aphasiological research. In order to develop methods of intervention in aphasia, knowledge of face-to-face interaction in aphasic conversation is greatly needed.

From the point of view of aphasic conversation, this orientation is very important. What kinds of interactional features are relevant in aphasic conversation and what consequences does their use have for the development of conversation? And is it even possible to compensate the loss of verbal abilities with specific interactional features?

There are a huge amount of various verbal and nonverbal details or characters in aphasic conversation and communication which may be influential from the point of view of mutual understanding. Because the interactional approach is relatively new, I decided to focus the study on some clearly observed and recurrent features in these aphasic group conversations.

The following characteristics of aphasic conversations are analysed in this study:

1.1. The appearance of potentially compensatory nonverbal behaviour in aphasic group conversation.
1.2. The appearance of written numbers, writing or drawing in aphasic group conversation.
1.3. The appearance of laughter and humour in aphasic group conversation.
1.4. The appearance of aphasic speakers' initiated collaborative repairs in aphasic group conversations.
1.5. The appearance of uninflected single-word turns in aphasic group conversation.

All aforementioned characteristics are analysed qualitatively in the conversational sequences. The focus of the analysis is the following:

Conversation as an
achievement in aphasics
Studia Fennica
Linguistica 6
1996.

A. Who initiates the use of the specific conversational characteristics
   (nonverbal behaviour, writing, drawing, laughter and humour, aphasics'
   initiated repair, single-word)?
B. How is a specific characteristic handled by the interlocutors of the group in
   the conversational interaction?
C. What kinds of consequences does the use of the specific conversational
   characteristics have for the development of aphasic conversation?

Very few studies within aphasiology apply the principles and method of
conversation analysis, although within sociology and sociolinguistics this
approach has developed into a new branch of investigation concerning
conversational interaction and social organization. As mentioned earlier, interest
in investigating aphasic conversation and interaction with this approach is only
just beginning. As the methods of such study are undeveloped within
aphasiology, the methodology of conversation analysis was chosen because, as
a rigorous empirical method, it offers a systematic analysis of detailed
interactional features. I will also evaluate the capability of conversation analysis
as a method for analysing aphasic conversation.

2.2. Organization of the thesis

The following chapter presents the subjects of study and the data of the study.
The transcription conventions and the sequence analysis of the material are
illustrated.

The next three chapters – on nonverbal behaviour as a compensatory
resource in aphasic conversation, writing and drawing in aphasic conversation
and humour in aphasic conversation – analyse the speech-related recurrent
interactional features in aphasic conversation which have until now received
no attention from the interactional and collaborative point of view. Each
chapter has a short introduction focusing on the literature on the topic,
analysis of the excerpts, and discussion in which the observations are
examined.

Chapter 8 deals with the aphasic speakers' other-repair initiations related to
the comprehension or hearing problems in conversation and to the notion of
collaborative repair in aphasic conversation, and chapter 9 analyses the use of
single words and the interactional consequences of their use in aphasic
conversation. The structure of chapters is similar to the three first chapters.

Chapter 10 presents a synthesis of the results of the substudies and
discusses their relevance for aphasia research. The method of this study is
discussed as well and suggestions for further research are offered. In addition,
clinical implications are discussed.

3. The main principles of conversation analysis

When utilising conversational data for research, one has to select the method best suited to the objectives and purposes of one's study. In the course of the present research project, my theoretical background changed from a generally pragmatic approach and from discourse analysis to a methodology based on conversation analysis. This change has taken place for several reasons that will be presented later. The next part outlines the basic principles of conversation analysis, and thereafter I will evaluate the relevance of conversation analysis for aphasiological research.

Conversation analysis has its roots in sociology, as part of the wider sociological movement called 'ethnomethodology' (Garfinkel 1967) which was not at first particularly concerned with conversational speech but developed as a theoretical and methodological critique of established forms of sociology (Taylor & Cameron 1987:99, Goodwin & Heritage 1990). Harvey Sacks introduced conversation as a focus of study during the 60's. Along with his colleagues Emanuel Schegloff and Gail Jefferson, Sacks developed a method for investigating spoken interaction known as conversation analysis (e.g. Heritage & Atkinson 1984:1).

According to Heritage (1989:22), the basic orientation of conversation analysis lies in the following four fundamental assumptions: 1) interaction is structurally organized; 2) contributions to interaction are both context-shaped and context-renewing; 3) these two properties are inherent in all the details of interaction so that no detail in conversational interaction can be dismissed a priori as disorderly, accidental or interactionally irrelevant; and 4) the study of social interaction in its details is best approached through the analysis of naturally occurring data.

The initial and most fundamental assumption of conversation analysis is that interaction is socially organized according to social conventions and consists of stable and recurrent structural features. Methodologically, this means that conversation, which has traditionally been viewed as unplanned and lacking overt structure, will be treated as a structured organisation that can be analysed, a study conducted independently of psychological or other attributes of participants.

Second, the relationship between language and context is assumed to be essential. Any conversational contribution is doubly contextual in being both context-shaped and context-renewing. The conversational contribution is

Conversation as an achievement in aphasics
Studia Fennica
Linguistica 6
1996.

context-shaped because it cannot be adequately understood without reference to the context in which it occurs. The local preceding context in which an utterance occurs is crucial, but the larger environmental activity is also taken into consideration. Thus, both speakers and hearers utilize the context as a conversational resource; speakers employ it in designing their utterances, and hearers in order to make adequate sense of what is said. Also, communicative action is context-renewing because it creates context for what follows. As the current utterance forms the immediate context for the next action in the sequence, it will contribute to the contextual framework for understanding the next action.

The third methodological assumption – that no order of detail in interaction can be dismissed a priori as insignificant – is also essential for conversation-analytic research. First, Heritage (ibid.) mentions, that as conversation analysis favours a strongly empirical approach in the study of social action, there has been a general retreat from premature theory construction. Another methodological consequence of this assumption is that the data will exhibit systematic and orderly properties which are meaningful for the participants in conversation.

Finally, the method of conversation analysis stresses the value of naturally occurring data, in accordance with its aim to analyse everyday social actions. From the descriptions of classroom discourse we know that three-part discourse structure seems to be characteristic; there is an initiating move, a responding move and a follow-up (Sinclair & Coulthard 1975). In contrast, everyday conversation seems to be structurally much richer and more varied than so-called institutional data. Although conversational speech is generally assumed to be incomplete, repetitive and hesitant, the systematic analysis of these features has shown that they are important in the organization of conversation.

Goodwin & Heritage (1990:301) point out that one of conversation analysis' strengths is that it directly describes events from 'the native's' point of view. Thus, the analysis is not based on reports about categories and appropriate behaviour, but instead on the analysis of participants' actions in the course of their social lives. In this way, conversation analysis offers an ecologically valid approach to assess the use of language in the natural context of interactive talk.

In the following sections I will introduce some of the central concepts of conversation analysis that are relevant for this work.

3.1   Turn-taking

According to Sacks, Schegloff & Jefferson (1974:696), the basic mechanism of conversation is **turn-taking**, a system that organizes conversational activity. They speak about a 'speech exchange system' where the turns suggest an economy. There are means for allocating turns and the use of these means affects their relative distribution, as in economies. Turns are complex, interactively constructed units that contain one or more turn-constructional units and turn-taking thus refers to the orderly sharing of time and sequencing of turns. One of the remarkable characteristics of conversation is its smoothness and fluency. Usually, one party talks at a time and turns are changed from one interlocutor to another with relatively little gap or overlap. Pauses between turns are often only microseconds long, which can be regarded as a result of exact timing.

Sacks et al. (1974) suggest that, in an actual everyday conversation, turn-taking is an open, local system where the interlocutors operate on a turn-by-turn basis. This local management system is based on conversational turns that are made up of **turn constructional units (TCU)**. Turn constructional units are sentential, clausal, phrasal, and lexical constructions and thus the unit-types may be sentences, phrases or words. The end of a TCU constitutes a point at which a speaker change may take place. This point is called the **transition relevance place (TRP)**. A speaker is initially allowed to have one such unit at a time, and whether s/he is allowed to have more TCUs in one turn is based on interactional work (Sacks et al. 1974:702-3). The literature on conversation analysis makes only sporadic mention of the use of intonation in conversation. In contrast, within phonetics, for instance Crystal (1975) and Cruttenden (1986:75-80) have found that intonational patterns may be important for recognizing the unit and its boundaries.

According to Sacks et al. (ibid.), 'turn constructional units' are basically syntactic units. However, several prosodic features have been identified as indicators of turn completion. Cutler & Pearson (1986) provided evidence of a downstep of fundamental frequency contours at the end of utterances. There are several prosodic features like pitch, tempo, loudness and duration movements that occur at turn-endings, and the recipients interpret these as turn-completions.

Besides prosodic information, there is evidence that some nonverbal cues may play an important role in turn-taking, for instance gaze and kinesic behaviour (Ellis & Beattie 1986:181-187). Goodwin (1979) has shown this relationship between turn construction and gaze. On the other hand, smooth transitions, as in telephone conversations for example, indicate that visual access to the interlocutor is not a necessary prerequisite for normal turn-taking.

Speaker-selection, which includes self-selection by a subsequent speaker and specification of a next speaker by the current speaker, is also a rule-based activity. Levinson (1983:298) has slightly simplified Sacks et al's rules for turn-taking:

(C is current speaker, N is next speaker)
Rule I - applies initially at the first TRP of any turn
    a) If C selects N in current turn, then C must stop speaking and N must speak next; transition occurring at the first TRP after N-selection.
    b) If C does not select N then any (other) party may self-select, the first speaker gaining rights to the next turn.
    c) If C has not selected N, and no other party self-selects under option (b), then C may (but need not) continue (i.e. claim rights to a further TCU)

Rule II - applies at all subsequent TRPs.
    When Rule I(c) has been applied by C, then at the next TRP, Rules I(a)-(c) apply, and recursively at the next TRP, until speaker change is effected.

Especially in multi-party conversation, turn-taking can be regarded as a competitive activity where speakers utilize various techniques to take and retain the floor. In the occurrences of turn completion, minor overlaps are common. Also, accidental misprojection of a turn-ending can lead to violative interruption. There are, nevertheless, repair techniques to restore the organization, for instance self-repetitions are used as a resolution of overlap, as well as raising one's voice to silence a competitor (Lesser & Milroy 1993:190).

The turn-taking organization outlined by Sacks et al. (1974) raises questions concerning aphasic conversation. One may ask whether aphasia in general, or only some specific subtypes of aphasia, has any effect on turn-taking. For example, the speech of a Broca's aphasic has been described as slow and hesitant with recurrent silent and filled pauses. How does a speaker with such aphasia manage the split-second timing of turn-taking, and, on the other hand, how do the interlocutors of Broca's aphasic speakers reason which pauses are due to aphasic disorders and which are true possible TRPs? The following example shows a typical instance of Broca's aphasic speech (A=aphasic, t=therapist):

```
01 t: missä päin Suomea oot syntynyt ja (0.6) ja minkälaiset
      whereabouts in Finland were you born and (0.6) what type of
02    (0.5) lapsuuden maisemat sulla on ollu.
      (0.5) childhood surroundings have you had.
03    1.5
04 A: kun,.(0.8) kun,. (0.7) syttynyt
      like,.(0.8) like,.(0.7) {was born}
05    (0.3) e on (0.6) öö (0.9) aah Helsingissä.
      (0.3) er is (0.6) er (0.9) uh in Helsinki.
06    0.4
07 t: hmm, mm-m? (0.5) no=
      hmm, mm-m? (0.5) well=
08 A:=ja (3.0) ö vaimo eiku (0.7) öö ÄIti, (0.3) on
      =and (3.0) er wife no I mean (0.7) er mother, (0.3) is
09    (2.0) ooh (1.6) öm (1.1) kuh (1.5) kun on (0.9) öm
      (2.0) uh (1.6) um (1.1) {like} (1.5) like is (0.9) um
10    (1.6) KOL+eiku (0.4) ne- (0.6) VIIden (.)POLven HELsin(.)kiläisiä.
      (1.6) THIR+no I mean (0.4) fo- (0.6) FIfth (.) GEneration's
      Helsinki born (NAURAHTAA/LAUGHTER)
12 t: ai jaah (NAURAHTAA) no niin nää on sitte sun lapsuuden
      I see (CHUCKLES) well then these are then your childhood
13    maisemia
      surroundings
14 A: (NAURAHTAA) on.
      (CHUCKLES) yes.
```

The speech of this aphasic person is extremely nonfluent. Silent pauses and hesitations occur before and after every word. However, the turn-taking *per se* does not present a problem for this aphasic speaker; for example, in line 8 we see that the aphasic speaker is able to take the turn fluently after the previous speaker. From this fluency we can conclude that the phenomenon of turn-taking is very complex and cannot be directly related to an aphasic speaker's speech problems.

Furthermore, one may wonder how a Wernicke's aphasic with extremely fluent, even overfluent, speech is able to react to the possible turn-taking signals of other interlocutors. In fact, until now this question has been very little studied. Schienberg & Holland (1980) have investigated the question of whether Wernicke's aphasics have turn-taking difficulties. Analysing two patients conversing with each other, Schienberg & Holland concluded that their subjects were not impaired in turn-taking and argued that conversational turn-taking behaviour remains intact in aphasia. However, this generalization may be excessive because they had only two subjects in their study.

Some findings suggest aphasic speakers systematically utilise various techniques for keeping the floor, for instance in the case of word-finding difficulties. These techniques include filling in pauses with extra 'noises' and interjections (Ahlsén 1985, Klippi 1991b); long, silent pauses are often interrupted by sighing, coughing, lip-smacking or sniffling (e.g. Klippi 1991b). Moreover, nonverbal means are often used, for instance tapping one's hand on the table while searching for a target word (Klippi 1991b) or raising one's hand and averting one's gaze (Ahlsén 1985, Laakso 1992). Lesser & Milroy (1993:191) refer to a study by Conway in which an aphasic speaker systematically altered her body posture during the conversation. During her own turn, she sat forward in her chair and she marked the point of turn completion by relaxing this posture. Also in the example above, the speaker's filled pauses, gaze direction and body posture seemed all to be important turn-keeping signals.

3.2   Intersubjectivity, sequencing and adjacency pairs

One of the core questions in human interaction is how the participants are able to build relevant and rational sequences of actions, which in verbal interaction are revealed by intelligible and coherent conversations. As was mentioned earlier, one of the central principles of conversation analysis is that, in contrast to methods involving the analysis of isolated sentences, conversation analysis investigates utterances or actions within their natural contexts, that is, in conversation. In the real world of interaction, utterances are never treated as isolated units but are understood to be forms of action situated within specific contexts and designed with specific attention to these contexts (Goodwin & Heritage 1990:287). In this way they reveal the architecture of intersubjectivity and reflexivity in conversation.

The **intersubjectivity** of action, expounded by Harold Garfinkel, and by Alfred Schutz before him, is an important notion within ethnomethodological school (Taylor & Cameron 1987:102-107). The sequential construction or architecture of intersubjectivity is built of linked actions, 'the basic building-blocks of intersubjectivity' (Heritage 1984:256). The main question is how individuals with private or different experiences achieve an intersubjective 'shared world' and are able to construct these linked actions. In interaction, the speakers operate under common assumptions. The principal assumption is that there are no interactionally relevant differences between the experiences. If some difference should arise, these will be made public through the interactants' behaviour and its normative accountability. Heritage, according to Schutz, states (1984:60): "...Actors, despite their non-identical experiences and despite their lack of access to the full particularity of one another's experiences, can nevertheless proceed on the basis that their experiences are 'identical for all practical purposes'. Persistently conducting themselves on this assumption, a world of shared experiences – extruded, as it were, through language – is brought into being". Hence, understanding is brought to a common ground that is 'identical for all practical purposes' by various methodological means (Taylor & Cameron, ibid. 104). To summarize, intersubjectivity refers to the means by which individuals in an interaction can reach a shared interpretation of the situation. Hence, conversation analysis describes and analyses those systematic practices that participants use to accomplish shared understanding (e.g. Goodwin & Goodwin 1987).

Naturally occurring conversation is an extraordinarily complicated issue. However, it is possible to isolate simple sequences in conversation, like adjacency pairs, paired actions (Schegloff & Sacks 1973:295, Sacks 1992b). They describe the notion of an adjacent pair in terms of five basic characteristics which Heritage (1984:246) has formulated in the following way. An adjacency pair is:
1. A sequences of two utterances, which are
2. adjacent
3. produced by different speakers,
4. ordered as a first part and second part, and
5. typed, so that a first part requires a particular second part (or a range of second parts).

In addition, there is a simple operational rule for an adjacency pair. Schegloff and Sacks, ibid. p.296) state:"Given the recognizable production of a first pair part, on its first possible completion its speaker should stop and a next speaker should start and produce a second pair part from the pair type of which the first (pair part) is recognizably a member." Hence, a first pair part requires the production of a reciprocal action, a second pair part, at the first possible opportunity after completion of the first. A participant analyses the developing course of others' actions in order to express relevant reciprocal action (Goodwin & Heritage 1990:288). Thus, an adjacency pair forms a coherent whole in which the second part presumes a relevant and expectable pair for the first part of the pair. Clear-cut adjacency pair types are, for instance, question-answer, greeting-greeting and offer-acceptance/refusal. On the other hand, a much wider and more loosely range of conversational actions is specified, such as assessment-assessment pairs or a piece of news and its evaluation.

Schegloff and Sacks (1973:297-298) suggest that by an adjacently positioned second, a speaker can show that s/he understood what a prior speaker aimed at and that s/he is willing to go along with it. Conversely, the first speaker can, by inspecting the second pair part, see if the first part has been understood. Hence the second pair part may display either understanding, or the failure to understand. This sequential property of conversation is called **sequential implicativeness**.

Heritage (1984:254) explains that, on the conversational level, the notion of intersubjectivity is well seen in an adjacency pair structure and it has far-reaching implications. He says:"...the recipient analyses the first utterance and whatever the conclusion of such an analysis, *some analysis, understanding or appreciation of the prior turn will be displayed in the recipient's next turn at talk*". This is precisely what Schegloff & Sacks propose with their notion of sequential implicativeness, which simply stated, means whatever is said and understood will be said and understood within the sequential context of preceding talk and action.

Sequential implicativeness links with the concept of **conditional relevance** (e.g. Schegloff 1972). Conditional relevance means that the first part of an adjacency pair builds a context for the next turn. This property permits speakers for instance to discover that particular conversational events are absent. If there is a lack of the expected second pair part, for instance the lack of reciprocal greeting or reply, this violates the rule, and is interpreted as a 'noticeable absence', and that there is a reason for its absence (e.g. Goodwin & Heritage 1990:287, Taylor & Cameron 1987:103). On the other hand, in the more loose adjacency-pair structures, the absence of the second pair part is not regarded as significant as it is in the more strict pairs.

Although the adjacency-pair structure is a central concept in sequence organization, conversations are not comprehensively analysable as sequences of chained pairs. Longer sequences can often be divided into embedded sequences. Frequently a second pair part may be delayed in various ways, and various pieces of structure can intervene. In place of a second pair part, one possibility is a question/answer sequence followed then by a second pair part. This sequence type has been called **insertion sequence** (Schegloff 1972, Sacks 1992b). Another possibility was noted by Jefferson (1972), who introduced the concept of a **side sequence** as a possible remedial procedure in conversation. There are also presequences and summonses to be found in conversations.

Methodologically, the concept of interactional sequence and sequential implicativeness has been an analytic innovation opening the way for cumulative empirical advances (Goodwin & Heritage 1990:287). One of the far-reaching consequences of sequential implicativeness is that the meaning of the utterance is the product of interactional work. In this way the meanings of utterances are seen as dynamic, in contrast with former theories that consider them to be relatively static. For example Searle, in developing the speech act theory, gives primacy to isolated utterances, which are analysed in terms of syntactic and semantic features (Lesser & Milroy 1993:176).

From the aphasiological point of view, the notions of sequential structure, sequential implicativeness and conditional relevance are essential, with several implications for research. Due to comprehension difficulties, aphasic speakers may have difficulties producing a coherent or expected second pair part. Thus, evidence suggests that aphasic conversation contains more embedded sequences than 'normal' conversation; in particular, numerous repair sequences, resulting from the aphasic speaker's expression or reception problems, seem to be typical of aphasic conversation (Milroy & Perkins 1992, Perkins 1993, Laakso 1993a). Due to aphasic problems, the participants often need to work harder together than they do in 'normal' conversations to establish the shared meaning 'for the current purposes'. These sequences are the key to understanding, how interlocutors co-construct meanings in aphasic conversations (cf. Goodwin, 1995).

On the other hand, there are also studies on aphasia that imply that an aphasic speaker produces the second pair part more easily than the first pair part of an adjacency pair in conversation (e.g. Thompson & McReynolds

1986, Springer et al. 1993). Anterior aphasics in particular seem to have problems producing e.g. questions, the first pair parts of the adjacency pairs. It would be relevant to study the natural compensatory means for producing questions to develop therapy programmes for such problems. Special features of severely handicapped aphasics include recurring utterances, stereotyped utterances and repetitive speech (e.g. Blanken 1991). Even a loss of initiative verbal behaviour can be observed in dynamic aphasia (Luria 1976a and b). In these cases, the production of all types of first pair parts (greetings, questions, assessments, etc.) may be missing, and possibly even the production of second pair parts (greetings, replies, etc.) may cause problems.

3.3   Repair organization

Repair organization refers to the processes whereby a natural language handles its intrinsic troubles. When talking in ordinary conversation, speakers address themselves to prior talk and most commonly, to immediately preceding talk. In doing so, speakers reveal their understanding or misunderstanding of the prior talk to which their own speech is addressed (Schegloff 1992). Hence, repairs are used for solving problems in speaking, hearing and understanding in conversation. The repair addresses the 'repairable' or the 'trouble source' (Schegloff et al. 1977) and repair work refers to the handling of the repairable or the trouble source. Schegloff et al. (ibid.) make two important distinctions in repairs: the one who initiates the repair operation and the one who overcomes the repair operation. There are self-initiated repairs versus other-initiated repairs. In addition, there are self-repairs carried out by the current speaker versus other repairs carried out by another participant. Thus, there are four possible ways to handle troubles in conversation: self-initiated self-repair, other-initiated self-repair, self-initiated other-repair and other-initiated other-repair.

Schegloff et al. (ibid. p. 366) also propose that self- and other-initiations have regular and different placements relative to the trouble source whose repair they initiate. Self-initiated repairs are encountered in three main types of positions. The first possibility is that they are within the same turn (T) as their trouble source; second, they are in the turn's transition space; and third they are in the third turn after the trouble-source turn. Other-initiated repairs typically take place in the second turn, the turn subsequent to the trouble-source turn and these are called 'next turn repair initiations' (NTRI). Levinson (1983:340) has formulated the organization of repair as follows:

T1 (includes repairable item) = first opportunity: self-initiated self-repair
Transition space between T1 and T2 = second opportunity: again self-initiated self-repair
T2 = third opportunity: either for other-repair or for other-initiation of self-repair in T3
T3 = fourth opportunity: given other-initiation in T2, for other-initiated self-repair

An important concept is the preference-organization of the self- and other-initiation of repair. Schegloff et al. (ibid.) suggest that both self- and other-initiated repairs yield self-correction and thus there is a clear preference for self-repair over other-repair. The trouble-source turns are overwhelmingly self-interrupted by the speaker of the turn for the self-initiation of repair. Hence, the troubles are resolved in the current turn, leaving the next turn free to carry on with the topic of discussion (the first and the second opportunity). Other-initiation is usually withheld, while the trouble-source turn is in progress, and initiated only when the trouble-source turn has come to completion. In this case, the speaker may have initiated the repair but is unable to complete it and it is left to the other interactant to initiate the repair. As other-initiations have the capacity to locate the trouble-source, they provide the speaker of the trouble-source with the third opportunity to repair the trouble in the turn that follows the trouble turn. There is still a fourth opportunity for repair. A speaker may realise that the co-participant has misunderstood a previous turn of the speaker and the speaker self-initiates repair on the trouble source in her/his earlier turn. This is called 'third position repair' (Schegloff 1992).

The notion of repair and its organization in conversation is extremely appropriate in aphasic conversation and it has already been studied to some extent in aphasic conversation (e.g. Milroy & Perkins 1992, Perkins 1993, Laakso 1993a and b). As there are frequent and recurrent troubles in aphasic conversation, the central issue is to analyse their consequences for interaction. In chapter 8 the collaborative repair sequences initiated by aphasic speakers will be analysed in greater detail.

3.4 Preference organization

One of the important concepts in conversation analysis connected to adjacency pairs and repair organization is **preference organization** (Levinson 1983: 332-337, Atkinson & Heritage 1984:53-56). The central idea is that not all the potential second parts to a first part of an adjacency pair are of equal standing; there are preferred and dispreferred types of responses. There is a range of adjacency pairs which allow for alternative second pair parts, for instance invitations can be accepted or rejected, requests can be granted or refused, etc. Such alternatives may arise at the level of lexical selection, utterance design, and action or sequence choice (Atkinson & Heritage 1984:53). It is important to note that the concept of preference is not a psychological claim but a structural notion and close to the linguistic concept of markedness (Levinson 1983:307).

Preferred second turns are unmarked and they are structurally simpler. They are normally stated explicitly and directly, with little delay. Dispreferred second pair parts are structurally more complex and marked by various kinds of features (Levinson 1983:334). According to Taylor & Cameron (1987:112) the characteristics of dispreferred second pair parts are (condensed and simplified from Levinson 1983):

a) pausing before delivery
b) the use of a 'preface'
e.g. (i) markers like "uh" or "well"
(ii) token agreements, appreciations and apologies
(iii) qualifiers

c) the use of accounts, i.e. explanations for why the preferred second pair part is not forthcoming

d) the use of a 'declination component': a form suited to the nature of the first part pair, but characteristically indirect or mitigated.

Pomeranz (1984) has found interesting features when studying the preference organization of agreeing and disagreeing with assessments. She noticed that a first speaker's assessment of someone or something invites a second assessment, with which the second speaker can agree or disagree with the first speaker. The design of the agreement and disagreement turns were different. In simple cases, agreement turns were preferred ones and they were fully occupied with turn components that asserted agreement, whereas disagreements were often prefaced. Agreements were accomplished with stated agreement components whereas disagreements were accomplished with a variety of forms ranging from unstated to stated disagreements. There were also often disagreements which were formed as partial agreements and partial disagreements, and they were weak forms of disagreement. Agreements were performed with a minimization of a gap between the first assessment turn and second assessment turn; disagreements were frequently delayed in production.

The relevance of the preference organization for aphasic conversation becomes evident if we think, for instance, about the numerous pauses and prefaces and their interactional consequences in aphasic conversation. It would be relevant to study whether the preference organization is preserved and how it is displayed in spite of aphasic speakers' linguistic problems. The concept of preference organization has been utilized in chapter 7 when investigating humour in aphasic conversation.

3.5   The relevance of conversation analysis to aphasiology

The perspective on interactive discourse offered by conversation analysts is a very new and fresh one within aphasiology in which the neuropsychological and cognitive perspectives have been prevailing. First, it seems that one interesting contribution of this theoretical background is that the focus of research is directed to actual communication situations, that is, to everyday mundane conversations (e.g. Heritage 1984, Goodwin & Heritage 1990) instead of language tests and experiments. For instance in clinical work, the standard approach to studying aphasic speakers is to assess an aphasic patient with the 'aphasia test batteries'. The traditional aphasia tests are primarily directed at measuring the linguistic reduction of the patient – not the communication of the patient and her/his skills of interaction. From an interactional viewpoint, the most problematic parts of 'ordinary' aphasia tests are tasks such as naming, recognition of objects and pictures, word fluency, etc. which are regarded as metalinguistic as to their quality (Lebrun & Buyssens 1982). These tests may measure linguistic ability, but they hardly simulate the language used in the context of natural interaction. The methodology used in assessing aphasic patients with aphasia tests, and in a wider perspective the methodology used in aphasia research as a rule, has given us knowledge of aspects of aphasia only to a limited degree. The demands of studying actual communication situations and interaction have consequences for methodology. The widely adopted test approach needs complementary methods to assess the communication skills of aphasic patients.

The second contribution is a shift to studying larger communication units, from words and sentences to linked turns to conversation (Goodwin & Heritage 1990:289). Hence, the scope of research is no longer a single utterance of an aphasic speaker with its syntactic, semantic or phonological errors, but rather the sequential development of the conversation. The study of conversation with an aphasic speaker or between aphasic speakers is of theoretical and practical importance. It is already known that, for instance, the structure of aphasic conversation differs from that of the normal because of the recurrent repair sequences (e.g. Perkins 1993). A major question is how these difficulties are handled and resolved in aphasic conversation, which can only be answered by analysing conversational sequences.

This leads immediately to the next important contribution to aphasia research, that is, the insight that conversation is a reciprocal activity where each participant must analyse the developing course of others' actions in order to produce the appropriate reciprocal action (Goodwin & Heritage 1990:288). Hence, it is assumed that the contributions to interaction are contextually oriented. Compared to various aphasiological traditions which have mostly studied isolated verbal utterances, this view inherently emphasizes context and its significance for analysis. Thus, the production of a turn involves, simultaneously, an ability to comprehend and form an utterance. As either of these skills may be impaired due to aphasia, the co-constructing of the meanings of conversation in collaboration becomes even more important in aphasic interaction.

When conversation is viewed as a reciprocal social activity that requires the coordinated efforts of both speakers, it is necessary to study the behaviour of all participants in the conversation. It is not enough that we study the communicative behaviour of aphasic speakers in interaction, but it is essential to study the interaction between the participants. This approach has already led to the study of conversation between an aphasic and a therapist, and conversation between an aphasic and a spouse or a relative (Klippi 1991b, Milroy & Perkins 1992, Laakso 1993a and b, Perkins 1993, Ferguson 1994, Goodwin 1995, Wilkinson 1995). As the interactive view stresses the role of both participants, an aphasic speaker is also seen as an active participant in interaction although her/his linguistic means may be limited. This view is also in contrast to the prevailing clinical practice where an aphasic speaker is often only seen as an object for rehabilitation.

Both neurolinguistic and psycholinguistic approaches to aphasiology have focused on identifying and describing deviation from assumed normal speech (cf. Ferguson 1994). This perspective can nevertheless turned instead to the identification and analysis of the processes that succeed in aphasic conversation. Conversation analysis focuses upon the notion of trouble, and abandons the notion of error as being essentially irrelevant to everyday conversation. Trouble may arise from the presence of error, but on the other hand, a detectable error is not crucial for the presence of trouble. Thus, trouble involves a difficulty in conversation which is indicated by the interactants, and errors which do not cause trouble for the interactants are regarded as insignificant for the interaction (Schegloff et al. 1977).

Another important aspect for the aphasiological research is contributed by the method of conversation analysis. Everyday interaction has several recurrent features such as silent pauses, hesitations, repetitions and overlaps which have not been systematically taken into consideration in other pragmatic approaches. The methodology of conversation analysis is the only approach within pragmatics which explicitly takes these interactional features into account (cf. Heritage 1987:23). The rigorously empirical basis of conversation analysis also yields an opportunity to account for and analyse the nonverbal behaviour connected with utterances. Although this interest is only in its infancy in conversation analysis (cf. however Goodwin 1981, Goodwin 1986, Goodwin & Goodwin 1986, Goodwin 1987), it displays promising possibilities for analysing communicative contributions which contain complex interactive resources. In exceptional interactions like aphasic conversation, this possibility is extremely relevant.

Finally, the ethnomethodological approach involves qualitative – as opposed to quantitative – analysis (e.g. Schegloff 1993), although recently there has been some interest in quantitative analysis. Traditionally, the quantitative approach is linked to the positivistic scientific approach typical of natural sciences, in which parameters can be objectively measured. This approach has been widely criticized in sciences studying human behaviour. As a qualitative method, conversation analysis is based on a phenomenological approach (Heritage 1984, Mäkelä 1990). For instance, in aphasia research, rather than being concerned with the number of times an individual performs a particular action correctly (words, sentences, etc.), conversation analysis involves a detailed examination of how the action is performed.

4. Data collection and transcription

4.1 Subjects

The main database for this study consists of four group conversations between five aphasics and a speech therapist in communication therapy. In addition, some excerpts were selected from conversations between an aphasic speaker and a therapist. The ages of the subjects ranged from 42 to 54 years when the group was formed. All aphasic participants had been working before the onset of the illness. At the time of the study, all aphasic participants had early retirement due to their aphasic problems. One speaker, Paavo was also dysarthric. Table 1 (p. 39) gives general information about the participants and Table 2 (p. 39) characterises their aphasia according to the Western Aphasia Battery, WAB (Kertesz 1982, a Finnish version, Lehtihalmes et al. 1986).

According to WAB, the two of speakers were Broca's aphasics and three were anomic aphasics in the group. The aphasia quotients of the WAB fell within the range of 68.9-92.2. The dyadic aphasic - therapist conversations were between Maija and the therapist, and Pekka and the therapist. Both aphasics had Broca's aphasia. The respective data concerning Pekka is in Tables 1 and 2.

Table 3 provides neurological information on the aphasic speakers. Based on medical and speech pathology reports, I have estimated the severity of aphasia after the onset of the illness according to the Aphasia Severity Rating Scale (Goodglass & Kaplan 1972). This study characterizes the present communicative and conversational abilities of these aphasic speakers. In the following pages, I will give a short description of the aphasic speakers in the beginning of the group. The pseudonyms are used, and the participants are called: Jaakko (J), Maija (M), Kalle (K), Elina (E), Paavo (P) and Pekka.

Jaakko was a 54-year-old right-handed man who became aphasic after a brain infarction. Immediately after the onset of aphasia, Jaakko's major symptom was jargon speech, and he had left-sided dyspractic paralysis. After becoming aware of his speech problems, he stopped communicating verbally and only gradually began speaking very slowly and haltingly as well as having severe problems in formulating propositions and in word finding. He received speech therapy periodically post onset. The aphasia group was established one-and-a-half years after his illness.

Maija was a 42-year-old right-handed woman who became globally aphasic after a complication in an operation. She also suffered mild right-sided upper limb paralysis. In the early stages of aphasia, her speech was

Conversation as an achievement in aphasics
Studia Fennica
Linguistica 6
1996.

extremely slow and laborious, with severe agrammatism and word-finding difficulty. She received speech therapy periodically for several years. Maija was aphasic already 12 years before the aphasia group was formed.

Kalle was a 43-year-old right-handed man who had suffered a head injury in a bicycle accident. After the accident, a large left-sided temporal intracerebral hematoma was evacuated and he suffered various cognitive-linguistic symptoms afterwards. Kalle's speech was extremely fluent but he had word-finding difficulties, and he often used circumlocutions and paraphasias in his speech. In the WAB-test, he also showed some problems in comprehending word meanings and sequential commands. In addition, he had problems with reading and writing. Qualitatively, his aphasic disorders resembled those of Wernicke's aphasia, but according to the WAB-test he had anomic aphasia. He had been in the accident only two months earlier and hence his condition was rather acute.

Paavo was a 49-year-old right-handed man who had suffered a left-sided brain infarction after which he became moderately aphasic. Having some transient motor symptoms on his right side, his hand movements were slow and inaccurate in the apraxia test. He also had dysarthria which made his articulation blurred. He had received speech therapy some months after the onset of the aphasia. The aphasia group was started two and half year after his illness. At that time his aphasic problems were rather mild; he had some problems in formulating propositions and minor naming problems. However, he had still evident motor speech disorder, dysarthria. His articulation was slow and slurred which sometimes made his speech difficult to understand.

Elina was a 45-year-old right handed woman who suffered a subarachnoidal haemorrhage but no paralysis. After the onset of her illness, her speech was totally jargon. She received speech therapy periodically and her recovery had been extremely good. When the aphasia group started, Elina had only slight aphasic speech problems, e.g. some occasional word-finding problems in conversation. The aphasia group was started three years and four months after her illness.

Pekka only participated in the dyadic conversations with the speech therapist. He was a 39-year-old right-handed man who suffered a left-sided brain infarction after which he became severely aphasic. His speech was very slow and laborious and he had severe problems in formulating propositions and in word finding. Pekka also had right-sided hemiplegia. He had received speech therapy periodically since the onset of aphasia.

According to the clinical categorization of the WAB-test, there were two Broca's aphasics and three anomic aphasics in the aphasia group. Classic descriptions of **Broca's aphasia** include observations of slow, laborious so-called non-fluent speech. Thus, Broca's aphasics usually have disordered articulation, short phrase length, abnormal prosody, paraphasic substitutions and a relative decrease in the number of syntactic words in the output (Benson 1988). Speech comprehension is usually relatively well-preserved in Broca's aphasia. Sometimes the considerably sparse speech is manifested in the form of expressing isolated content words only, sometimes even expressed in an uninflected form. This kind of speech has been referred to as 'agrammatic' or 'telegraphic' (e.g. Luria 1970; 1976). According to Goodglass & Menn (1985:1-2), descriptions of agrammatism by French, German and Russian writers show remarkable parallels, and they summarize the changes in the linguistic structure of agrammatism according to Tissot, Mounin & Lhermitte:

1. The lack of function words in discourse, that is, the leaving out of conjunctions, prepositions, articles, pronouns, and auxiliary verbs, and copulas (notable exceptions to this are the conjunctions *and*, *because*).
2. The predominance of nouns, at the expense of verbs, in some form of agrammatic speech.
3. The loss of verb inflection, with substitution of the infinitive for finite verb forms.
4. Loss of agreement of person, number, and gender, most notably in inflected languages. In languages with case declensions for nouns, nouns revert to the nominative form.

Table 1. General Information on the Aphasic Participants

Aphasic speaker	Sex	Age: years	Former Occupation	WAB, AQ max. 100	Type of Aphasia
Jaakko	M	54	engineer	68.9	Broca
Maija	F	42	graduate of a commercial institute	75.0	Broca
Kalle	M	43	foreman	72.9	Anomic
Elina	F	45	graduate of a commercial institute	92.2	Anomic
Paavo	M	49	restaurant manager	85.2	Anomic, Dysarthria
Pekka	M	39	telephone assembler	50.2	Broca

Table 2: Aphasic Participants' Scores in the Western Aphasia Battery (WAB)

Subject	AQ max. 100	Spont. speech max. 20	Comprehension max. 10	Repetition max. 10	Naming max. 10	LQ max. 100
Jaakko	68.9	13	7.85	6.7	6.9	51.9
Maija	75.0	13	8.7	7.2	8.6	73.7
Kalle	72.9	17	8.95	7.2	3.3	77.1
Elina	92.2	18	9.9	9.9	8.3	95.6
Paavo	85.2	15	10	8.2	9.4	92.4
Pekka	50.2	11	7.8	2.5	3.8	–

AQ = Aphasia Quotient, LQ = Language Quotient, – =not tested

Table 3: Neurological Information about the Aphasic Participants

Subj	Time post onset; years months	Etiology	Lesion localization	Hemiplegia at the time of onset	Side of Lesion	Severity of Aphasia in the time of onset
Jaakko	1:6	stroke	CT:lesion in the right temporo-parietal area	left facial palsy; left dyspractic hemiplegia	right	1
Maija	12:00	stroke	EEG: left-sided irritative theta activity	mild right-sided hemiplegia	left	1
Kalle	0:2	trauma	CT:left-sided large intracerebral hematoma operated	• none • visual problems?	left	2
Elina	3:4	S.A.H.	CT:subarachnoidal haemorrhage, status post ligaturam ophthalmic artery, posterior cer.artery and middle cer. artery	• some right-sided • weakness in limbs • visual problems	left	2
Paavo	2:5	stroke	CT:left-sided temporal lobe; (old) right-sided fronto-temp. lobe	right-sided hemiplegia	left	2–3
Pekka	1:11	stroke	CT: no information	right-sided hemiplegia	left	1

CT = computerized tomography
EEG=electroencephalography
S.A.H.=subarachnoid haemorrhage

* The severity of aphasia is rated according to the Aphasia Severity Rating Scale (Goodglass & Kaplan 1972):

0 = No usable speech or auditory comprehension.

1 = All communication is through fragmentary expression; great need for inference, questioning, and guessing by the listener. The range of information that can be exchanged is limited, and the listener carries the burden of communication.

2 = Conversation about familiar subjects is possible with help from the listener. There are frequent failures to convey the idea, but patient shares the burden of communication with the examiner.

3 = The patient can discuss almost everyday problems with little or no assistance. Reduction of speech and/or comprehension, however, makes conversation about certain material difficult or impossible.

4 = Some obvious loss of fluency of speech or facility of comprehension, without significant limitation on ideas expressed or form of expression.

5 = Minimal discernible speech handicaps; patient may have subjective difficulties that are not apparent to the listener.

Some recent studies (e.g. Heeschen 1985, Heeschen & Kolk 1988, Miceli et al. 1989) have problematized the distinction between agrammatism and paragrammatism, the latter label referring to the posterior aphasics who are observed to have complex syntactic structures but often misuse grammatical morphemes (but see also Grodzinsky 1991 and, for Finnish, Kukkonen 1993). If we, however, accept the label of agrammatism, it seems evident that there are various types of agrammatism (e.g. Howard 1985, Saffran et al. 1989). This notion has also appeared in the few studies on Finnish-speaking aphasic subjects. Niemi et al. (1990) describe the speech of two Finnish agrammatic aphasics who did not delete suffixes in speech, and this study reported that the few instances of morphological errors were substitutions. The impairments of these Finnish aphasics were mostly failures to produce syntactic phrases in a proper manner, low use of coherent discourse, and dysfluency. Based on these results, Niemi et al. suggest that since Finnish is a synthetic language, Finnish aphasics do not lose bound grammatical markers as easily as do speakers of an analytic language, such as English. On the other hand, Kukkonen & Pajunen (1986) have observed that Finnish-speaking aphasics may use uninflected words or they may delete or choose faulty inflections. Traditionally, agrammatism has been explained by referring to defective morphosyntactic processing (e.g. Goodglass & Menn 1985), but some recent studies show evidence that the primary problem may be a semantically based defective conjunctive processing (e.g. Persson 1991 and 1995).

Anomia is probably the most general and persistent problem in aphasia, and it can be observed in all its clinical categories (Whitehouse & et al. 1978). Albert & Helm-Estabrooks (1988) define anomia as the inability to generate word names in confrontational tasks and in spontaneous speech. When anomia becomes the predominant feature in relation to other problems in aphasic disorders, the term 'anomic aphasia' is used. Spontaneous speech may be rather fluent, although severe word-finding difficulty is observed. Auditory and reading comprehension, reading aloud and repetition are all relatively normal in anomic aphasia. The speech output of an aphasic speaker with word-finding problems is often disconnected; there are hesitations and filled or unfilled pauses. Especially significant are those pauses that occur at non-grammatical junctures, not within clause or sentence boundaries; these types of pauses are more typical of non-fluent than fluent aphasics (see Hadar & Clifford Rose 1988). On the other hand, word-finding problems are also observed in normal conversation, and word search pauses at non-grammatical junctures occur with normal speakers, too (Goodwin & Goodwin 1986). Ellis & Young (1988: 117-123) describe several plausible impairments which cause anomia, for instance category-specific and non-category-specific semantic impairment. On the other hand, some aphasic speakers may experience word-finding problems for words whose meanings were available to them in full detail. It has been suggested that in these cases, a possible explanation might lie in the activation state of the speech output lexicon (e.g. Stemberger 1985).

4.2   The aphasia group

Literature on aphasia contains sporadic mention of aphasia group therapy already after the first world war (e.g. Schuell, Jenkins & Jiménez-Pabón 1969). However, descriptions of the activities employed in group treatment are few (see however Aronson, Shatin & Cook 1956, Bloom 1962, Schlanger & Schlanger 1970, Bollinger, Musson & Holland 1993, Kagan & Gailey 1993, Pachalska 1993). Marquardt, Tonkovich and DeVault (1976) state that literature generally reflects three types of group therapy for aphasics: a speech-centred approach, a socio-therapeutic approach and a psychotherapeutic approach. Kearns (1986) presents five types of aphasia group treatment: direct, indirect, sociolinguistic, transitional and maintenance-oriented. Direct language treatment is usually didactic, structured and directed by the clinician, with activities similar to those used in individual treatment. Indirect treatment groups are unstructured and largely undefined in content and procedure; they may consist of general conversation, social groups, role-playing and field trips. Sociolinguistic treatment focuses on interactive communication among participants with minimal clinician direction; among the aims is maximization of the patients' communicative strengths to improve interpersonal communication. Transition groups are conducted to help aphasics adjust to communication deficits by adapting and reinforcing the skills obtained in individual treatment through group interaction. Finally, maintenance groups provide regular communication stimulation activities of a social nature to maintain post-individual treatment abilities.

In Finland, group therapy treatment for aphasics has been either an adjunct to individual aphasia therapy or a transition tool after individual therapy. The speech-centred groups use often direct language therapy similar to individual treatment. On the other hand, some aphasia groups provide social objectives such as possibilities to meet other aphasic persons and to handle the problems caused by aphasia complementing transition treatment. In this particular aphasia group, the aim was to allow practice in communicative and conversational abilities (Klippi & Pyyppönen 1988, Klippi 1990). As individual aphasia therapy, at least in Finland, usually concentrates on facilitating speech comprehension and production processes, group therapy provides opportunities for using different speech functions in socially motivated contexts.

Before the aphasia group was started, the therapist contacted aphasics who no longer received individual aphasia therapy within the public health care system but who were known to actively seek an alternative source of therapy. Five aphasics were enrolled for the group. The participants' ages and general life situations were rather homogeneous and the amount of women and men was balanced. However, the time since the onset of aphasia and the severity of aphasia varied among participants. Maija had been aphasic for 12 years whereas Kalle had been for only two months (see Table 3). In addition, Jaakko, Maija and Kalle were regarded to have at least moderate aphasic problems whereas Paavo and Elina had only mild aphasic problems.

Apart from the differences in aphasic disorders, the group seemed to be balanced, according to my clinical experience. Hence, it was easier to find generally interesting topics for the group. On the other hand, heterogeneity in terms of aphasia and its severity may even be an advantage. From the point of individual experience, these types of differences give possibilities to compare one's own situation to others and see the variability of aphasic problems. Those who have been aphasic longer have the change to support more acute aphasics. At the same time, word-finding problems are found in all aphasia types, and all participants had similar interactional difficulties in this respect. This evidently gave a sense of solidarity to the participants as in a peer group for the learning of language and culture (e.g. M.H. Goodwin 1990).

The group sessions contained various types of group exercises and conversations, usually according to a given theme. The beginning and the end of each meeting were reserved for free conversation. The thematic conversations covered different topics: for example, the illness, previous work, and so on. The data for this study were obtained from these conversations in the aphasia group therapy sessions.

The aphasia group met at the Department of Phonetics at the University of Helsinki once a week during the fall term. The group sessions were videotaped with VHS-equipment with the permission of the participants. The camera was placed behind a mirror to minimize the disturbance caused by the recordings. Students of logopedics were also following the group sessions from behind the mirror.

4.3 Database

The aims of the research and the methodology chosen imposed certain requirements on the data of the study, including that it should be derived from an actual communication situation, conversations (cf. Heritage 1984, Goodwin & Heritage 1990). Another criterion was that the data should be videotaped to be able to analyse the nonverbal behaviour as well. Due to technical problems, the data could not be collected from everyday situations. As I was just starting to work with an aphasia group, I decided to videotape the group sessions.

Table 4. The speaking time per participant in the group conversations.

Disc.	Jaakko	Maija	Kalle	Elina	Paavo	Th.	Total
I	1.26	2.00	3.27	3.07	–	2.54	15.08
II	0.42	0.11	0.52	1.29	2.25	2.39	8.40
III	0.10	0.02	0.08	0	3.35	1.22	4.30
IV	13.42	0.32	–	2.32	2.22	3.22	25.41
Total	16.00	2.45	4.27	7.08	8.12	10.17	54.00

Disc.= discussion   – = absent
Th. = therapist   0 = not participated in conversation

The core of the data consists of four conversations in the aphasia group. The lengths of speaking times per participant were measured manually by stopwatch. The time spent in each speaker's turn was measured three times and the final time was defined to be the means of the two nearest measures. Hence, the total duration of the transcribed group conversations was 54 minutes and time spent in talking ranged from 2.45 to 16.00 minutes per participant (see Table 4). In addition, a few excerpts were obtained from the aphasic-therapist dyads.

4.4   Transcriptions

In the first phase, a rough transcription on the turn-by-turn basis was made from the videotapes of the aphasic group discussions. This transcription described the verbal part of the conversations in orthographical symbols but did not take up the length of pauses within and between the turns. The speakers' speech-related nonverbal behaviour was described in detail. However, especially from the interactional point of view this transcript has shortcomings, main one being that it reveals only one speaker's communicative behaviour at a time and pays no attention, for instance to the simultaneous nonvocal behaviour of an interactant which nevertheless may be crucial to understanding the development of the interaction.

A transcription can never be a complete description of spoken interaction; Gail Jefferson (1985:25) has mentioned: "...when we talk about transcription we are talking about one way to pay attention to recordings of actually occurring events." Nettelbladt (1994:54) refers to Linell who for his part has pointed out the great problems that exist in the transmission from the acoustic (and visual) signal to the written notation:" ...a projection of a dynamic, temporally distributed stream of behaviour onto a spatially organized, static object...". Also, selectivity of the transcript is to be encouraged; a transcription that is too detailed is difficult to follow and assess (Ochs 1979). These problems have been extremely obvious in the present study. As one of the main aims has been to analyse aphasic conversation and interaction and its various means, taking the linguistic problems of aphasic speakers into consideration, the other aspects of interaction – the non- or quasi-lexical speech objects (Heritage 1989:29) – have become extremely relevant in some analysis. For this reason, the more advanced versions of the transcriptions have been applied and developed according to the aim of the specific questions of the substudies. Three various transcription modifications have been applied and they will be described in the following.

4.4.1   The basic transcription

In the second phase, the more detailed transcripts and analyses carried out on the excerpts of this study have been transcribed according to the conventions of conversation analysis. The transcription notation used in conversation analysis has been developed by Gail Jefferson and it has been presented in several sources (e.g. Levinson 1983, Atkinson & Heritage 1984, Button & Lee 1987, see also the Finnish versions Hakulinen 1989 and Tainio et al. 1991). The symbols used in this study are presented in the beginning of the work. Audiotapes have been made from the original video recordings of the group sessions and accordingly the more detailed transcriptions, based on conventional Finnish orthography, have been made. If problems have arisen in listening to the material and reshaping it into the transcription, the audio and video recordings have been compared because sometimes the lip movements of a speaker have clarified the problem. Also, another trained listener has been used in some trouble places to make the transcripts more reliable. In this study, there was one dysarthric speaker. His speech was sometimes blurred and in some occurrences his speech intelligibility was poor which caused trouble for the orthographical transcription. One solution might have been to use a phonetic transcription for his speech but because of the occasional overlaps and the periodic technical shortcomings in the quality of the recordings, it turned out to be impossible. It was decided to accept the rough orthographical transcription because these problematic occurrences were only few and they were not crucial from the point of view of the research questions.

The turns of the speakers have been transcribed consecutively and hence the spatial arrangement of turns by different speakers is vertical (Edwards 1993). The occurrences of overlaps have been marked. In group discussions there were some occurrences of overlaps which were extremely difficult to transcribe, which were mainly the laughing occurrences. For this reason, the modified transcript notation was used and we will describe it later.

The silent pauses between the turns and within the turns were measured. The duration of a pause was defined as 200 ms or more. The durations of the pauses have been measured from the audiotapes using either a Farallon MacRecorder digitizer and a SoundEdit program or Signalyze TM Version 2 (Keller 1992). The transcriptions also contain a description of some prosodic features, for instance the intonation contours of a turn's ends and some other factors like tempo and stress.

The examples in chapter 8 (Collaborative repair initaited by aphasic speacers) and in chapter 9 (Uninflected single-word turns) have been mainly presented according to the above described conventions. An example of the conventional transcription is in the following:

Example

```
1  t:no mut haastatel|ka|a vaikka Jaakko|a.(.)minu|st se ol|is
      PRT but      interview-IMP-2PL  for instance 1name M-PAR   I-ELA   it   be-CON
   well but go ahead and interview Jaakko(.)I think it would be

2  ihan(0.8)°hyvä°,
   PRT         good
   all(0.8)°right°,

   (2.8)

3  M:h.*$ehe|i oshaa$[san-*
             NEG3  can {say}
     h.*$channot $[sa-*

4  E:               [missä sä ol|i|t tö|i|ssä.
                     what-INE  you  be-PST-2  work-PL-INE
                    [where were you working.

   (1.3)

5  J:°mitä.°=
      what-PAR
     °what.°=

6  E: =°mi|ssä sä ol|i|t,.°
         what-INE  you  be-PST-2
      °where were you,.°
```

```
   (0.6)

7   J: Lemminkäinen.{Ø INE}
        company name-NOM
        Lemminkäinen.{Ø INE}

8   E: Lemminkäinen.{Ø INE}
        company name-NOM
        Lemminkäinen.{Ø INE}
```

4.4.2 Transcriptions with speech-related nonverbal behaviour

As one of the aims of this study is to describe and analyse the various means with which aphasic speakers are able to participate in conversation, it was relevant to add nonverbal acts in the transcriptions. Chapters 5 (Nonverbal behaviour as a compensatory resource) and 6 (Using written numbers, writing and drawing) analyse the nonverbal behaviour which, according to the literature, has the potential to convey meanings and thus to compensate aphasic speakers speech problems in conversation. Hence, a modification of the conventional transcription system of conversation analysis was developed. Certain nonverbal acts, containing speaker's head, hand or body movements, have been described in the transcript with the help of the some additional symbols (see Transcript notation). The spatial arrangement of turns by different speakers is vertical.

A rough synchronization of a nonverbal act with the speech has been indicated with asterisks.

Example

```
1   E: e|t|kö sä ol|lu(0.4)tuolla.(2.6)ol|i|t|+sä ulkomailla.
        NEG-2-Q   you be-PPC    there           be-PST-2-(-Q)+you abroad
        weren't you(0.4)there.(2.6)were you abroad.

2   (.)Venäjä|llä° tai°
       Russia-ADE    or
       (.)in Russia°or°

3   J:*joo.*=
      *yes.*=
      *Onod,GE*

4   E:=*°ol|i|t°*
       be-PST-2
       *°you were°*
       *Onod,GJ*
```

4.4.3 Synchronized transcriptions with nonverbal behaviour

A third version of transcribing was developed to analyse the complex interaction of mutual laughter and humour in aphasic conversation. As one of the questions studied was aphasic speakers' means for entering and inviting other participants to mutual laughter, a more detailed and synchronized transcript was needed which could handle the simultaneously occurring acts in interaction. In this transcript system several acts, gaze, vocal behaviour and nonverbal behaviour were transcribed.

During the development of this more sophisticated transcript, a syncWRITER programme was published (*med-i-bit* GmbH 1990). Because this programme yielded the possibility to describe synchronized actions of different speakers, it was adopted. This transcript is based on a form of musical notation where each instrument or voice in a composition is assigned its own stave in the score. Hence, the spatial arrangement of turns by different speakers is in partiture form (Edwards 1993). The score notation enables the descriptions of the simultaneously occurring acts (e.g. gaze, vocal behaviour and nonverbal behaviour) of several speakers. In the following transcription, every speaker has three tracks: a gaze track (if observed), a speech track and a gesture track which are marked below each other. The linear progression of the events is also preserved.

Mgaze	GJ..
M	minä(.)edistyy(.)koko ajan. NAURAA
	I progress-3 all time-ACC
	I (.)progress (.)all the time. LAUGHS
Mgesture	***LH stepwise↑, Onod***
t	mm.mm.
	DM
Jgaze	Gpaper..........
J	(0.6)aha.(1.7)
	(0.6)oh. (1.7)
Jgesture	***Onod***

4.5   Translations of transcriptions into English

The conversational excerpts have been translated into English and the translations are offered together with the original Finnish transcription. There are several characteristics in Finnish which influence such a translated transcript. Finnish is a synthetic language where the basic principle of word formation is suffixations, the addition of suffixes to stems. Finnish has 14 morphological cases and the case endings normally correspond to prepositions in English. Also, Finnish sometimes uses endings, for instance possessive suffixes, where English generally has independent words. Similarly Finnish has clitic particles which always occur in the final position after all other endings. This makes words longer in Finnish than in, for instance, English. In addition, there is no grammatical gender, and there are no articles before Finnish nouns (Karlsson 1983:12-14). As the structures of Finnish and English are so different, the translations were not possible to do on a word-by-word basis. For this reason, the text contains the original Finnish excerpts and 'free' translations from Finnish into English. The examples offer the original

Finnish excerpts, the English gloss and the 'free' translations from Finnish into English.

One participant of the group, Paavo, had dysarthric problems in addition to his aphasic problems which made his articulation inaccurate and sometimes slurred. Also Jaakko had occasional problems in switching from one articulation to another. Luria (1973:185) explains this as a typical feature of Broca's aphasia (efferent motor aphasia in his classification) which is due to a disturbance in the kinetic organization of articulations. Hence these speakers had either articulatory or phonological-articulatory problems in their speech. The inaccurately pronounced words have been marked in italics in the Finnish text, for instance *si-sirontaa sirontaa* for "seurantaa" and if the target word could clearly be reconstructed, it has been marked within summation brackets in the English translation, for example, {fo-follow-up follow-up}. If a word was incomprehensible, it has been marked with a question mark in the English translation.

The two speakers with Broca's aphasia, Jaakko and Maija, had lexical and/ or morpho-syntactic loss or deviations in their utterances, for instance:

```
Maija: minä (.) edistyy (.) koko ajan
       I         progress-3   all time-ACC
       I (.) progress (.) all the time
```

In Finnish, the verb agrees with the subject. In this example, however, the third person singular form (*edisty+y*), which could also be regarded as the unmarked form, is used for the first person singular form (*edisty+n*). The unagreement, however, does not cause problems in comprehension. From the communicative point of view, more problematic are fragmentary utterances in which the speaker has such severe problems in word finding and in the expression of grammatical relations that all grammatical morphemes are missing. In its extreme form this leads to nonverbal turns or to turns that contain only one uninflected lexical item.

5. Nonverbal behaviour as a compensatory resource

5.1 Introduction

Charles Darwin began the tradition of the empirical study of nonverbal behaviour with his work *The Expressions of the Emotions in Man and Animals* in 1872. Darwin was mainly interested in two issues: the first is the question of the innateness versus the social learning of nonverbal behaviour, and the second is the communicative use of expressive signs (Scherer & Ekman 1982:1-2). The latter question is particularly important from the point of view of aphasics' communication. In fact, this issue goes back as far as to the beginning of the nineteenth century to 1825 when J. Bouillaud presented the hypotheses that body communication may substitute or compensate for speech in the event of a speech disturbance (Ahlsén 1991). The interest in this question was already present in the first writings about aphasia. For example, in 1861 Paul Broca wrote that his aphasic subject, called 'Tan', tended to make up for his inability to speak with various gestures (Kann 1950:17).

However, four years after Broca, in 1865, Armand Trousseau questioned the aphasic patients' ability to express their thoughts by gesture or by drawing, and concluded that the great majority of their intellectual activities are impaired (Gainotti 1988). Furthermore, Finkelnburg proposed that aphasia is merely one consequence of a more general symbolic disorder (1870: translation with commentary in Duffy & Liles 1979). He further pointed out that aphasia not only extended beyond speech and language, including comprehension, reading and writing, but was also linked to many nonverbal disturbances of symbolic usage. To support his argument, Finkelnburg presented five cases of aphasia which demonstrated, along with linguistic disturbances, various other symptoms: hemiplegia, memory disorders, dementia and especially loss of understanding and use of symbols (e.g. Christian symbols, notes, loss of comprehension of money). He concluded that aphasia could not be seen as a simple verbal impairment, but instead proposed a more accurate and complete definition of the disorder, referred to as 'asymbolia'. He defined this as a "disturbance of function in which there is a partial or complete loss of the ability to comprehend and express concepts by means of acquired signs" (Duffy & Liles 1979).

This conception of asymbolia addresses the fundamental issues concerning the relationship between nonverbal and verbal actions. Pierre Feyereisen has

Conversation as an achievement in aphasics
Studia Fennica
Linguistica 6
1996.

analyzed the interaction between gestures and speech in his review article of 1987, noting that it has traditionally been hypothesed that body movements and language constitute parallel, separate systems. Thus, gestural processing is independent of the processing involved in speech production, and the mechanisms are not connected. In the occurrence of aphasia the nonverbal system stays intact. On the other hand, Feyereisen mentions the diametrically opposing viewpoint that gestures and speech are closely interconnected, and that they arise from a common cognitive source. According to this latter view, aphasia is then related to disordered nonverbal behaviour.

This interactive theory is supported by several facts. First, Feyereisen (1987) mentions McNeill's (1985) notion that gestures occur only during speech in synchronization with linguistic units, and could be direct manifestations of the speaker's ongoing thinking process. McNeill (1985:350) argues that: "Gestures share with speech a computational stage; they are, accordingly, parts of the same psychological structure". To further support his claim, McNeill noted that there is simultaneous dissolution of linguistic and gestural abilities in aphasic patients. Second, Feyereisen (ibid.) refers to studies which show that some gestures reveal difficulties experienced by the speaker in speech production and thus relate to the mechanism controlling the verbalization processes. Third, some studies suggest that the coordinative structures between speech and gesture are evidence for the interactive theory. However, several notions also support separability between the mechanisms of gesture and speech. In support of this theory, Feyereisen (ibid.) cites studies that show that aphasia without apraxia is common and that aphasics often pantomime the use of objects they are unable to name. Furthermore, this position – that speech and gestures have same underlying mechanisms – is challenged by the observations of left-handers with both aphasia and apraxia who recover from aphasia, but not from apraxia. Feyereisen does not clearly favour either theory, but urges researchers to develop alternative views on the interaction between gestures and speech. For Feyereisen, the main problem is that researchers must determine which computational stage is shared by the two systems, and when they begin to diverge.

As we see, studying aphasic patients has been used in defence of both hypotheses. Because aphasia causes several disordered linguistic functions, the clearest of which is the inability to find proper words for utterances, an alternative area of research has emerged that studies the possibility of nonverbal behaviour compensating for aphasic disorders in conversation. In aphasic speech, the most common problem is word-finding difficulty when words are not accessible to a speaker. In aphasiological literature, this symptom is called anomia and it is one of the most general and persevering features of aphasia, regardless of clinical type (Whitehouse et al. 1978:63). According to Lesser (1989:197-198), there are several reasons for a failure to produce the correct word, although different kinds of behaviour can be observed. An aphasic speaker with a semantic disorder may produce semantic paraphasias for the target words, whereas an aphasic speaker with a difficulty in accessing the item in the phonological lexicon may produce circumlocutions (for instance that is what one throws [a ball]) and exploratory phonemic paraphasias. Problems also arise in the 'phonemic assembly' which lead to phonemic paraphasias when searching for a word; yet these phonemic paraphasias are more closely related to a target word than in the other cases mentioned. In addition, difficulties can arise at the stage of planning the phonetic realization which corresponds to the definition of apraxia of speech. Moreover, consistent articulatory problems at the most peripheral level of speech production may cause difficulties in naming.

The main idea in the compensatory hypothesis has been that, with the occurrence of anomia or other difficulty in speaking, a speaker may use nonverbal means to express the intended meaning. Hence, nonverbal behaviour may offer an alternative means for communication, either by substituting for, or by augmenting speech, when it is impossible or difficult. So, for example, the increased use of the nonverbal channel has been assumed to support the compensatory hypothesis. However, studies report conflicting results about the compensatory use of nonverbal behaviour in aphasia. Some researchers have doubted the existence of the compensatory abilities, because of, among other things, apractic disorders (Glosser et al. 1986) which impair the execution of learned movements (see e.g. Geschwind & Damasio 1985). For example, Cicone et al. (1979) and McNeill (1992) maintain differences between various types of aphasia and the use of nonverbal behaviour. According to Cicone et al. (ibid.), Wernicke's aphasics used more elaborate and complex movements and the largest proportion of gesturing was nonreferential, whereas Broca's aphasics produced simple, unelaborate units with a high degree of referentiality. Cicone et al. concluded that the results offer little support for the view that aphasic speakers spontaneously enhance their communicative efficacy through the use of gesture. Furthermore, Glosser et al. (1986) provided evidence that aphasic speakers are impaired in their gestural communicative competence under natural conditions of communication.

On the other hand, several investigators have found that aphasic speakers use more nonverbal cues than do normal speakers (Larkins & Webster 1981, Feyereisen 1983, Ahlsén 1985, Smith 1987a, Le May et al. 1988, Herrmann et al. 1989, Hadar 1991). Many of these studies suggest that aphasic speakers compensate for their verbal deficit by increasing the frequency of their nonverbal behaviour (Smith 1987a, Feyereisen et al. 1988, Le May et al. 1988, Herrmann et al. 1989, Klippi 1990, Ahlsén 1991, Hadar 1991). In addition, the latest reports indicate that severe and moderate aphasic speakers tend to use nonverbal behaviour to compensate to their verbal disorders more than do mild aphasics (Smith 1987b, Feyereisen et al. 1988, Herrmann et al. 1988, Hadar 1991).

Studies also report that healthy speakers gesture while searching for words. Goodwin & Goodwin (1986) have studied healthy speakers' use of nonverbal behaviour as an interactive resource. They describe gaze aversion, thinking face, producing talk connected to the trouble, for instance w't th'hellwz'er name, perturbation in the talk, sound stretches and hand movements. Indeed, according to empirical observations, these features are also found among aphasic speakers experiencing word-finding difficulties.

Goodwin & Goodwin (1986) and Goodwin (1987) used different method than did the previously mentioned aphasia studies. They criticized investigations that study nonverbal behaviour by isolating gestures from the local, interactive circumstances of their production. Their approach, conversation analysis, stresses the detailed qualitative analysis of nonverbal behaviour and the co-participation of a recipient in the local interactive context. According to Goodwin & Goodwin (ibid.), this method yields the possibility to make a detailed investigation of, how the participants themselves not only find meanings for the gestures but how they use them as social facts. Thus, the participants' verbal and nonverbal behaviour have clear consequences for the organisation of the activity they are engaged in (Goodwin & Goodwin 1986:72). Goodwin & Goodwin further stress that the most important question involves speech in connection with nonverbal behaviour, and these communicative factors' relationship to the interpretation of turns. The linguistic tradition has excluded the analysis of nonverbal behaviour related to speech in the interpretation of the conversational contributions. However, it seems reasonable to suppose that both verbal and nonverbal behaviour are important for the interpretation of turns.

In the following pages, nonverbal actions of aphasic group participants, their categorization and their interactional consequences have been investigated in their local interactive context as Goodwin & Goodwin (1986) and Goodwin (1987) have suggested. Simple quantifications have also been included. My departure point has been to analyse nonverbal behaviour which has, according to the literature, the potential to convey meanings and thus to compensate for aphasic speakers's speech problems in conversation. Hence, I will analyse nonverbal behaviour in conversation from the point of view of compensation, as compensation can facilitate the development of aphasic talk and the establishment of mutual understanding for current purposes. To clarify, nonverbal behaviour that does not convey meanings such as turn-allocations or turn-keepings will not be studied even though this behaviour can influence interaction. Finally, I will discuss possible explanations for the variability in the use of nonverbal behaviour.

The aims of this chapter are:

1. To analyse the conversational sequences where aphasic speakers use potentially compensatory nonverbal behaviour combined with speech or without speech.
2. To evaluate the functions of potentially compensatory nonverbal behaviour combined with speech or without speech in aphasic conversation.
3. To analyse the usage of nonverbal behaviour to convey meaning, especially by observing cases where a speaker changes the mode of expression to a nonverbal channel, and by analysing the consequences of nonverbal behaviour for the development of conversation.

According to the literature, three types of nonverbal behaviour can substitute for speech and as such, compensate speech; these are emblems, illustrative movements and deictic movements (Ekman & Friesen 1969 and 1972, Wiener et al. 1972). As a basis for the analysis, I have partly taken up these classifications, but I will also show some examples of nonverbal behaviour that are difficult to classify using these classes as criteria.

The data presented in this chapter is selected from four aphasic group discussions. Two additional examples are derived from the aphasic-therapist dyads, and these are analysed in connection with illustrative movements. The potentially compensatory nonverbal acts – emblems, illustrative movements and deictic movements – were defined according to the literature. Whereas these definitions helped to focus on the potentially compensatory movements, the final classification of the nonverbal acts was made according to their sequential context (cf. Goodwin & Goodwin 1986), revealing the function of nonverbal acts within conversation. Regardless of these tentative classifications, other types of potentially compensatory nonverbal behaviour were also sought, although there was not an exact fit between movements and definitions.

In the first phase, each speaker's nonverbal behaviour was described in the transcription. In the second phase, the emblems, illustrative movements and deictic movements were identified from the video recordings, one nonverbal act type at a time. Each nonverbal act was interpreted and classified according to its local interactive context. In the third phase, the interactional consequences of their use were analysed.

5.2 Emblems

The first group of nonverbal behaviour to be observed is emblems. According to Ekman & Friesen (1969:63, 1972), emblems are arbitrarily-coded nonverbal acts that have been regarded as having a direct verbal translation or dictionary definition, usually consisting of one word or more, or perhaps even a phrase. The verbal definition or translation of the emblem is well known by all members of the group, class or culture. An important feature of an emblem is that it may repeat, substitute, or contradict some part of concomitant verbal behaviour; a crucial question is whether it can be replaced with a word or two without changing the meaning conveyed. Wiener et al. (1972:210) describe a class of pantomimic gestures which they divide into two classes, formal and improvisational. The formal pantomimic gestures very closely resemble emblems because they are defined as stylized movements of the arms and hands and they have a culturally prescribed consensual meaning. As examples of such nonverbal behaviour they give the waving of goodbye, or the forming of a circle with the index finger and thumb to signify 'okay' or 'perfect', which are the same examples that Ekman and Friesen (1969, 1972) give for emblems.

Furthermore, Ekman and Friesen (1969:64) mention that emblems occur most frequently when verbal exchange is prevented by noise, external circumstances (such as while watching a play), distance (between hunters), by agreement (in the game of charades), or by organic impairment (the deaf). Typically in such instances, emblematic exchange carries the bulk of messages that would normally be communicated through words. In contrast, most common emblems, such as nodding or head-shaking in affirmation or denial, are often seen in normal conversations. These types of nonverbal behaviour are typical in simple question-answer adjacency pairs.

From the point of view of aphasic speakers' communication, emblems are the most important items of nonverbal behaviour because suffice to substitute a word or words with nonverbal behaviour. An aphasic person may compensate for her/his speaking problems, at least partly, with emblematic behaviour. However, most aphasics have some verbal abilities that they try to maximally utilize, often accompanied by nonverbal behaviour. For this reason, the temporal relationship between a nonverbal act and a verbal act is crucial from a theoretical standpoint. Do the verbal and the nonverbal acts occur simultaneously or sequentially? And if they occur sequentially, in what order? These questions can be asked when observing aphasic conversations.

First we will study adjacency pairs within conversation and analyse how aphasic speakers behave verbally and nonverbally in these simple adjacency pairs. The following examples illustrate some frequently observed cases. In these examples, the second pair part consists of a verbal expression yes or no and the respective simultaneous nonverbal behaviour, the head nod or the head shake (example 1, line 3 and example 2, line 2).

Example 1

```
1   E: e|t|kö sä ol|lu(0.4)tuolla.(2.6)ol|i|t|+sä ulkomailla.
        NEG-2-Q   you  be-PPC       there        be-PST-2-(-Q)+you  abroad
        weren't you(0.4)there.(2.6)were you abroad.

2   (.)Venäjä|llä°tai°
       Russia-ADE      or
    (.)in Russia°or°

3   J:*joo.*=
      *yes.*=
      *Onod,GE*

4   E:=*°ol|i|t°*
          be-PST-2
      *°you were°*
      *Onod,GJ*
```

Example 2

```
1   E: on|ko lähellä Tsernob?
        is-Q   near      place name
        is it near Chernob?

    (1.1)

2   J:*.hh ei.*=
          NEG
      *.hh no.*=
      *Oshake*

3   E: =ei
          NEG
        =no
```

The following example shows an excerpt where one of the members, Maija, gives only a nonverbal reply to the question (line 4). Those examples were very rare in the data. The previous discussion concerned the European Security Conference and its functions:

Example 3

```
1   t:nii mitä nää seurantako[koukse|t palvele|e oikein.]
      PRT what+PAR these  follow-up meeting-PL       serve for-3   really
    well what do these progress report me[etings serve for.]

2   P:                              [mitä se tekee joo(.)nii]nii.
                                     what  it does  PRT    PRT PRT
                                    [what does it do yes(.)yeah]yeah.

    (0.3)

3   t:on|k|s ke|lle|kään muodost|u|nu selvä|ä,.=
      is-Q-CLI  anybody-ADE-CLI  form-REF-PPC     clear-PAR
    has anybody got a clear (idea),.=

4   M:*Oshake*

        GM
5   P:=kakkos kori ja kolmos kori(0.2)ja mi|tä se,
      number two  basket and number three basket    and  what+PAR it
    =second basket and third basket(0.2)and what it,

6   t:nii jo[o.
      PRT  PRT
    yeah ye[s.

7   P:      [mi|tä si-sironta|a sironta|a pitää tapahtu|u.
             what-PAR {follow-up-PAR    follow-up-PAR}  must   happen-INF
    [what {progress report meetings} has to happen.
```

Here the therapist and Paavo are discussing the function of follow-up meetings. The therapist first directs her gaze to the group, then to the newspaper clipping that the discussion has been based on, and then asks, has anybody got a clear [idea],. At this point, Maija shakes her head. Because this is a silent turn within the group, it could have gone unnoticed. The therapist may have overlooked it and subsequently moved on to the next question. However, Paavo's following contribution shows that he has acknowledged Maija's head shake. Paavo turns his gaze to Maija and expands the discussion with debating the meaning of the meetings.

The head-shaking emblem was very typical of one speaker in this data. Jaakko used recurrent head-shaking movements, sometimes several times in a sequence. This act was usually synchronized with his verbal phrase. The next two examples are exceptional in that in both cases Jaakko begins his turn with the nonverbal head shake followed by his verbal contribution. The meaning of the examples are of a similar type, expressing that he is unable to contribute to the conversation.

Example 4

```
1   t:mite|s Jaakko.(0.7)jos sä esittä|yty|si|t nyt
        how-CLI  1name M      if  you introduce-REF-CON-2    now
    how about Jaakko.(0.7)if you would like to introduce yourself

2   sitten,(0.6)mu|i|lle.
        then            other-PL-ADE
    now,(0.6)for the others.

3   J:* * ei tu *ei tule mitä|än.*
            NEG come NEG come  nothing-PAR
        * * nothing come(s)*nothing comes (out).*
    *Oshake*                  *Oshake*

4   t:miks|ei.[heh heh]
        why+NEG
    why not.[heh heh]

5   J:         [*ei ole*]
                 NEG be
            [*there is nothing*]
               *Oshake*
```

Example 5

```
1   t: no Jaakko.
        PRT 1name M
    well Jaakko.

    (0.7)

2   J:* * ei tuu mitä|ä.
            NEG come nothing-PAR
    * *  nothing comes (out).
    *Oshake*

    (0.6)

3   t:#o:#(.)o:n|ko varma[heh-heh-heh]
             is-Q     sure
    #a:r#(.)a:re you sure[heh-heh-heh]

4   J:               [ei heh-heh ]mää koit|i|n.
                      NEG            I    try-PST-1
                     [no heh-heh ]I tried.
```

Examples 4 and 5 have similar structures. In these samples, the therapist allocates the turn to Jaakko, who begins to give excuses that he is unable to say anything. In the first case, the general theme of the conversation was to introduce oneself to others and in the second example, the general topic was to tell about one's work. In both cases Jaakko shakes his head before giving the verbal contribution (example 4, line 3 and example 5, line 2). It is possible that Jaakko has developed a fixed behavioural pattern with nonverbal and verbal behaviour for these kinds of situations. In these examples, it is interesting that he begins his turn with a nonverbal act which can be classified as an emblem.

The most frequent emblems in these conversations were head shakes and head nods. Other types of emblems were infrequent for instance, hand shrugs, to express "what can be done?" (cf. Bavelas et al. 1992). These emblems were always combined with speech. The following example illustrates the use of such an emblem (line 3):

Example 6

```
1   t:no mut haastatel|ka|a vaikka Jaakko|a.(.)minu|st se ol|i|s
        PRT  but  interview-IMP-2PL     for instance  1name M-PAR      I-ELA    it   be-CON
    well but go ahead and interview Jaakko(.)I think it would be

2   ihan(0.8)°hyvä°,
    PRT          good
    all(0.8)°right°,

    (2.8)

3   M:h.*$ehei oshaa$[san-*
            NEG3   can       say (?)
      h.*$channot $[sa-*
      *LHlifts palm up, lays down*

4   E:                    [missä sä ol|i|t tö|i|ssä.
                           where    you be-PST-2  work-PL-INE
                          [where were you working.
```

Figure 1: Emblem (cf. line 3)

The previous notion is in accordance with Herrmann et al's (1988) results. In their study, the aphasics used mostly 'codified gestures' which were mainly head nods and shakes as well as shoulder shrugs. Ekman & Friesen (1969) have suggested that emblems possibly carry less personal information than do other nonverbal features. Emblems resemble linguistic units because they are arbitrarily coded, and they may replace certain words. Ekman & Friesen (ibid.) have also proposed that emblems are perhaps used around the more ritualized aspects of conversation, such as greetings and departures or changes in status or topic. The present data does not include the openings or closings of the group sessions which might have contained greetings or goodbyes with the concomitant nonverbal acts. This may explain why other emblems than head nod and shake were so little observed in these aphasic conversations.

In adjacency pairs, head-nodding and shaking emblems typically function as signs of approval or disagreement. From an interactional point of view, these are easy to interpret within conversational context. Furthermore, even in this data they usually occurred in relation to speech, and hence the nonverbal and verbal part of the contribution supported each other. In other words, no interactional troubles were observed in connection with the use of these emblems.

The speakers in this group rarely utilised only a nonverbal code to indicate affirmation or denial. On the other hand, the words "yes" and "no" are so basic in our vocabulary that they usually remain in aphasic speech except for the most severe forms of aphasia. In fact, so basic are these responses that in many globally aphasic persons' communication, they are the only words the speaker can express (cf. Goodwin 1995).

It is possible that the strong synchronization between nonverbal and verbal approval or disagreement may occur because there were so few occurrences where the verbal and nonverbal contributions were expressed in sequence or separately in this data. Nevertheless, these occurrences might have some important implications. Although the most typical case combines verbal and nonverbal behaviour, there are possibilities for the dissociation of the verbal and nonverbal behaviour (cf. McNeill 1985 and 1992, Feyereisen 1987). Often a speaker used only verbal affirmation or denial. In a few cases, only nonverbal contributions were seen, and in some cases there were occurrences where the contributions began with a nonverbal act. This data contained too few cases to draw conclusions from, but theoretically it would be an interesting question to analyse these types of occurrences in different aphasic speakers and compare the results to healthy speakers.

5.3   Illustrative movements

The next group of nonverbal behaviour to be observed is that of illustrative movements. This is a large group of mainly hand movements that draw a picture of their referent or action and thus are iconically coded. According to Ekman and Friesen (1969:68-69), illustrative movements are directly tied to speech and can repeat, substitute, contradict or augment the verbal information. Cohen and Harrison (1973) claim that illustrative movements facilitate communication by amplifying and elaborating the verbal content of the message, and Le May et al. suggest (1988) that furthermore, these movements may also be used to provide gestural illustrations if the speaker has difficulties to express her/his meaning verbally. Ekman and Friesen (1969:68-70) present a large group of illustrative movements divided into six subclasses: batons, ideographs, deictic movements, spatial movements, kinetographs and pictographs. Batons are movements that time, accent or emphasize a specific word or phrase, whereas ideographs are movements which sketch a path or direction of thought. Neither of these movements convey independent meanings. Deictic movements point to an object that is present, spatial movements depict a spatial relationship, and kinetographs are movements which depict a bodily action; these can convey something of the speech content. Wiener et al. (1972:210) have a somewhat similar class of movements which they called 'improvisational pantomimic gestures'. In this work the illustrative movements include chiefly what Ekman and Friesen called spatial movements, kinetographs and pictographs, because these movements can potentially be used to compensate for speech.

In this data, the most usual cases of using illustrative movements were related to speech. Thus the recipient obtains verbal and visual information simultaneously. The following excerpt is typical of an illustrative movement:

Example 7

```
1   M:  *minä*(.)*edistyy(.)koko aja|n.*[NAURAHTAA
         |            progress-3    whole   time-AAC
        *I*(.)*progress(.)all the time.*[LAUGHS
        *Onod*     *raises LH stepwise*

2   t:                                    [*mm.mm.*

    (0.6)

3   J:aha.
      PRT
      I see.
```

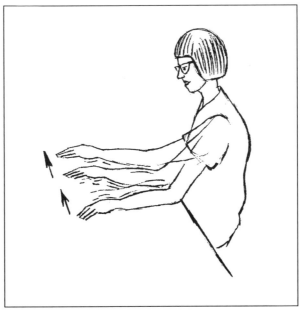

Figure 2: Illustrative movement (cf. line 1)

In this example, Maija tells how she is constantly making progress with her speech although she has been aphasic for years. While she states this, she raises her left hand step by step (line 1). This gesture is iconical, and it elaborates the meaning of her verbal contribution. In this case the nonverbal behaviour seems to form a single, united expression with the verbal meaning. A similar type of iconical gesture is the following:

Example 8

```
1   E:                                    [vähä humalassa liiku|n
                                           little   drunk      move-1
                                          [little drunk I walk

2   (-)*noin horju|skele|n* kun kävele|n paljon.=
        PRT     shake-FRE-1    when  walk-1   a lot
    (-)*I stagger a bit* when I walk a lot.=
        *RHshows wriggling movement*

3   K:*jaaha.*$jooh niin$
        PRT      PRT  PRT
      *oh.*$yes uhuh$
      *Onod*
```

Figure 3: Illustrative movement (cf. line 2)

In this excerpt Elina explains how her visual problem disturbs her walking. She describes that she walks as if she were drunk, and she staggers when she walks a lot. At the same time she makes a wriggling gesture with her hand (line 2), which can be interpreted as elaborating the verbal part of her contribution.

In example 9, the topic concerns a trip in which Paavo and Jaakko had participated:

Example 9

1 t:sa|i|tte|ko mitä|än alennus|ta sii|tä.(.)vai ol|i|k|s tää ihan
     get-PST-2(PL)-Q   any-PAR   reduction-PAR   it-ELA   or   be-PST-Q-CLI this   PRT
   did you get any reduction for it.(.)or was this just the

2 normaali hinta.
   normal   price
   normal price.

   (2.6)

3 P:ei si|tä oikee osa|a sano|a.(0.5)siellä(-)lipu|ssa luk|i(-)
     NEG it-PAR   exactly can-3 say-INF   there   ticket-INE   stand-PST
   one can't really say.(0.5)there(-)on the ticket it said(-)

4 seitsekymmentä viis prosentti|a,.(0.6)ol|i hinna|sta.
        seventy five   percent-PAR   be-PST price-ELA
   seventy-five percent,.(0.6) of the price.

5 t:°**m-hmm mm**°

6 P:°joo°(3.0)lipu|ssa*luk|i pien|i|n kirjaim|i|n*tse.
       PRT   ticket-INE   stand-PST small-PL-INS letter-PL-INS   it
   °**yes**°(3.0)**on the ticket*was written in small letters*{*it*}.**
                          RHshows small space

Figure 4: Illustrative movement (cf. line 6)

Here the therapist asks Jaakko and Paavo if they received a reduction in the price of the trip, and Paavo answers that the text of the reduction was printed with small letters on the ticket. At the same time he shows a small space between his thumb and forefinger (line 6). This nonverbal act can also be regarded as an elaborative one.

In some cases a speaker could not find the proper words and tried to rely on the nonverbal behaviour supporting the speech with hand movements. In the following example Jaakko was unable to find a word, and so he resorted to nonverbal behaviour in order to convey his meaning to others:

Example 10

```
1   J: sitte.(10.4 huokailee)* *kier-,(0.4)*mikä se on,.*=
           then                               what    it   is
        then.(10.4 SIGHS)*         *twi-,(0.4)*what is it,.*=
               *twirls his pen on the paper**RHtwirls his pen in the air,GP*

2   P: =*joo*
          yes
        =*yes*
         *GJ*

    (0.7)

3   M:*kierre|tä|ä.
          twirl-PASS-4
       *twirling.*
        *LHmakes a circle in the air,GJ*

4   P:*joo*
         PRT
       *yes*

    (1.7)

5   J:*ympäri.*=
         around
       *around.*=
        *RHmakes a circle in the air,GP*

6   P: =*nii*
          PRT
        =*yeah*
          *GJ*
```

Figure 5: Illustrative movement (cf. line 1)

Jaakko explains the operating of the chipboard factory and he has drawn a sketch of a machine. In this excerpt he searches for the right word and he is able to utter the beginning of the word *twirl* or *twist* (in Finnish *kiertää*) (line 1) but cannot express the end of the word and asks, <u>what is it.</u>. At the same time, he makes a gesture of twirling. Thus, he was able to support his goal while appealing for help. In this excerpt the speaker is able to show clearly with a compensative gesture the trouble spot in the conversation. He turns to the recipients and appeals for help with his problem, using an open question. At the same time he is able to assist the others with a relevant gesture. Thus, this is also an example of an exposed self-initiated other repair with the aid of a gesture (cf. Jefferson 1987).

In the following pages, I will focus on two comparable examples of the compensatory nonverbal behaviour in aphasic conversation. In these examples gestures do not directly fit the classifications found in the literature, but here I will include them in the group of illustrators, although they are not connected with the concrete features of an object or action. In both cases the nonverbal behaviour refers to an abstraction, that is, to a temporal order of the events. The examples reveal how the speakers, unable to express the sequence of events grammatically, used nonverbal means for the expression of sequentiality. The gestures appeared during storytelling in a dyadic interaction between an aphasic speaker and a therapist. The group discussions did not have instances of this kind of nonverbal behaviour.

The first example is an excerpt of a conversation between Maija and the therapist.

Example 11

```
1  t: joo(.)no mi|llä sä se|n saa|t sit,.(1.3) [puhu|ma|lla.]
        PRT      PRT  what-ADE you it-ACC    get-2  then          speak-INF-ADE
       yes(.)well then how do you get him,.(1.3)[by speaking.]

2  M:                                               [*M MYöhästy.*]
                                                         be late-PST
                                                     [*was L-LAte.*]
                                                     *raises eyebrows*


3    (0.3)*MYöhästy.*
              be late-PST
     (0.3)*was LAte.*
          *LHopens*


     (0.3)

4  t: hmm. hmm. hmm.=

5  M: =*m MUistutus.*(.)*Muistus.*
            a note          a note
       =*n NOte.*      (.)*NOte.*
       *puts LH on the table* *moves LH forward*


     (0.3)

6  t: hmm.
```

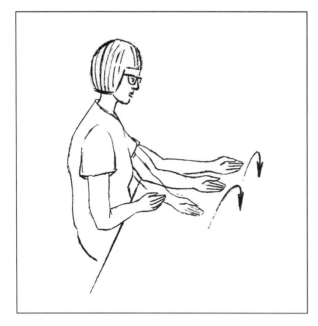

Figure 6: Illustrative movement (cf. line 5)

The topic involves Maija's problems in waking up her son in the mornings. In the beginning of the conversation, Maija tells the therapist that <u>every day,.everybody is late.</u>. Later she continues that she cannot get her son up. The therapist asks <u>yes (.) well then how do you get him,.(1.3) [by speaking.]</u>. During the final words Maija breaks in and continues her story, repeating twice the same lexical unit <u>was late.</u> (in the past tense) amplifying her verbal contribution by raising her eyebrows on the first word and by shrugging her hand on the second word. The therapist gives three acknowledgement tokens and Maija continues to explain <u>n Note.(.)NOte.</u> (a teacher's note sent home for lateness) stressing the words and moving her hand forward twice on the table (line 5). The important point in this example is that Maija is clearly unable to verbally express the recurring character of the events by any other means other than by repeating the verb, and the recurrency is revealed by using nonverbal behaviour.

The next example is a story told by a Broca's aphasic speaker, Pekka, and it shows a similar type of nonverbal behaviour as the previous example. This example is derived from a conversation between Pekka and the therapist.

Example 12

```
1  P:ja SItten,.(0.8)*ööh tota,.* (0.4)
      and then                PRT
      and THen,. (0.8)*uh well,.*(0.4)
                     *raises finger*

2  *Pantta*(.)ja*sitte,.*(1.4)
    name         and then
    *Pantta*(.)and*then,.*(1.4)
    *taps on the table*

3  *tämä näin,.*=
    this      PRT
    *this one,.*=
    *moves his finger back and forth on the table*

4  t:  =hmm?=

5  P:  =*kaks*=
        two
        =*two*=
    *moves his finger back and forth on the table*

6  t:  =*aha su|l ol|i kaks sitte[yhtä]aika|a.*
          PRT  you-ADE be-PST two   then   same  time-PAR
        =*I see you had two[at the same]time then.*
        *both hands forward*

7  P:                          [joo](0.5)ja sitten,.
                                PRT           and  then
                               [yes](0.5)and then,.

8  (0.7)ööh,(0.6)*KUol|i.*ja sitte,.(0.4)*KUol|i.*
                  die-PST   and then        die-PST
    (0.7)uh,(0.6)*DIed.*and then,.(0.4)*DIed.*
              *taps on the table*   *taps on the table*

   (0.3)
```

```
 9  t:hmm.=

10  P: =ja sit (.)*Paragon.*
          and then          name
       =and then(.)*Paragon.*
                *circles with finger on the table*

(0.3)

11  t:*aha sit se|n jälkeen ot|i|t [tämä|n.*]
       PRT  then  it-GEN after  take-PST-2  this-ACC
     *I see after that you took [this one.*]
     *GP, hands forward.*

12  P:          [joo.]
                [yes.]

13  t: = joo. joo..hmm
          yes   yes
        yeah. yeah.  .hmm
```

Figure 7: Illustrative movement (cf. line 8)

The story is about Pekka's three dogs. First he tells the names of his dogs and then says three. which the therapist acknowledges. Then he continues the story, telling that he had two of them at first and when these two died he took the third one. It was remarkably difficult for him to tell this story. First, he has such a severe word-finding disability that he could only with extreme effort produce the names of his dogs and still after he had managed to say them, he has the same difficulty when he needs the names again (lines 1-3). In lines 5-7 the therapist and Pekka reach the mutual understanding that he used to have two dogs. Then comes the crucial point where he expresses the temporal progression of the events; he tells and THen,. (0.7) uh,(0.6) DIed. and then,.(0.4) DIed.. He utters the verb *died* twice with a stress in the first syllable and at the same time he taps his finger twice forward on the table (line 8). This nonverbal act is similar to the one in the previous example and it is used similarly, amplifying the scant verbal contribution. The sequential development of the conversation displays that the participants managed to reach mutual understanding for current purposes.

To summarize, this part of the chapter has focused on the illustrative nonverbal behaviour in aphasic speaker's conversation, in particular, on the compensative illustrative hand movements. Illustrative movements were not common in these conversations although they have been attested to provide gestural illustrations when speech problems occur (Le May et al. 1988). In this data, these gestures were most frequently used with speech, and only in the few above-mentioned cases were they used as compensation for word-finding difficulties, or for the more profound syntactic difficulties. All speakers had at least one illustrative gesture that was either related to speech or was without speech. In any case, illustrative nonverbal acts were not prominent in these conversations.

The few illustrative movements showing compensatory function were revealing. In the first case – example 10 – Jaakko clearly illustrates the missing word with a gesture. Unable to find the proper word, he begins a self-initiated repair directed to the other participants, and uses an illustrative gesture to help him recall the target word with the illustrative gesture. The next two cases (ex. 11 and 12) were remarkably similar although they were used by different speakers. In both examples the structure of the verbal utterances were very simple. In the first case, the speaker repeats the noun *muistutus* (*(a) note*) twice and in the second case, the speaker repeats the verb *kuoli* (*died*) twice. In both cases the verbal expression was amplified with a hand gesture, expressing the recurring nature of the events by forward directed hand movements.

The speakers utilized the spatial area directed in front of themselves for these illustrative movements, but the occurrences of these movements showed wide variation. For example, when Maija described her progress with her speech, she raised her hand upwards. Elina, who illustrated drunken walking, moved her hand forward in front of her. When Maija and Pekka recalled recurrent events they moved their hands forwards on the table. The direction of a movement could also be an important illustrative means for facilitating the interpretation of the intended meaning.

Some studies report that aphasics, particularly Broca's aphasics, frequently use illustrative nonverbal behaviour. For instance in Ahlsén's study (1985), the aphasics used illustrative, turn-taking and emotional gestures more than healthy controls. In this study, however, the class of illustrative gestures was wider than in the present study; Ahlsén included general illustrators, general emblems and pointing movements. Le May et al's (1988) results also indicate that illustrative hand gestures are used most by Broca's aphasics, but the category of illustrative gestures had again a broader definition than in this study. Their results indicate that aphasic patients as a group use more spontaneous illustrative gestures than do normal controls, but the frequency and the subtypes of illustrative gestures vary according to the type of aphasia. For instance, Le May et al. (1988) suggest that the Broca's aphasics used batons and ideographs (which were regarded as illustrative gestures) significantly more than do Wernicke's aphasics.

Due to the small amount of the illustrative gestures in this study, it is impossible to discuss the qualitative or quantitative difference between the aphasia types in the use of illustrative gestures as Le May et al. (1988) suggest. From the compensatory point of view, the most revealing cases were Jaakko's twirling gesture when seeking a proper word, and Maija's and Pekka's illustrations of the recurring events. In these occurrences the speakers' movements can be regarded as compensation for the verbal part of the speaker's contribution, and thus they facilitated the interpretation of those contributions. These occurrences may be regarded as supporting one of Le May et al's (ibid.) results, according to which aphasic speakers will resort to using illustrative gestures when faced with speech problems.

5.4 Pointing movements

The third category of nonverbal behaviour which will be analysed here is pointing movements, which are regarded as deictic behaviour. In certain contexts, pointing movements can stand for a word or two and thus they can compensate for speech. A pointing movement is a simple gesture which in contrast to pantomimic gestures or illustrative gestures, does not even require use of hands. Pointing movements are performed with some part of the body, usually with finger(s) or hand(s), but also with the head. They are usually directed to a person, to a part of the body, to an object or to a place. In most cases they point to the surrounding physical context but it is also possible that the referent is a more abstract attitude, attribute, affect, direction or location (Ekman & Friesen 1969:62). If the referent is in the immediate physical context, pointing movements may be a rather powerful means for communication, for instance in word-finding difficulties. In that sense they are interesting in aphasic speakers' talk.

Based on my earlier work (Klippi 1990), a classification system was developed for analysing pointing movements. These movements were classified into four groups in order to analyse them in more detail, and to investigate their ability to convey meanings and to facilitate the reaching of mutual understanding. The groups are:

1. A pointing movement to the immediate context connected with a verbal utterance.
2. A pointing movement to the non-immediate context connected with a verbal utterance.
3. A pointing movement to the immediate physical context connected with a vague or missing verbal reference.
4. A pointing movement to the non-immediate context connected with a vague or missing verbal reference.

This classification can also be described in terms of four fields (Table 5).

Table 5. The categorization of pointing movements.

+ +	+ −
1. verbal utterance + pointing to immediate context +	2. verbal utterance + pointing to non-immediate context -
− +	− −
3. vague verbal reference − pointing to immediate context +	4. vague verbal reference − pointing to non-immediate context −

In the first field, a speaker utters a verbal reference connected with a pointing movement, and thus the expression receives the value of (+ +). In the second field, a speaker uses a verbal utterance of the reference but the pointing movement is directed to the non-immediate context and the expression is assigned a value of (+ −). In the third field, a speaker uses a pointing movement to the immediate physical context connected with a vague or missing verbal reference, which earns the expression a value of (− +). In the last field, a speaker points to an external context and uses a vague or missing verbal reference and the expression gets the value of (− −). It is noteworthy that a pointing movement in the immediate context may refer to a person or an object but it may also refer to the numbers or the drawing made by Jaakko which represent concrete objects. Thus, there are several examples in which the participants are talking, for instance, about Jaakko's work, chipboard manufacturing, and as Jaakko has drawn a scheme of the manufacturing process, the speakers often point to the scheme during their talk. These cases have been grouped into a class where the referent is found in the immediate physical context.

Table 6. Pointing movements in the aphasia group discussions.

Speakers	J	M	K	E	P	t	Total
1. categ.	13 (26%)	2	8	17 (71%)	10	35 (70%)	85 (53%)
2. categ.	3 (6%)	0	2	1 (4%)	3	2 (4%)	11 (7%)
3. categ.	33 (66%)	3	5	5 (21%)	2	12 (24%)	60 (37%)
4. categ.	1 (2%)	0	1	1 (4%)	1	1 (2%)	5 (3%)
Total	50	5	16	24	16	50	161

J = Jaakko, M=Maija, K=Kalle, E=Elina, P=Paavo and t=therapist

In the following pages, I will give a short description of the categories of pointing movements and provide examples of them. As they are easy to recognize and often used, I will also give the frequencies and the percentages of the various categories of the pointing movements per speaker, presented in Table 6. From the point of view of aphasic communication, the focus of analysis is on the third group of pointing movements, which may be potentially compensatory movements.

5.4.1 A pointing movement to the immediate context connected with a verbal utterance

The first category consists of cases where a speaker's utterance includes a verbal part referring to the surrounding context connected with the pointing movement. These speech-related pointing movements were used by all the speakers in the group and were mostly connected with the naming of the interlocutors, with the concrete objects or with the naming of some parts of Jaakko's drawing. They were also the most frequently used pointing movements in these conversations, amounting to 53% of all the pointing movements. In fact, Kalle, Elina, and the therapist used them most frequently of their pointing movements.

Elina used proportionally most speech-related pointing movements, in 17 cases of all her 24 cases (71%). She used pointing movements on several occasions, most often pointing to the numbers which Jaakko had written or the drawing he had made, but she also pointed to the next speaker or to an object. Especially in the fourth discussion, she pointed to Jaakko's drawing or to the numbers he had written down. The following excerpt presents an example of this type. Jaakko wrote down the number 18 and Elina made an other-repair initiation with a question containing the numeral 18, pointing simultaneously to the paper (line 3):

Example 13

```
1   J:  sitten,(1.9).hhhhh(2.6)noin,(4.6)sitten,
        then                    like          then
        then,(1.9).hhhhh(2.6)like,(4.6)then,

    (0.8)

2   M:°kaheksantoista°
        eighteen
        °eighteen°

    (9.6 J:hhh.)

3   E:*ol|i|k|s+tei|t kaheksantoista kaikenkaikkiaan vai,*=
        be-PST-Q-CLI+you(PL)-PAR  eighteen        altogether        or
        *were you eighteen altogether or,*=
        *LHDpaper*

4   J:=juu(.)[juu sitten,(4.6) minä.
        PRT       PRT    then              |
        =yes(.)[yes then, (4.6) I.

5   E:          [*aha.*
                 PRT
                [*I see.*
                *Onod, finger on the paper*
```

For the sake of comparison, the therapist also used speech-related pointing movements most frequently of her all pointing movements, that is, in 35 cases of 50 (70%). Unlike Elina, her pointing movements were most often connected to turn allocation. She used the speech-related pointing movements interactionally, directing the next turn to a next speaker. She often formulated questions or requests directed to one of the participants as in the following excerpt:

Example 14

---

1   t: m-hm?(0.7)no hyvä.(0.7)*no Maija*kerro|pa sinä.
              PRT   good   PRT 1name F   tell-CLI   you
     m-hm?(0.7)okay. (0.7)*well Maija* come on tell us.
                         LHDM

The name of the recipient was omitted in several occurrences as it is in the next excerpt:

Example 15

---

1   t: m-hm?m-hm?(2.2)no*kerro|ppa pikkusen su|n*
                      PRT   tell-CLI   a little   you-GEN
   m-hm?m-hm?(2.2)well*tell (us) a bit about your*
                   RHDJ

2   *alkutilantee|sta.*(2.0)
      startingpoint-ELA
   situation in the beginning.(2.0)
   twirls the pen in the air

3   sen *jälkeen* ku sä *ol|i|t sairastu|nu|t.*
   it-GEN   after   when you be-PST-2   become ill-PPC-2
     after when you *had become ill.*
     RHDJ   ****RHDJ****

The therapist requests Jaakko to tell about the time following his illness and while speaking she points to him with her pen, then makes a circular movement with the pen pointing to the others and finally stops her pen again at Jaakko. The therapist's pointing movement towards Jaakko is very clear but also her circular movement can be interpreted as a pointing movement without a connected verbal utterance because she pointed to all the participants but didn't mention them explicitly (*kerroppa pikkusen / tell (us) a bit*)(lines 1-2). Evidently Jaakko took the therapist's pointing movements into consideration as he directed his gaze and his answer to the whole group, not only to the therapist.

Also, Jaakko himself often pointed to the numbers or the drawing he had made when naming the referent. In the following example, Elina seeks clarification for the meaning of the number which Jaakko had written down. At first she points to the drawing, uttering the number (lines 2 and 4), and Jaakko completes the utterance giving the reference for the number and at the same time pointing at it (line 5).

Example 16

```
1   M:°vii[s°
       five
      °fi[ve°

2   E:    [*viis*,(2.5)*venäläis|i|ä v#ai#*
            five            russian-PL-PAR    or
          [*five*,(2.5)*Russians o#r#*
      *Dmoves finger on the paper**Dfinger on the paper,G->J*

3   J:ei kun,=
      NEG PRT
      no but,=

4   E:=*ol|i**viis[ ol|i,*
        be-PST   five    be-PST
      =*was**five[was,*
      *LHDnumber,Onod**Onod,finger on the paper*

5   J:            [*#ö ö#*]suomalais|i|a.=
                            finnish-PL-PAR
      [*#er er#*]Finns.=
          *RHDpaper*

6   E:=*suomalais|i|a.*
                  finnish-PL-PAR
      =*Finns.*
      *Oupwards a little*

7   J:m-hm.

8   Y:mm

9   J:nii.
      yes.

10  E:joo joo
      yes yes
```

In the following example Jaakko names a part of his drawing (line 3):

Example 17

```
1   t:niih-hih-hih-heh$mi|tä]tekee kahde|n kilometri|n pi[tui-$
                       what-PAR does  two-GEN  kilometre-PAR  {long}
      yeah-hih-hih-heh$what]does one do with a two kilometres l[on-$

2   J:                                                [*ja(.)
                                                       and
                                                      [*and(.)
                                                      *RHDt,Gt*

3   taas,.*(1.5)*kuli*-*kuljetin.*
    again            conveyer
    again,.*(1.5) *con*-*conveyer.*
              *Gpaper,Dpaper**Gt,Dpaper*
```

In the next example he gives a reply to Elina while showing his drawing (line 4):

Example 18

```
1   t:kaks kilometri|ä.
        two      kilometre-PAR
    two kilometres.

2   J:nii.
        PRT
    yeah.

3   E:jooh(1.0)°mitä(0.5)kaks kilometri|a ni,
        PRT        what-PAR      two   kilometre-PAR    PRT
    yeah(1.0)°what(0.5)two kilometres yeah,

4   J:*lastulevy|ä*
        chipboard-PRT
    *chipboard*
     *Gt->M, twirls the pen on the paper*

5   E:aj+jaa.
    oh+yeah.

    (0.6)

6   J:hmm.
```

Of all possible pointing movements, Paavo and Kalle most often used speech-related ones although they had individual differences in their use. Kalle directed his pointing movements mostly to the interactants whereas Paavo directed them mostly to Jaakko's drawing or to numbers. Maija used speech-related pointing movements for two of her five pointing movements; both occurrences were directed to herself.

5.4.2 A pointing movement to a non-immediate context connected with a verbal utterance

The second possibility is that a speaker combines a verbal utterance with a movement pointing to a non-immediate context. Thus, the meaning of the utterance is conveyed by both verbal and nonverbal means. This type of combination was not often used; there were only eleven cases in all the data, but all speakers except Maija used this combination at least once. Two examples are provided below:

Example 19

```
1   t:no(.)kerro vaikka että mi|tä sä tä|llä hetke|llä tee|t
        PRT    tell     PRT  CNJ  what-PAR you this-ADE  moment-ADE  do-2
    well(.)tell about what you're doing

2   nyt[te.](.)su|ll+o-hm=
        now          you-ADE+is
    now[adays.](.)youv-hm=
```

```
3   J:[kato,]
       look
      [look,]

4   J:=ö(0.2)*paha juttu**kuule.*
               bad    thing    listen
      =er(0.2)*bad thing**listen.*
              *RHDhimself**RHmoves*

    (0.3)

5   t:°m-hm?°

6   M:°joo°
      °yes°

7   J:*°e#i#°(0.8)ei ymmärrä*(1.1)°kato°(1.9)*Lauttasaare|sa
         NEG         NEG-3 understand      look           place name-INE
      *°n#o#°(0.8)not understand*(1.1)°look°(1.9)*in Lauttasaari
      *RHback and forth*                          *RHDforward.*

8   ö**YH(0.8)sisä(-) kaikki.*
                        all
      er**UH(0.8)in(-) all.*
        *RHswings*

    (0.9)

9   t:m-hm?

10  M:kohta(.)ymmär|tää.
       soon      understand-3
      soon(.)understand.

11  J:mm(.)joo
      mm(.)yeah

12  M:kohta ymmär|tää.
       soon    understand-3
      soon understand.

    (1.0)

13  t:m-hm?
```

In this example, Jaakko's turn is rather long and confusing with rich nonverbal behaviour. His turn begins with the utterance n#o# (0.8)not understand.. In the middle of his turn he refers to the district of the town where he lives in Lauttasaari and at the same time swings his hand forward (line 7). Evidently the recipients found the content of Jaakko's speech to be vague, but Maija caught an intelligible part of it and continues the conversation uttering soon understand. (lines 10 and 12).

Example 20

```
1  K:  *mu|ll+on*(1.0)*kesäpaikka*mi|nkä kanssa mä ol|i|n tuolla
        I-ADE      is              summer place    what-GEN   with    I   be-PST-1   there
   K:  *I've got*(1.0)*a summerplace* with which I was there
        *RHmoves*                *RHDforward*
```

Example 20 is derived from Kalle's story where he refers to his summerplace and while doing so, he swings his hand forward. This example differs from the previous in that Kalle mentions the referent *summerplace* but does not mention the name of the place.

In the first two groups, a speaker's verbal utterance was supported by a pointing movement. I will move now to analyze the occurrences where a pointing movement was dominant in the sense that the co-occurring verbal reference was vague or missing.

5.4.3 A pointing movement to the immediate context connected with a vague or a missing verbal reference

The third class of the pointing movements is fascinating from an aphasic speaker's point of view. In these cases a speaker produces a vague verbal reference or the verbal reference is totally missing, and simultaneously s/he points to the surrounding physical context in order to make her/his meaning public. Thus, the nonverbal act gives the meaning for the contribution, and the verbal part, if present, supports the contribution. With aphasic speakers, the most evident cases are when a speaker cannot find proper words for his expression but is able to use a pointing movement to the immediate context and hence compensate the trouble.

All speakers used pointing movements with an vague or missing verbal reference (category 3). In fact, these gestures accounted for 37% of all pointing movements. Jaakko used category three pointing movements (Table 6, p. 69) most often, and more frequently than did other speakers. He used these movements 33 out of 50 cases, for a total of 66 % of all his pointing movements. Kalle used these movements in five of sixteen cases, Elina in five cases of 24 and Maija and Paavo together used them only five times. Possibly this combination is commonly used by healthy speakers too, because the therapist used these twelve times out of 50 (24%).

The targets of these pointing movements varied. Maija's three and Kalle's five such movements were directed to another interactant without mentioning her/his name. On the other hand, Elina had these pointings five times and they were all directed to the physical context, for instance to Jaakko's drawings. Paavo had only two cases of the pointing movements with the indefinite verbal reference of his total 16 pointing movements. One of these was directed to a recipient and one to an object.

If we take a closer look at speaker Jaakko's pointing movements connected with a vague or a missing verbal reference, we notice that he was able to utilize his context efficiently. He directed his pointing movements to various targets, most often to the numbers and the drawing he had made (17 cases), to directions (six cases), to the map (five cases) and to the recipients or to himself (five cases). Particularly in the fourth conversation, which concerned Jaakko's earlier work, one can detect a constant pattern in the use of these movements. The fourth conversation was predominantly based on a question-answer structure so that the participants presented questions and Jaakko answered them. Questions were mainly connected with the time he had spent working abroad in a factory, the number of workers there, the amount of production, etc., and often demanded answers with numerical information which Jaakko was not able to express verbally. In these occurrences, he used paper and a pen and wrote down numbers or made a drawing in order to explain the operation of the factory. During the discussion which follows numerous instances of written information was utilized and Jaakko referred to these with a pointing movement to the numbers or to a scheme he had drawn.

The next example illustrates that kind of occurrence. Note Jaakko's and the therapist's pointing behaviour in lines 5 and 9:

Example 21

```
1   J:(3 KOPUTUSTA)tä|n(0.9)aika|na,.(*14.0*)
                   this-GEN    time-ESS
    (3 TAPS)this(0.9)time,.(*14.0*)
                              *writes*

2   (2 KOPUTUSTA)(12.0) tul|i|n,.(2.0) ja,(KOPUTUKSIA)
                         come-PST-1       and
    (2 TAPS)(12.0)I came,.(2.0) and,(TAPS)

3   M:°neljä vuot|ta°
       four     year-PAR
    °four years°

4   (8.8 *J sighs, writes*)

5   t:mi|tä,(.)mi|tä tapahtu siis *tä|nä,(.) seiskytkuus viiva
      what-PAR  what-PAR happen-(PST) PRT  this-ESS      seventy-six    clash
    what,(.)so what happened *this,(.)seventy-six dash
                                      *Dnumbers*

6      [kahdeksankymmentä.*
        eighty
       [eighty.*

7   J:[hhhhh.

8   t:nyt+mä e|n ihan(.)tarkkaan pääs|sy,.
      now+I  NEG-1 quite   clearly    get-PPC
    now I didn't quite(.)clearly get,.

    (1.9)

9   J:*lastulevy.*
       chipboard
    *chipboard.*
     *Dpaper*

    (0.6)
```

```
10  t: aha.(0.3)sillon|ko sä ol|i|t juuri siellä,.=
        PRT         then-Q      you  be-PST-2  just   there
    oh.(0.3)were you there just at that time,.=

11  J:=juu=
    =yeah=

12  t:=Neuvostoliito|ssa.=
       Soviet Union-INE
    =in the Soviet Union.=

13  J:=jooh=
    =yeah=

14  M =jooh=
    =yeah=

15  E:=hmm
```

Jaakko had written down some numbers earlier in the conversation and in line 1 he audibly points (taps) to those numbers several times and explains (3 taps) this (0.9) time,. (14.0 WRITES DOWN)(2 taps) I came,.(2.0)and,. Maija leans forward and reads from the paper four years and Jaakko makes again some marks on the paper. The therapist joins the conversation (line 5) and makes an other-repair initiation (cf. chapter 8) by asking what happened during the years (19)76-80, also pointing at the numbers. Her explicit formulation of the question gives Jaakko the possibility to answer with a single word (line 9) (cf. chapter 9), pointing at the numbers on the paper. It turned out that Jaakko had been at that time in the Soviet Union to set up a chipboard factory. In this excerpt, Jaakko's verbal contribution *this time* was vague. This utterance revealed that he was referring to a point of time but he could not specify it verbally. On the other hand, he was able to give some information through writing, pointing and directing his gaze, but the matter became clear only after the cooperation of other participants. Thus, this is also a revealing example of how the meaning of numbers is co-constructed between the interlocutors (cf. Goodwin 1995).

The next excerpt presents a series of pointing movements connected to Jaakko's word-finding problem (a point of the compass). The vagueness of his contribution led to a long repair sequence before the matter became clear. However, with the help of a pointing gesture he is able to convey his meaning to the therapist who is capable of giving a verbal expression to the gesture. The therapist's verbal interpretation is possible only after several of Jaakko's pointing movements. In the following I will show parts of this negotiation (the whole repair sequence is dealt with in chapter 8):

Example 22

```
          GM             GM        GM
1  J: on Sarja,(2.1)*sinneh.(.)sin[ne.]*
       is   name          there+to    there+to
    Sarja is,(2.1)*thereh.(.)the[re.]*
              *Onod,RHDL↑         RHDL↑  *


                              GJ           GJ
2  M:                        [jooh](0.7)°joo°
                              PRT          PRT
                             [°ye:s°](0.7)°yes°


                          Gpaper         ,,GM
3  J: hhh.(KIRJOITTAA 7.2) [on|k|s oikein(2.3)Sae-Sarja
                            be-Q-CLI  right         name
    hhh.(WRITES 7.2)       [is it alright(2.3)Sae-sarja

4  M:                      [*G paper LHDpaper*

   (0.9)


              GM......,,Gt
5  P: se paika|n se [nime|ltä] Sarja
      it   place-GEN it  name-ELA    name
    it of the place [called] Sarja


                          GP
6  M:                    [joo]
                         [yes]


7  E: *Onod*

8  t: hmm


9  J:*t[änne]*
        here+to
    *the[re]*
      *RHDL↑ *


            GP
10 M:  [°Sarja°]
          name
      [°Sarja°]


       GM
11 J: juuh=
      ye:ah=

12 t: =ahaa=
      =I see=
       *Onod*


       Gpaper
13 M: =joo
      =yes
       *Onod*
```

(1.1)

```
        GM              G↑              G↑
14  J:*tonne.(.) tonne.*(2.4) [hhhhh.3.8]
      there+to      there+to
    *over there.(.) over there.*(2.4) [hhhhh.3.8]
      *RHDL↑          RHDL↑  *

15  t:                              [*takes a map*]

                                    GJ  ,,Gt
16  P:                              [ei se löyd|y sieltä.=]
                                    NEG it  find-REF there+from
                                    [cannot find there.=]
```

Figure 8: Pointing movement (cf. lines 1 and 14)

The topic of the conversation is the geographical position of the factory where Jaakko worked abroad. In the earlier discussion it was revealed that Jaakko worked as an engineer in a project setting up a big factory in the Soviet Union. In the first turn (line 1) of the excerpt he introduces the name of the place, *Sarja* (in this conversation the word refers to the place but it is also a meaningful word in Finnish), to the conversation and immediately continues with a deictic proadverb there while pointing diagonally left with his pen (line 1). Apparently, the referent for the word *Sarja* is unclear and the participants concentrate on resolving it. Later, Jaakko returns again to the location of Sarja explaining over there (.) over there pointing again diagonally leftwards (line 14). This presents a new problem in the conversational, and in response, the therapist takes a map and begins to look for the place. This trouble is resolved and later the therapist returns to the geographical direction of the place, making an other-initiation of repair (example 23, line 1):

Example 23

```
1   t:hmm-mm.(0.4)elikkä se(0.8)ol|i|k+se*sinne POHjose|en
                    that means  it       be-PST-Q+it  there+to   north-ILL
    hmm-mm.(0.4)in other words it(0.8)was it*to the NOrth-
                                                    *RHD↑ *

2   #päin vai.#*
     wards    or
    #wards or.#*

    (0.8)

            Gmap
3   J: ei kun,=
        NEG PRT
       no but,=
       *RHDmap*

4   t=eei
       NEG
       no:

5   P: itä|än.[et(-)]
        east-ILL
      to the east.[sou(-)]

6   J:         [*RHmoves his pen DR↑ *

    (0.7)

7   t:*HETkinen.*
       moment
      *just a MOment.*
         *RHD↑ *

            Gt
8   J:*ylös.*
       up+to
      *up.*
       *RHD↑ *

    (1.5)
9   t:*koillise|en.*
        north-east-ILL
      *north-east.*
       *RHD↑ *

            Gmap
10  J:[joo]
      [yes]

            GJ
11  P: [hmm.]
```

Figure 9: Pointing movement (cf. line 6)

Paavo suggests that the direction is east (line 5), but Jaakko is not content with this and continues to point diagonally upwards (line 6), this time changing the direction to the right. The trouble is solved only when the therapist imitates Jaakko's gesture and suggests that the direction is instead northwest. This example is the most complex with several trouble sources. However, the essential point here is that Jaakko, being unable to express his meaning verbally, resorts to nonverbal resources and collaboration between the interlocutors led to resolution of the trouble.

Actually, one may argue that Jaakko's gesture in line 1 of example 22 was deictic-iconic because it was a pointing movement, but at the same time this gesture showed iconically the direction of the place. In any case, the other participants could not interpret the nonverbal act before they had more knowledge of the place's location. Mutual understanding was finally reached when the therapist imitated Jaakko's gesture and on the basis of that imitation she could offer a candidate understanding which Jaakko accepted.

The majority (66%) of Jaakko's pointing movements were connected with a vague or missing verbal reference, with a total of 33 pointing movements out of 65. In these cases, the connected verbal utterances were mostly deictic proadverbs, e.g. there (sinne, tonne), here (tässä, tossa, tänne, täällä), this (tää, tämä). These utterances do not carry lexical meaning but they provide information about the place or direction of movement of the referent.

In Jaakko's case, the pointing movements were clearly connected to the specific problem, his inability to find proper words, and in particular, to express numerals. In the WAB test Jaakko's aphasia quotient (AQ) was 69 points of a total 100 and his aphasia type was Broca's. In the subtest of object naming, he was able to utter the names of the common objects (20 pieces) rather easily; he had 56 points out of 60. However, it was apparent that in conversation and in picture description tasks, he had considerable word finding difficulties. On the other hand, his communicative behaviour showed a clear ability to compensate for his aphasic disorders. From the interactional point of view, it is interesting that Jaakko was able to externalize some of the elements which were beyond his verbal expression. Let us take for example his ability to write numbers or to draw. With these means he was able, at least to some extent, to make his meaning recognizable for the others. What was even more interesting was that he was able to use these externalized meanings during the conversation. On several occasions he used deictic movements in order to refer to the issues which were under discussion. In this sense, he could externalize his meaning by making use of the immediate physical context. Hence, although he had a limited ability to renew the conversational context (Heritage 1989:22) with verbal resources, he could compensate his trouble through nonverbal resources, and thus renew the conversational context.

Kalle had a lower frequency of pointing movements with a missing or vague reference than did Jaakko, but Kalle did use them on several occasions (five times). However, Kalle used the pointing movements as an interactional resource, directing them towards his interactants without naming his interactant. He displayed no evidence of compensative pointing behaviour in case of word-finding difficulty. According to the WAB's naming subtest he had considerable word-finding difficulties, he had only 33 points out of 100. In the object-naming task, he scored only nine points out of 60. He was able to name seven objects out of 20; one object was named without help and six with a phonemic cue. While Jaakko often relied on nonverbal resources in conversation, Kalle clearly had another strategy to convey meanings. Kalle often tried to describe the use of objects, for instance he said that is what one throws (a ball) or that is a thing in the hand (wrist) (a watch) pointing to his watch. These kinds of circumlocutions were easy for him, and his speech was very fluent. In other words, he clearly relied on his verbal abilities rather than exploited nonverbal resources. Hence, his pointing movements did not indicate the compensatory functions.

5.4.4 A pointing movement to the non-immediate context connected with a vague or missing verbal reference

The fourth class consisted of an unclear verbal reference connected with a pointing movement to a context outside of the surroundings. These cases were rather few, only five instances altogether, which is 3% of all the pointing movements. All speakers, except for Maija, had one such case, including the therapist. In the latter case, the definite reference was verbally mentioned immediately before her turn. In any case, it is possible that normal speakers also use vague utterances in certain contexts.

Example 24

```
1  P:[nii se ol|i se](-)se ol|i se(0.5)tota kiertoanna-annelu
      PRT  it be-PST it          it be-PST it     PRT    {guided tour}
     [yeah it was it](-)it was it(0.5)well {a guided to-tour}

2  mutta se ol|i yksi(0.4)manneliini mannekiini näytös
   but     it be-PST one           mannequin        show
   but it was a(0.4) {fashion fashion } show

3  *saman tien sie-siellä.*
    same   time      there
   *at the same time the-there.*
       *ODleftwards*

4  Y:.hh

5  t:*Tukholma|ssa.*
        Stockholm-INE
    *in Stockholm.*
       *Onod*

6  P:[(-)nii]       (-)              [lai]va|ssa ol|i.
       PRT                            ship-INE    be-PST
     [(-)yeah]      (-)              [on b]oard it was.

7  J:[nii ]juu juu juu se on laiva|s[sa.]
                         it is  ship-INE
     [yeah]yes yes yes it is on bo[ard.]
```

In this excerpt Paavo tells about the programme during a trip to Stockholm. At the end of his turn, he uses a deictic proadverb <u>there</u> pointing to the left at the same time (line 3). In this case the therapist is able to infer the reference for the proadverb "there" in her next turn because it had been explicitly mentioned in the earlier context.

To summarize, pointing movements in conversation are an absorbing group of nonverbal behaviour from the point of view of compensation. To analyse, them I developed a classification system based on my earlier work (Klippi 1990). The pointing movements were divided into four groups in relation to the accuracy of the verbal utterance related to the pointing movement and the existence of the referent in the immediate context. Thus, in my classification, the main division was made between the pointing movements with an accurate verbal reference and those with a vague or missing verbal reference.

The categorization of the pointing movements was unproblematic on the whole. However, there were some unclear cases which were excluded from the analysis, mostly connected to the pointing movements related to Jaakko's drawing or writing. The following excerpt is an example:

Example 25

```
1   t:tarkota|t|ko että ehd|i|t ol|la kolme vuot|ta Suome|ssa.
        mean-2-Q        PRT    manage-PSF-2 be-INF  three   year-PAR   Finland-INE
        do you mean that you managed to be three years in Finland.


    0.5


2   J:juu ei|kun,
        PRT NEG-PRT
        yeah no but,


3   t:vai,=
        or
        or,=


4   J:=juu-u ei|kun,(1.3)ö-men|i|n,(0.7)tonne tonne
        PRT    NEG-PRT        go-PST-1       there+to   there+to
        J:=ye-yeah no but,(1.3)er I went,(0.7)there there


5   hh.(1.2)kato|s,.hh (0.5) Valmeti|lle.(0.7)  *
            look-CLI              company name-ALL
        hh.(1.2)look,.hh (0.5) to Valmet.(0.7)  *


6   Valmeti|lle.(0.7)* *[*Valmeti|lle*
    company name-ALL        company name-ALL
    to Valmet.(0.7)* *[*to Valmet*
    *2 taps on the table*[*taps on the table*


7   E:                        [°vaihdo|i|t firma|a°
                                change-PST-2   firm-PAR
                              [°you changed firms°


8   t:                        [hmm?
```

In this excerpt Jaakko mentions the name of the company he had worked for ('Valmet', line 5). He repeats the name of the company twice and at the same time taps on the paper (line 6) on which he had written numbers related to his story. As a matter of fact, it is possible to regard this act as a 'baton', a movement which accentuates or emphasizes speech. In this case, it is justified to determine that the movement has a double function, having both emphasizing and deictic functions. There were also some more examples in which the target of the pointing movement was unclear due to the camera's limited angle.

The conversations contained a total of 161 obvious deictic movements. The two groups of pointing movements (group 1 and 3) with a reference to the immediate context cover 88% (145 cases) of all the data.

The speakers in this group had various profiles regarding the pointing movements (see Table 6, p. 69). The total amount of pointing movements of Maija, Kalle, Paavo and Elina was under 30 cases per speaker, and one should be careful in analysing them. The most interesting finding was the difference in the profiles of Jaakko and the therapist. Jaakko had 13 cases (26%) of type 1 (a pointing movement to the surrounding context combined with a verbal utterance) whereas the therapist had 35 cases (70%) of those. This distribution was opposite to the pointing movements of type 3 (a pointing movement to the immediate context combined with a vague or missing verbal reference); Jaakko had 33 cases (66%) and the therapist, 12 cases (24%). In fact, the proportional profile of Elina was rather similar to the therapist's profile, although the frequencies were lower; type 1 was the most prominent and type 3 the next most frequent type of movement. The profiles of Kalle and Paavo showed a similar tendency but, as mentioned before, the frequencies were low, with only 16 cases per speaker.

Pointing movements with a vague or missing verbal reference were mostly used by Jaakko; 66% of all his pointing movements were of this type. Besides Jaakko, the therapist likewise had 12 cases (24%) of this type which indicates that this combination is also used by normal speakers. On the other hand, in Jaakko's case, type 3 pointing movements were evidently related to his aphasic disorders, principally to his word finding difficulties. This result indicates that Jaakko had a tendency to rely on the immediate context in the speech problem situations, and he compensated for his speech problems by referring to his immediate physical surroundings. It is interesting that although Maija used only five pointing movements in all, two of these were speech-related, whereas three type 3, the pointings with a missing or vague verbal reference. This displayed some similarity to Jaakko's use.

Jaakko's amount of pointing movements with a vague or missing verbal reference indicate that, from the communicative point of view, these deictic movements may play a decisive role in the process of reaching mutual understanding for current purposes in aphasic conversations. The crucial point seems to be a speaker's ability to use the nonverbal pointing movement in order to compensate for the speech problems. If the referent is in the immediate context, the pointing movement, although connected to the vague or missing verbal reference, offers at least an initiation for the repair sequence in order to co-construct the meaning for the insufficient utterance (cf. Goodwin 1995). Excerpts 22 and 23 present good examples of such cases.

When closely observing Jaakko's pointing movements, we noticed that they were often connected to the numbers he had written down or to his drawings. This indicates that he had developed a behavioural pattern in which the first phase was the use of written numbers or drawing when having word-finding difficulties. However, in many cases this information was not sufficient for the recipients, and the trouble led to a collaborative repair sequence where the participants and also Jaakko himself often pointed to the numbers or Jaakko's drawing. In these occurrences, the topic of the conversation may be decisive for the use of such externalized means. On the other hand, at least concrete events have certain attributes connected to the time, place and participants which one can express with numerical, written or drawn information.

5.5   Discussion

The aim of this chapter has been to observe and analyse the potentially compensatory use of nonverbal behaviour in aphasic conversation and its consequences for interaction. I have focused my analysis qualitatively and partly quantitatively on the prominent, potentially compensatory nonverbal behaviour in aphasic conversation, observing the variation in their use by aphasics. This question is theoretically related to the interaction between verbal and nonverbal behaviour, and the possibility of nonverbal behaviour to substitute or compensate for speech, to convey meanings and to be interpretable by recipients in conversation.

This analysis has its departure from the nonverbal categories of Ekman & Friesen (1969, 1972) and Wiener et al. (1972). The nonverbal acts have been classified as emblems, illustrative gestures and pointing movements, as these nonverbal acts are, according to the literature, principally able to convey meanings in conversation, and can be used to replace one or two words. This study excludes speech-related rhythmic gestures and nonverbal behaviour which mainly regulate the interaction and do not convey independent meanings.

Emblems resemble linguistic units because they are arbitrarily coded and they may replace words. In these conversations, emblems did not turn out to be prominent nonverbal acts of a compensatory nature. The most frequent emblems were head nods and head shakes, usually combined with a verbal utterance. Other types of emblems were infrequent. One may question why emblems other than head-noddings and shakings were missing from all the speakers in this group, including the therapist's interaction. Ekman & Friesen (1969) have suggested that emblems possibly carry less personal information than other nonverbal categories and possibly are used around the more ritualized aspects of conversation. The data of this study did not contain such occurrences, and this may have influenced the restricted amount of emblems.

The distinction between emblems and illustrators is that emblems are arbitrarily coded, whereas illustrators are iconically coded. Ekman & Friesen (1969) and Cohen & Harrison (1973) have pointed out that illustrators are related to speech. On the contrary, Le May et al. (1988) have suggested illustrators are used in the occurrence of speech problems. In this data, illustrators were usually related to speech. Purely compensatory illustrative movements were rare, although there were some interesting occurrences. For example, one case was connected to an obvious word-finding difficulty; two others were observed in dyadic interactions, both involving longer storytelling turns, and both were used to express the recurrence of the events.

From the compensatory point of view, the third group, pointing movements, were the most interesting ones. The pointing movements were classified into four subgroups according to their relation to the present or absent referent in the context and to the concomitant verbal reference or the vague or missing verbal reference. The frequencies of the four types of pointing movements were quantified for each speaker; Maija, Kalle, Elina and Paavo had less than 30 cases. The most interesting difference was found between the pointing profiles of Jaakko and the therapist. Their profiles were in fact quite opposite. The result that Jaakko was primarily using the gesture with a vague verbal reference indicates that he compensated for his speech disability with the pointing movements.

The systematic study of speech-related nonverbal behaviour was limited before film and video equipment were available at a reasonable price. Consequently, the empirical study of this issue is rather new. The picture concerning aphasic speakers' speech-related nonverbal behaviour is not simple. Several studies have made quantitative analyses of aphasics speakers' nonverbal conversational behaviour (e.g. Cicone et al. 1979, Larkins et al.

1981, Feyereisen 1983, Ahlsén 1985, Glosser et al. 1986, Smith 1987a, Le May et al. 1988). However, there have been no studies related to aphasics' nonverbal behaviours' interactive consequences. The methodology used here is based on sequential analysis, an approach of conversation analysis found, for instance, in the works of Goodwin & Goodwin (1986) and Goodwin (1987), but previously unknown within aphasiology.

As a result, there is currently a great need for knowledge of aphasic speakers' nonverbal behaviour and its variation for therapeutic purposes. Within aphasiology, the prevailing group study -methodology has been based on the categorization and quantification of nonverbal acts. Le May et al. (1988) mention some methodological problems which reflect the general difficulties of group studies; first, some studies have distinguished between the types of aphasia while others have categorized subjects only according to severity. Second, the materials used in the studies are not always representative because the segments of conversation are often very small. Third, the interactions studied are not homogeneous in terms of the topics discussed; it is possible that contextual factors and the particular topic of a conversation may influence for the use of gestures. Fourth, some studies lack a descriptive classification with an explicit set of rules. Finally, there is often a lack of statistical analysis in the interpretation of the data. In addition, Herrmann et al. (1988) suggest that partners perhaps increase and modify their normal nonverbal behaviour in order to facilitate communication with the aphasics, which too may have consequences for aphasics' nonverbal behaviour.

Furthermore, the use of the group-study design has led to more serious methodological problems. In these studies, nonverbal acts have been categorized according to external criteria derived from the literature of 'normal' nonverbal behaviour. It is, however, quite possible that 'normal' behaviour may not cover all aphasics' nonverbal behaviour. Furthermore, the analysis has been based on the researchers' interpretation of the nonverbal acts, which may ignore context-bound interpretation.

This is in contrast with the method of conversation analysis which is based on the sequential analysis and the contextual interpretation of the interlocutors. For instance Goodwin (1986:30) points out that it is quite possible that many movements, for a variety of reasons, do not support the recipient's understanding of the talk, although they appear to be gestures which should contribute to understanding. Another important factor is that a speaker may produce something which is clearly recognizable as a gesture but the recipient has directed her/his gaze elsewhere and does not notice this gesture. Furthermore, some body movements can be identified as clear examples of gestures, while in other cases it is not always certain. For this reason, Goodwin (e.g. 1986) developed an analysis in which gestures are interactively attended to by participants within conversation, as evidenced by responses to the gestures as events in themselves. In addition, according to my observations, a nonverbal act may have a double function in conversation (e.g. example 25). Hence, the idea of only one function per gesture may give a misleading picture. It is not always possible to determine the primary function of the nonverbal act. Also, methodologically, the use of two cameras would be beneficial when recording the material for the study of nonverbal behaviour (e.g. Goodwin 1993).

The methodology used in this study is a mixture of the previously mentioned approaches. In this research, nonverbal acts have been analysed in their local interactive circumstances and categorized according to that analysis. Emblems and illustrators have been analysed qualitatively, whereas pointing movements have been studied both qualitatively and quantitatively. The frequencies of various pointing movements have been counted, and this allows comparison of the speakers in terms of various pointing movements.

If we compare the results of this chapter cautiously to those reported in the literature, we notice some interesting parallels with recent investigations concerning aphasics' nonverbal behaviour in conversation. As mentioned earlier, there were very few emblems other than head nodding and shaking in these conversations. These findings are in accordance with Herrmann et al's (1988) results which also showed small number of other emblems in aphasic conversation. This may be due to the situational aspects of the conversations. However, the rare use of compensatory illustrators was fairly unexpected. In this data, there were actually only three such occurrences; thus it is evident that they do not form a marked group of compensatory gestures in this material. According to Le May et al. (1988) and Ahlsén (1985), aphasic speakers used more illustrative gestures than do normal controls yet their category of illustrative movements was much broader than in this study.

Some investigations suggest that the type of aphasia relates to the type of gestures used in conversation (e.g. Cicone et al 1979 and McNeill 1992). Cicone et al. (1979) claim that Broca's aphasics use more simple, unelaborated nonverbal units with a high degree of referentiality, which is in accordance with their verbal output, whereas Le May et al. (1988) suggest that Broca's aphasics use batons and ideographs significantly more than do Wernicke's aphasics. It is not possible to evaluate this question in this study. The only finding that might give some support for Cicone et al's result is that Jaakko, who had Broca's aphasia, used compensative pointing movements most, and these can be regarded as simple gestures with a high degree of referentiality.

In fact, the only comparison between the previous studies and this study can be made with regard to the pointing movements. In the present research the speakers' profiles of pointing movements were different. The results indicate that at least Jaakko made compensative use of pointing movements, and this compensative behaviour often formed a fixed behavioural pattern. Jaakko clearly used an externalizing strategy; using a pen and a paper, he was able to write down or draw some of the meanings he aimed at. However, it was not always possible to express the whole issue by writing or drawing and there often followed a collaborative repair sequence with several pointing movements to the numbers or drawing. The growing use of pointing movements in aphasics has been found in Le May et al's (1988) and Ahlsén's (1985) study. Smith (1987a) also reported that aphasics used more nonverbal behaviour, especially with high semantic loading like pointing movements, than non-aphasics and controls.

The complex question concerning the relationship between verbal and nonverbal behaviour is beyond the scope of this study. However, according to earlier studies it seems evident that aphasic speakers use more nonverbal behaviour than do normal speakers (Larkins & Webster 1981, Feyereisen 1983, Ahlsén 1985, Smith 1987a, Le May et al. 1988, Herrmann et al. 1989, Hadar 1991). Furthermore, some recent studies have highlighted the compensatory functions of nonverbal behaviour in aphasic communication (Smith 1987 a and b, Feyereisen et al. 1988, Le May 1988, Herrmann et al. 1988, Klippi 1990, Ahlsén 1991, Hadar 1991). The results of this study support the research findings that state that nonverbal compensative behaviour can be found among aphasic speakers. These results do not, of course, exclude the possibility that nonverbal behaviour deteriorates with aphasia, but from a communicative point of view, it is more important to analyse the possibilities of nonverbal behaviour in compensating for or facilitating aphasic communication and interaction, whether or not it has deteriorated. This analysis can therefore only be conducted in the local, interactive circumstances of production. Hence, it seems that this approach might be worthwhile developing further within aphasiology.

6. Using written numbers, writing or drawing

6.1 Introduction

Some aphasic speakers use written numbers, writing and drawing as alternative means of communicating when they have word-finding or word-pronouncing difficulties. Like gestures, these activities have two roles as communicative aids; they may substitute for language or they may be an augmentative form of communication (e.g. Lyon 1995). Usually these observations are connected with Broca's aphasia and/or with global aphasia and especially with apraxia of speech. Although this is common knowledge among people accustomed to communicating with aphasics, aphasiological literature rarely includes observations of this type of alternative means of communication, and there is very little mention of their value in everyday conversational situations.

Recently, Lyon (1995) published an excellent review of drawing and its value as a communication aid for aphasic adults. In this work, he presents some features of drawing which, when combined with the residual language of adults, offer potential enhancement of communication not otherwise attainable through conventional forms of expression, speech and gestures. As Lyon points out, speaking and gesturing exist only momentarily through acoustically or visually coded patterns, whereas drawing provides a permanent, fixed, graphic record of content. Writing is also a fixed graphic form, but it requires access to, and proficiency with, linguistically-coded letters. Another feature of drawing compared to speaking or writing is that drawings are largely free of linguistic symbols. Lyon refers to a report that eight artistically untrained, normal adults could satisfactorily draw and communicate the basic content of a variety of topics without reliance on written or spoken descriptors. This research led him to conclude that simplified drawings can adequately communicate both basic needs and wants without the supplementation of spoken or written words. Finally, drawing may represent the most direct, and thus most effective, route to inner thought and its expression. Accordingly, drawing is occasionally used to augment communication when other expressive forms are not available.

Regardless of hemispheric locus, brain damage interferes with drawing ability (e.g. Benton 1985). Most aphasics are not able to draw normally following the onset of their illness. Lyon (1995) describes typical features of

Conversation as an achievement in aphasics
Studia Fennica
Linguistica 6
1996.

drawing associated with left and right brain damage based on literature. The form and style of drawing change when left-brain damage occurs, and the drawings tend to become simpler. In these drawings, there is little detail, the size of figures is reduced, and multiple perspectives may appear simultaneously. Right hemisphere lesions mainly cause spatial disorientation, giving rise to, for example, faulty perspective, and scattered or fragmented parts or enlarged parts. The causes of drawing dysfunction have been linked to problems in the visuoperceptual, visuospatial and visuoconstructional abilities (Benton 1985).

Gainotti et al. (1983) studied experimentally the ability of aphasic patients to draw from memory common objects with a characteristic shape (e.g. a glass, a comb). They observed a significant relationship between impaired drawing and a disruption of semantic processing abilities. This result also appears to confirm Luria's (1976a:145-146) notion – that patients with a disturbance both of the nominative function of the speech and of the ability to evoke visual images in response to a given word, and whose lesions are due to the disturbances of the posterior zones of the left temporal region – are not able to draw a picture of named object although they are still perfectly capable to copy it. Hence, not all aphasic speakers may be able to use drawing to alleviate speech problems.

Although there has been interest in drawing ability in aphasia and in brain damage in general, few studies evaluate the aphasics' use of drawing for communicative purposes. Lyon (1995) summarizes eight published and seven unpublished studies that analyse several aspects of drawing by aphasics, for instance, the recognizability of drawings, their communicative value, their ease of use, and the use of drawing in natural settings. Two studies were based on the same aphasic subject. The latter studies' summarized results revealed how the drawings' recognizability varied from poor to excellent and how their communicative value also varied greatly; in most cases, however, the communicative value was rated as good or as at least functional. These studies rarely reported on the ease of use, and only three studies mentioned self-initiated drawing. From the communicative point of view, observations about the use of drawing in natural settings were the most interesting. In seven studies it was not observed, in four studies it was unclear but seemingly present, and in one study (two Broca's aphasics) it was present when probed. Only in two studies, both on one Broca's aphasic, was drawing present in natural settings. In fact, this review reveals excellently how little aphasic individuals' compensatory communication skills have been observed, not to mention studied, in natural settings.

Aphasia is also typically associated with various grades of agraphia. Mild aphasia is usually accompanied by mild agraphia. But the more severe the forms of aphasia, the more obvious becomes the writing disorder (Goodglass 1993). Leischner (1969) divides the concept of agraphia into three forms: agraphia due to language disturbances, constructional agraphia and apraxic agraphia. All types may be connected with aphasia. In sum, agraphia is obligatory in total aphasia, and in other forms of aphasia, agraphia appears much more distinctly. According to Kaplan & Goodglass (1981), Broca's aphasics usually have severely impaired writing, whereas Wernicke's aphasics usually write easily with their dominant hand, showing an analogy to their facile articulation of speech. Wernicke's aphasics' writing may show, for instance, semantic paraphasia, neologistic jargon, and paragrammatic sentence forms, as does their speech. In contrast to these findings, Leischner (1969) reports that in the majority of cases where the writing of letters and words is disturbed, the writing of single numbers is still preserved.

Hatfield & Zangwill (1974) described a patient with Broca's aphasia who was able to use single words. This patient often tried to circumvent his speech problems by writing, but this writing had limited communicative value due to his phonological-processing impairments. When comparing two anterior and two posterior aphasics to four normal speakers, Cicone et al. (1979) noticed that anterior speakers used numerical and writing information more than did either of the other groups. Moreover, when studying aphasic patients' communicative strategies, Holland (1982) reported that one patient used pencil and paper for writing in her communication. The patient described by Hatfield & Zangwill (ibid.) also used drawing as a means of expression. These researchers presented several examples to support their observation that drawing can serve as a helpful vehicle of communication in the presence of severe expressive disorders, although there were the inadequacies characterizing most of the patient's drawings.

Information-processing theories offer explanations of processing problems in aphasia. Linguistic processing is considered to be slow or inefficient, and sometimes to be a total block of linguistic knowledge due to brain-tissue damage. This brain damage causes problems in accessing and integrating linguistic knowledge. Nevertheless, knowledge of the target word is accessible through a visual form. If this is true, a speaker should be able to use writing or drawing to express numerical or other information. Another possible explanation is speech apraxia, according to which a speaker has succeeded in processing the linguistic information, but s/he is not able to activate the articulatory programme and utter the information needed.

This chapter focuses on how written numbers, writing or drawing are used to facilitate conversation either by substituting or by augmenting language.

The specific questions studied here are:
1. Where and when are number writing, writing or drawing used in aphasia group conversations?
2. What kind of consequences do written numbers, writing or drawing have for the development of conversation?

In the following pages, I will investigate the use of writing and drawing and their interactional consequences in their local interactive context.

6.2   Writing in conversation

In this data, one person, Jaakko, systematically and on his own initiative, used written numbers as an alternative means of communication. This observation is especially important because Jaakko had, in fact, total agraphia, and he consequently had difficulties in writing even single letters. He was able to write his name and some ideographs (e.g. the names of the former presidents of Finland) but he could not write words even for most ordinary objects. He could, however, write numerical information, for instance dates, times, numbers of amounts, etc. In fact, he used written numbers in three discussions, but only a few times in the first and in the second discussions. In the fourth discussion, Jaakko used written numbers and drawings several times. He drew a scheme of the chipboard plant and developed the drawing step by step. Here he wrote down a word only once, a name of a place (see chapter 8, example 7). In the whole database only one case occurred where another speaker, Maija, wrote down a number, and this actually happened at the request of Jaakko. I will analyse this excerpt, too.

The following example is a sequence taken from the beginning of the second discussion and it indicates how written turns are used. The topic of this conversation is the trip in which Jaakko and Paavo had participated.

Example 1

```
1   t:mi|nä päivä|nä te lähd|i|tte.
        what-ESS day-ESS     you-(PL) go-PST-2PL
        on what day did you leave.

    (1.4)

2   P:keskiviikko ilta|na.
        wednesday       evening-ESS
        on Wednesday night.

    (0.7)

3   t:mm?

4   (2.3*J draws 15 on the surface of the table*)

5   M:viisitoista{Øord} °päivä°.
        fifteen              day
        fifteen{Øord} °day°.

6   t:viidestois[ta,
        fifteenth
        the fifteen[th,

7   J:            [i-i-ilta|na.
                    evening-ESS
                  [e-e-evening.

8   t:mm=

9   P:=mm=

10  t:=mm

11  (2.6*J draws 16 on the surface of the table*)

12  t:ja[kuudestoista]
        and    sixteenth
        and[the sixteenth]
```

```
13   P:   [torstai|na   ]joo ol|t|i|in siellä.=
              thusday-ESS     PRT  be-PAS-PST-4  there
         [on Thursday  ]yes (we) were there.=

14   t:=hmm?(1.4)ja sitte seuraava|na aamu|na.
                    and  then   next-ESS    morning-ESS
         =hmm?(1.4)and then the next morning.

15   P:takas joo.[KRÖHM
         back   PRT
         back yes. [CLEARS THROAT

16   t:              [tul|i|tte takas joo.
                      come-PST-2PL  back  PRT
                     [you came back yes.

         (3.2)

17   J:iltapäivä|llä.
         afternoon-ADE
         in the afternoon.

         (1.5)

18   t:mm.
```

The participants were aware from earlier conversations that Jaakko had difficulties in expressing numerical information orally. In this excerpt, he informed them with written numbers of the departure date and of the arrival date of the trip he had participated in with Paavo. However, in this conversation, no identifiable trouble places occur with usual hesitations or longish pauses, in spite of the exceptional means of communication. This excerpt begins with the therapist's question on what day did you leave.. After a short pause (1.4 sec.), Paavo answers on Wednesday night. which the therapist acknowledges. Jaakko continues by writing down the number 15 with his finger on the surface of the table (line 6). Maija, who is sitting next to Jaakko, utters the number "15" (line 5) aloud. She expresses this in its basic form fifteen day which reflect her problems in inflecting words. The therapist corrects her utterance to the inflected form fifteenth day, which in this case represents a type of embedded correction (Jefferson 1987) because it does not discontinue the ongoing talk. After several acknowledgement tokens, Jaakko continues to contribute to the conversation by writing down the number 16 on the table (line 11). At this time the therapist utters aloud a number in the ordinal form with connector and, implicating the sequentiality of events. Paavo simultaneously initiates his turn and explains that they spent Thursday the sixteenth in Stockholm. By the end of the sequence it is apparent that they returned the next day. Considering the participants' difficulties in this exchange, the conversation progresses fluently, although the means of communication were exceptional.

Even though most of the sequences containing written numbers were clear like the previous excerpt, occasionally there were problems. In the following example, there is no problem in Jaakko's written contribution but the difficulty occurs in Maija's next turn.

Example 2

```
              Gmap
1   t:  [mi]ten pitkä matka Moskova|sta.
        how      long    way    Moscow-ELA
        [ho]w far from Moskow.

    (1.5)

         Gmap      ,,Gt      ,,Gpaper      ,,Gt
2   J:(hhh. 4.3) ö-ö (1.6)*kato.(.) tossa.*=
                              look       there
        (hhh. 4.3) uh-uh(1.6)*look.(.) there.*=
                           *RHmoves paper,RHDpaper*

3   M:=°kaheksan kymmentä°=
         eight       hundred
        =°eighty°=


              Gmap
4   t:  =kaheksan sataa.=
          eight      hundred
        =eight hundred.=



                Gmap
5   M:  =     [joo]
        =     [yes]

6   E:        [°kaheksan sataa°]
               eight       hundred
              [°eight hundred°]

    Gt
7   J: jooh [joh]
       ye:s [yes]

8   t:       [kah]eksansataa kilometri|ä Mosko[va|sta.
             eighthundred         kilometre-PAR   Moscow-ELA
             [ei]ght hundred kilometres from Mos[cow.

                                          Gt
9   M:                                    [mm

                                          Gt
10  J:                                    [jooh
                                          [ye:s

11  t:hmm-mm.
```

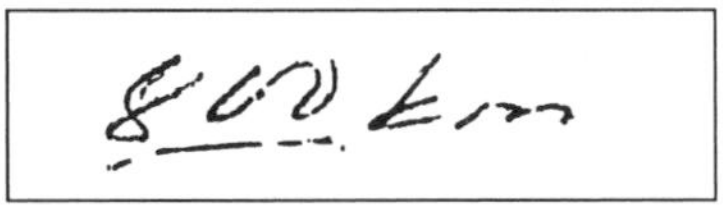

Figure 10: 800 kilometres (cf. line 2)

Jaakko had previously written the numeral 800. This excerpt begins with the therapist's contribution to Jaakko how far from Moscow. (line 1). Jaakko tries to express the number "800" which he has written on the paper, trying to find the proper lip positions for producing the number but failing to utter it. Consequently, he gives up (line 2) and points to the number on the paper and says look.(.) there.. Maija, looking at the number on the paper, utters eighty instead of 'eight hundred'. The therapist immediately produces a direct other-initiated repair which Jaakko acknowledges. Subsequently, the therapist further clarifies the matter with a specification directed to Jaakko, saying eight hundred kilometres from Moscow. Jaakko confirms this, and the therapist moves to the next contribution. Evidently there was no need to handle the correction further and it remained as an embedded correction. Although the correction was directed at Maija's utterance, the therapist did not shift her gaze to Maija and this could account for Maija's lack of response to the repair. Seemingly, the correction and Jaakko's immediate acknowledgement made it unnecessary to continue discussion of the error.

Furthermore, in the next excerpt, Jaakko's written contribution is clear, but in this case Maija's hesitation in expressing the written number also causes minor troubles.

Example 3

```
1   J:minu|l on,
        I-ADE    is
        I have,

2   (4.0 *J writes*)

3   M:yksi,.(1.7)puolitoista.°joo°
        one              one and a half
        one,.(1.7)one and a half.°yes°

    (1.9)

4   J:[on|k|s oikein.=
         be-Q-CLI right
        [is it right.=

5   M:[puolitoista,
         one and a half
        [one and a half,

6   t:=on?
        is
        =yes?

7   M:vuot[|ta.
         year-PAR
        ye[ars.

8   t:      [hmm

    (0.7)
```

```
 9  J:suunilleen.
       approximately
       approximately.

    (0.4)

10  M:joo-o.
       PRT
       ye:s.

    (0.5)

11  t:    elikä puolitoista vuot|ta on kulu[|nut.
          so        one and a half   year-PAR is   pass-PPC
       in other words one and a half years have go[ne.

12  J:                                            [joo.
                                                  [yes.

    (0.4)

13  t:hmm?hmm?
```

In the earlier discussion Maija told that she had been aphasic for 12 years. After that, Jaakko begins to tell about the length of his illness. He manages to utter I have (''minulla'':Sg1+ADE.) but is unable to go on. During the pause he takes a pen and writes down a numeral. Maija reads the number aloud but utters at first only one which, after a short pause, she self-corrects to one-and-a-half (literally 'half+of second' in Finnish) and continues by saying yes. It seems that Jaakko is a little bit uncertain of Maija's utterance and turns to the therapist and asks for a check saying is it right., while simultaneously Maija repeats the expression one-and-a-half-year. The therapist gives an affirmative reply to Jaakko after which Jaakko adds the word approximately. which Maija acknowledges. The therapist once more explicitly interprets Jaakko's written contribution (line 11), in other words one-and-a-half-years have gone.. Only after that did the speakers close the sequence with acknowledgements which implied that mutual understanding was reached.

The previous excerpts are revealing examples of how this kind of exceptional communicative behaviour is treated in conversation. Typically, one of the other participants uttered aloud the number which Jaakko had written down. In the first excerpt this occurred very naturally without interrupting the flow of the talk, but in the second and third excerpt some confirmation was needed before the conversation could go on. Despite this, in these excerpts Jaakko's contributions were adequate and unambiguous and the need for repair was due to Maija's paraphasic interpretations of Jaakko's written contributions.

On the other hand, there were also occasions where Jaakko's contributions were somewhat fuzzy and they caused problems in conversation. These problems led to long repair sequences. Next, there is an example where Jaakko himself was uncertain of the name of the number which he aimed at. Later on it turned out that he had aimed at expressing *two kilometres* but uttered at first "20 kilometres".

Example 4

1 J:on|k+se,.(0.6)kakskyläm,.(0.4)°kakskys,.(0.3)kaks
    be-Q-it   {twenty }   {twenty }   two
  J:is+it,.(0.6){tweln,.(0.4)° twens,.(0.3)two

  (1.7)

2 *kilommetr,.*°(0.7)kilometri|a.(*0.9*)on|k+se,
                     kilometre-PAR   be-Q-it
  ***kilommetr,.}*°(0.7)kilometres.(*0.9*)is+it,**
           writes "2"

3 t:mmm kak[si.
      two
  mmm tw[o.

4 J: *[kakskylmene,.*
           {twenty }
        [twenly,.

5 t:nyt nyt su|l+on siinä kaksi vasta.(0.4)kaksi.
    now now   you-ADE+is there   two   only   two
  now you only have two there.(0.4)two.

6 (3.5 **J writes "km"**)

7 t:kaks kilometri|a.
    two   kilometre-PAR
  two kilometres.

8 J:nii.
   PRT
  yeah.

  1.2

9 E:mi|tä.(0.7)kaks kilometri|a,.=
    what-PAR   two   kilometrePAR
  what.(0.7)two kilometres,.=

10 J:=ö-ö-lastulevy|ä.
         chipboard-PAR
  uh-uh-chipboard.

11 E:°aha m°
    PRT
  °I see m°

12 Y:.hjoo
  .yeah

13 J: **hmm.**

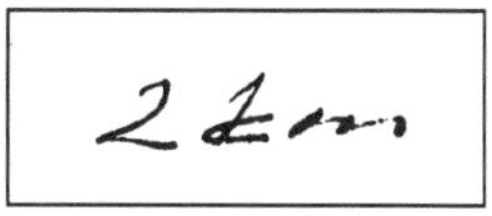

Figure 11: 2 kilometres (cf. lines 2 and 6)

The excerpt includes the repair sequence which followed Jaakko's unsure contribution (lines 1 and 2). Jaakko clearly anticipates the problems and begins a self-initiated self-repair appealing for help, looking at the therapist and asking is+it,.(0.6) tweln,.(0.4) twens,.(0.3) two kilommetr,.(0.7)kilometres.(0.9)is+it, and at the same time he writes the number "2" which the therapist utters aloud. After that there follows a negotiation where Jaakko begins to repeat perseveringly twenly but stops this utterance. The therapist states that he had written only the numeral 2 and Jaakko writes the abbreviation km (line 6) after the 2. Next, the therapist utters two kilometres which Jaakko acknowledges. Thus, the negotiation concerning the amount of kilometres terminated successfully.

The sequence which followed Jaakko's self-repair initiation resembles a negotiation more than a clear repair-sequence. Of interest is that Jaakko himself initiates a self-repair. From the start he is unsure of the number he is offering. He writes down the numeral 2 but utters it, although with hesitation, as "20". The therapist gazes at the number and reads two. For this reason, the therapist's turn (line 3) cannot be regarded as a clear instance of other-repair; rather, it is a reply or an interpretation of Jaakko's contribution. In line 5, the therapist informs Jaakko that he has only written the numeral 2. However, Jaakko still expresses a hesitant twenly and the therapist continues by explaining that, now you only have two there. (0.4) two. Jaakko adds to the numeral 2 with an abbreviation of 'kilometre' (km), and the therapist reads it aloud. Thus, the therapist acts as the 'voice' of Jaakko rather than as an instructor. At the end of this excerpt it is evident that the interactants did not understand the reference of 2 km. In line 9, Elina makes an other-repair initiation (a next turn repair initiation, Schegloff et al. 1977) and asks what Jaakko means by 2 km. At this point Jaakko manages to express that his contribution 2 km refers to the chipboard. The beginning of this excerpt shows, interestingly, the collaboration between Jaakko and the therapist. This is in accordance with Milroy's and Perkins' (1992) observations of aphasic conversations. They propose a term 'collaborative negotiation of repair' instead of the term 'repair-sequence' for an accurate description of the repair-process in aphasic conversation.

In the following, I will show a complicated example where the aspect of negotiation is very obvious. The excerpt begins with Elina's elliptic question (line 2) [did you get ill] while being the-there (in Russia). Quite soon, however, the topic shifts to handling the time Jaakko spent in chipboard production in Russia. Jaakko characteristically contributes to the conversation with several pieces of numerical information but the conversation has critical points where the information offered is insufficient.

Example 5

```
1   J:on vaan. (0.4) on vaan. (2.4)[koo oo pee.]
       is  just        is  just        K  O  P
    it is just. (0.4) it is just.(2.4)[K O P]

2   E:                        [°sairastu|i|t]+sä si-siellä
                                get ill-PST-2 +you  there
                              [°did you get ill]when being the-

3   ol|le|ssa.°
      be-INF-INE
    there.°

    (0.8)

4   J:*mitä.*=
       what
      *what.*=
      *G,,,,E *

5   E:=ol|i|t+sä siellä(.)kun(.)sairastu|i|t.
       be-PST-2+you  there    when    get ill-PST-2
      =where you there(.)when(.)you get ill.

    (0.5)

6   J:ei ei ei ei ei(2.7)hhhhh.
       NEG NEG NEG NEG NEG
      no no no no no(2.7)hhhhh.

7   (9.6*J WRITES*)

8   M:°kolme vuotta°
        three   year-PAR
      °three years°

    (0.8)

9   J:*koo(0.6)°k° kolme vuot|ta.*(*5.8*)sitten,.(0.4)kaue|mmin
       K              three  year-PAR            then        long-COM
      *K(0.6)°k° three years.*(*5.8*)then,.(0.4)longer
           *Gpaper**makes some marks on the paper*

10  kauen,.(*4.3*)suunilleen.(0.7)ei|kun,.(*2.3*)juu-u juu
                   approximately      NEG-PRT            PRT   PRT
    {longer},.(*4.3*)about.(0.7),.(*2.3*)ye:ah yeah
           *Gpaper**makes some marks on the paper*

11  juu (2.2)RYKÄISEE
    PRT
    yeah (2.2)CLEARS THROAT

    (0.5)

12  t:[°mm°

13  J:[hhhhh.

    (1.5)
```

14 t:tarkota|t|ko että ehd|i|t ol|la kolme vuot|ta Suome|ssa.
        mean-2-Q   PRT manage-PSF-2 be-INF   three   year-PAR   Finland-INE
     do you mean that you managed to be three years in Finland.

    (0.5)

15 J:juu ei|kun,
      PRT NEG-PRT
     yeah no but,

16 t:vai,=
      or
     or,=

17 J:=juu-u ei|kun,(1.3)ö-men|i|n,(0.7)tonne tonne
      PRT   NEG-PRT   go-PST-1   there+to   there+to
     =ye-yeah no but,(1.3)er I went,(0.7)there there

18 hh.(1.2)kato|s,.hh (0.5) Valmeti|lle.(0.7) *
          look-CLI   company name-ALL
     hh.(1.2)look,.hh (0.5) to Valmet.(0.7) *

19 Valmeti|lle.(0.7)* *[*Valmeti|lle*
     company name-ALL   company name-ALL
     to Valmet.(0.7)* *[*to Valmet*
     2 taps on the table[*taps on the table*

20 E: [°vaihdo|i|t firma|a°
                                change-PST-2   firm-PAR
                             [°you changed firms°

21 t: [hmm?

    (0.7)

22 t:hmm?

23 J:men|i|n.*   *
      go-PST-1
     I went.*   *
        koputtaa paperia 4 kertaa

24 t:hmm?

25 (13.2 J:*KIRJOITTAA HUOKAISEE*) °yks°
                                  one
     (13.2 J:*WRITES SIGHS*)   **°one°**

    (3.8)

26 t:kahdeksankymmentä.
      eighty
     eighty.

27 J:hmm.

    (0.6)

28 t:siis MUUt|i|t silloin firma|a vai.
     so   change-PST-2 then   firm-PAR or
     so you CHANged the firm then or.

29 J:juu kato ei ei kato|s .hh=
      PRT look NEG NEG look-CLI
      yes look no no look.hh=

30 t:=ei?
       NEG
       =no?

31 J:öm
      um

     (1.5)

32 t:öö,
      uh,

33 J:(3 KOPUTUSTA)tä|n(0.9)aika|na,.(*14.0*)
                   this-GEN   time-ESS
      (3 TAPS)this(0.9)time,.(*14.0*)
                         *_writes_*

34 (2 KOPUTUSTA)(12.0) tul|i|n,.(2.0) ja,(KOPUTUKSIA)
                        come-PST-1   and
     (2 TAPS)(12.0)I came,.(2.0) and,(TAPS)

35 M:°neljä vuot|ta°
       four   year-PAR
      °four years°

36 **(8.8 _J *sighs, writes*_)**

37 t:mi|tä,(.)mi|tä tapahtu siis *tä|nä,(.) seiskytkuus viiva
      what-PAR what-PAR happen-(PST) PRT this-ESS   seventy-six clash
      what,(.)so what happened *this,(.)seventy-six dash
                                     *_Dnumbers_*

38   [kahdeksankymmentä.*
        eighty
       [eighty.*

39 **J:[hhhhh.**

40 t:nyt+mä e|n ihan(.)tarkkaan pääs|sy,.
      now+I NEG-1 quite   clearly   get-PPC
      now I didn't quite(.)clearly get,.

     (1.9)

41 J:*lastulevy.*
       chipboard
      chipboard.
       *_Dpaper_*

     (0.6)

```
42  t: aha.(0.3)sillon|ko sä ol|i|t juuri siellä,.=
        PRT          then-Q    you be-PST-2  just  there
    oh.(0.3)were you there just at that time,.=

43  J:=juu=
    =yeah=

44  t:=Neuvostoliito|ssa.=
       Soviet Union-INE
    =in the Soviet Union.=

45  J:=jooh=
    =yeah=

46  M =jooh=
    =yeah=

47  E::=hmm
```

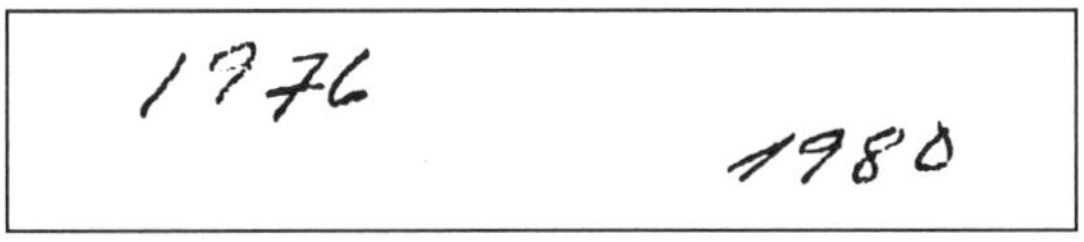

Figure 12: Years 1976–1980 (cf. lines 25 and 33–36)

Jaakko strongly denies (line 6) Elina's question (line 5) by repeating *no* five times with head shakes. Jaakko then writes the number 3 followed by an abbreviation v (v = vuotta; years in Finnish). From the point of view of the conversation's organization, this is an interesting turn. His writing comes after an adjacency pair where the first part is a Wh-question and the second part of the pair is a denial. Thus his strong denial could have been interpreted as an initiation of an explanation because Jaakko is able to keep the turn, in spite of the long pause, and he continues, grasping the pen and writing down number "3". Once again, Maija reads Jaakko's written contribution aloud, saying three years (line 8). Evidently this contribution needed explanation, which Jaakko himself recognises, and he offers a rather long turn with rich nonverbal behaviour (lines 9-11). Even so, Jaakko's explanations remained unclear for the therapist because she formulates a request for clarification (line 14) and begins an other-initiated repair with an acknowledgement token and *do you mean*-initiation, which is a typical NTR-initiation (Schegloff, Sacks & Jefferson 1977). However, the therapist's interpretation was incorrect and so in line 18 Jaakko manages to explain that he began to work in a well-known Finnish company.

Jaakko continues to tap the paper and, after a short pause (0.7), an important confirmation follows where Jaakko repeats the same information, but this time by dividing it into parts, first repeating to Valmet (line 19). At this point Elina's silent candidate understanding is observed, but Jaakko does not react to it. Instead he goes on uttering I went and again taps the paper with his fingers (line 23). This may have been turn-keeping behaviour to gain time to write down the numbers. Subsequently he wrote again some numbers that turned out to be a year (1980) although he only utters the first number of it, one (line 25). The therapist reads aloud eighty which Jaakko acknowledges. But the issue remains unclear to the therapist because she formulates the next request for clarification beginning with the particle so (siis in Finnish) so you CHANged firms then or (line 28). The content of her repair initiation is the same as Elina's former repair initiation (line 20), but this time the form of the repair-initiation is more clearly a question. Jaakko obviously regards this as a question because he first confirms it, but then immediately afterwards denies it. In lines 33–36, he manages to give additional written information, which causes Maija to utter four years. Next, the therapist explicitly asks what,(.)so what happened this,(.)between seventysix dash eighty.now I didn't quite (.)clearly get,.. This seems to be a critical question because now Jaakko manages to reply with a single-word chipboard (line 41)(see also chapter 9) and this turned out to be some solution for the long repair sequence.

Several trouble sources arose in this excerpt. The first trouble source – in lines 9 and 11 – was because Jaakko was not able to provide an explanation for the written number 3. The therapist and Elina began to collaborate and formulated the requests for clarification (lines 14, 20, 28, 37, 42). In addition, there were turns where the other participants read aloud Jaakko's written numbers (lines 8, 26, 35, 37-38). Thus, a cooperative pattern emerged in the conversation so that Jaakko introduced information in a numerical form and the other participants uttered it aloud, and they also tried to give interpretations for written numbers, inferring their suggestions from the earlier conversational context. In this sense, these excerpts display real interactional achievement in these conversations. Jaakko's communicative behaviour needed the cooperation of the other participants and the cooperation offered resolutions for the troubles.

6.3 Discussion

The above examples show some of the events which took place in connection with the use of written numbers in order to develop the conversation. In all cases, Jaakko substituted his oral inability to express the numerical information by writing down the target numbers. The first excerpt shows a very fluently proceeding conversation without any signs of problems, although written numbers were used instead of oral expressions. In the next two excerpts (ex. 2 and 3), mutual understanding was rather easily reached, although some collaboration was needed before the conversation could continue. In both cases, Jaakko has written the right number but the trouble appeared after Maija's contributions because they were inaccurate interpretations of Jaakko's numerical turns. In these excerpts, the conversational topic was already established and the turns that offered numerical information can be regarded as topic-continuing with additional information. Although Jaakko was not able to contribute verbally to the conversation, he was capable of giving additional information in written form when such information was relevant.

The two other excerpts illustrate more profound problems in conversation connected with the use of numerical information. In example 4, Jaakko himself incorrectly named his own written number, causing the other participants to negotiate which number Jaakko was aiming at. The most complicated excerpt was example 5, where Jaakko introduced several numbers. In this case, he participated in the conversation with additional information but was unable to give reference for the numbers. However, discussion of the issues relevant to this excerpt occurred earlier on in the conversation, and the interactants began their collaboration based on the earlier conversational context. As a consequence, they were able to infer some possible interpretations from the earlier discussion and mutual understanding was reached with the help of collaboration by the co-participants.

Thus, in simple cases, the written numbers were excellent substitutes for speech. These numbers renewed the conversational context (e.g. Heritage 1989) as well as the speech itself. The easiness of example 1 shows that numbers can be well used in conversation in some occurrences, instead of orally produced words, because they contain explicitly coded information. In these cases, the context of the conversation (cf. Schegloff & Sacks 1973, Heritage 1989) supported the search for the meaning of the number offered by Jaakko. However, in more complicated cases, there were clearly problems in reaching the meaning for the number(s). The recipients were not able to infer directly the meaning for the number(s) offered. Obviously, their knowledge of the issue was too scant, or they could not process the fragmentary information offered. These excerpts also show that there is always the likehood of misproduction or misinterpretation in aphasic conversation.

Jaakko was the only speaker to use written numbers of his own initiation. The examples indicate that his behaviour was systematic in this respect. Whenever he had to express time, dates, prices or other information which could be offered through numbers, he did so. Thus, as this communicative behaviour ties in with his verbal inability, it can be regarded as compensatory. Jaakko clearly used an externalizing strategy; using a pen and a paper he was able to write down some of the meanings he aimed at. This finding is in accordance with earlier observations of aphasic speakers' communication (Hatfied & Zangwill 1974, Cicone el al. 1979, Holland 1982). However, these conversations show that it was not always possible to express the whole matter with writing, and there often followed a collaborative repair sequence to Jaakko's numbers.

The previous excerpts display a fascinating communicative pattern by Jaakko. Although he was not able to participate verbally in conversation, he was in certain cases able to contribute to the conversation with written information. In other words, he changed the mode of communication from oral expression to writing and thus in these examples writing served as a tool for communication (cf. Vygotsky 1931/1982) In order to do this, he had to be able to utilize contextual resources; first he used the physical resources, a paper and a pen; second, at least in some cases, he was able to place the numbers in such positions in conversation that the interlocutors were able to combine the numerical information and the earlier contextual knowledge; and third, if problems followed, he was able to get his interlocutors to work in co-operation with him to make guesses about what he meant with the numbers (cf. Goodwin 1995).

The writing down of numbers turned out to be a very constant feature in Jaakko's communicative behaviour. When I met him some years later he still used the same compensatory strategy in conversation. Apparently this was connected to his specific inability to express numerical information orally.

Thus, it is possible that his conceptual knowledge concerning numerical information is preserved, and his problems may be in the phonological and/or the articulatory level (cf. Lesser 1989). On the other hand, he sometimes had problems understanding verbally uttered numbers. As he clearly had slow auditory processing of verbal utterances, he probably suffered from the defect called "alienation of the meaning of words" identified by Luria (1976).

Generally speaking, these examples can be regarded as 'problem-solving' instances in conversation. In the first examples the solutions were self-evident, but especially in the last example it was more difficult to find the solution. The participants obtained hints from Jaakko for the collaboration, numbers, but they did not know the reference of the phrases with numbers. Thus, they inferred the meanings from the earlier conversation or from the knowledge acquired earlier and offered the candidate interpretations to Jaakko. In these sequences, the collaboration led to successful repair work.

6.4 Drawing in conversation

Drawing was another alternative means of communication. Jaakko was the only participant to use this form of communication and his contributions occurred in the fourth discussion after a confusing misunderstanding had arisen. He tried to explain the size and functioning of the chipboard factory where he previously had worked. Problems arose after Jaakko's turn in which he combined the words *two kilometres* and *chipboards*, from which the recipients interpreted that the length of the chipboards was two kilometres, which was, of course, impossible. After an exhausting long repair sequence which lasted several minutes, it turned out that Jaakko had tried to express that it was the production line that was two kilometres long. During this long repair sequence he drew a scheme of the chipboard plant.

The initiation of this trouble is found below:

Example 6

```
1  E:=mi|tä toi(.)kilometri|a lastulevy|ä, ö-ö(1.2)tarkottaa.
       what-PAR  that   kilometre-PAR   chipboard-PAR          means
     =what this(.)kilometres chipboard, er-er(1.2)means.

   (3.2)k[aks,(3.9) kilometri|ä
        two            kilometre-PAR
   (3.2)t[wo,(3.9) kilometres.

2  P:    [(RYKÄISEE)
         [(CLEARS HIS THROAT)

3  J:kaks kilometri|ä.(2.2) lastulevy|ä.(5.5) HUOKAISEE
       two   kilometre-PAR        chipboard-PAR
     two kilometres.(2.2)chipboard.(5.5)SIGHS

4  M:hirvee (0.8)  i[so.
       enormous         big
     enormous (0.8)b[ig
```

```
 5   J:              [juu
                     [yes

 6   E:hirvee pät[kä.
          enormous  piece
        enormous pie[ce.

 7   J:              [juu juu
                     [yes yes
     (.)

     (.)

 8   E and t:[heh-heh-heh-heh-heh-heh-heh

 9   J:       [juu juu juu
              [yes yes yes

10   M                    [$iso[(.)firma.$
                            big      company
                          [$big[(.)firm.$

11   J:              [kuule.(0.8)kuule.[(0.6)      [kato nyt
                      listen       listen           look  now
                     [listen.(0.8)listen.[(0.6)    [look now

12   t:                                       [heh-heh-heh
                                              [heh-heh-heh

13   M:                                            [heh-heh
                                                   [heh-heh

14   .hhh
     .hhh

     (0.8)

15   J:ei usko kato|s.* *
        NEG believe  look-CLI
        cannot believe look.* *
                       *puts pencil on the paper*
```

In this trouble spot, Elina poses a question (line 1) that was connected with the chipboard and two kilometres. In line 3, Jaakko attempts to explain the relationship but is unable to utter more than two kilometres(.) chipboard.. Maija and Elina are surprised at the length of the chipboards. In lines 11 and 15, Jaakko clearly suspects that the others do not believe him and so he continues his attempts at explanation by first putting his pencil on the paper, but he does not yet draw. However, the trouble cannot be solved and the conversation continues with the evident misunderstanding. The recipients continue to make other-initiated repairs and Jaakko attempt to assure them that something (the line) is two kilometres long. As the trouble continues and Jaakko's verbal means do not allow a more elaborated explanation, Jaakko begins to draw the scheme while simultaneously listing the production line phases (example 7, lines 4 and 7).

Example 7

```
1   t:niih-hih-hih-heh$mi|tä]tekee kahde|n kilometri|n pi[tui-$
                         what-PAR does   two-GEN   kilometre-PAR
    yeah-hih-hih-heh$what]does one do with a two kilometres l[on-$

2   J:                                               [*ja(.)
                                                      and
                                                     [*and(.)
                                                      *RHDt,Gt*

3   taas,.*(1.5)*kuli*-*kuljetin.*
    again          conveyer
    again,.*(1.5) *con*-*conveyer.*
          *Gpaper,Dpaper**Gt,Dpaper*

    (0.5)

4   J:[*kuli-kuljetin.* * *
          conveyor?
      [*con-conveyor.* * *
       *Dpaper*       *DRAWS*

5   E:[kahe|n kilometri|n,.
        two-GEN kilometre-GEN
      [two kilometres,.

    (0.4)

6   M:°kuljetin°
        conveyor
       °conveyor°

    (0.7)

7   J:*taas,.(1.2)pönttö.*
       again        container
    *again,.(1.2)container.*
       *DRAWS*

    (0.8)

8   M:pönt[tö.
        container
      contai[ner.

9   J:        [pönttö.(0.6)sitten,
               container       then
              [*container.(0.6)then,*
                   *DRAWS*

    (1.5)

10  M:kuljetin,(0.5)VIelä [heh-heh.
      conveyor        more
      conveyor,(0.5)AGain [heh-heh.

11  K:                    [NAURUA
                          [LAUGHS
```

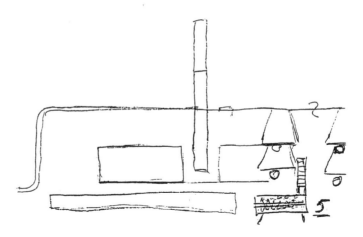

Figure 13: A scheme of the chipboard plant

The above misunderstanding was very confusing because the recipients did not know the referent, which they learned was two kilometres long, and furthermore, Jaakko did not comprehend what was problematic for the others. As a result, during the long repair sequence, he drew the whole scheme of the factory on paper in order to convince the recipients of the size of the factory. The flow of conversation was interrupted on several occasions because of the drawing.

In this case Jaakko used drawing to augment his communication, not to replace his linguistic communication. Hence, his communication continued partly through the use of language and partly through the use of drawing. With the help of the drawing, he managed to give an idea of the different phases of chipboard production to the recipients. Thus, he used drawing as a facilitating means which compensated his limited verbal expressions. He needed time for drawing and it is interesting that the others yielded time for him. Clearly, the recipients got more elaborate information with the help of the drawing than Jaakko's verbal explanations could give them. At last, after drawing the scheme and after several attempts at collaboration by the recipients, the misunderstanding was resolved.

6.5 Summary

In this data, one participant, Jaakko, used paper and a pen for two types of alternative communicative means, writing and drawing. He used written numbers to substitute for language when his verbal expression was hindered, whereas drawing was used in association with speech. They were both used in problems of speaking, in order to give more detailed information of the current topic of the conversation. One can say that Jaakko made use of writing and drawing as compensatory strategies in his communication.

The given excerpts show that writing down the numbers did not self-evidently facilitate the conversation. In some written turns it was easy for the interlocutors to infer the meaning of the numbers, as in example 1. On the other hand, there were some problems when the recipients were not immediately able to infer the reference for the number written by Jaakko. Also, there were sequences in which written turns only partly gave the information needed for understanding a turn, and in these cases further collaborative negotiation was needed in order to make sure of the meaning which Jaakko aimed at.

These conversations also contain examples in which the trouble is caused by the aphasic misinterpretations or mispronunciations. There is an excerpt where the next speaker acts as the voice of the earlier contributor but utters a wrong number (ex. 2) and, on the other hand, there is an excerpt (ex. 4) where Jaakko himself wrote the right number but read it out incorrectly and this led to the negotiation about which number was the target of his expression.

In cases of drawing, the contribution (the figure) got its form gradually and the other participants did not explicitly verbalize all the steps. However, Jaakko's drawing clearly illustrated his explanation of the chipboard plant, and the interlocutors did not begin repair sequences in connection with the drawing itself.

There are sporadic observations in the aphasiological literature that especially Broca's aphasics use writing (Hatfied & Zangwill 1974, Cicone et al. 1979, Holland 1982) or drawing (cf. Lyon 1995) in their communication. These few remarks do not justify estimating their generality in aphasic conversation. However, the studies mentioned by Lyon (1995), as well as my own clinical observations, indicate that there are aphasic individuals who are able to employ them, at least to some degree, in their communication. There has been very little evaluation of the communicative value of using these alternative means of communication. Although the examples of this chapter show that the use of writing and drawing are not self-evidently successful as alternative means of communication, they show one important communicative resource in impaired conversation. In some occasions, writing and/or drawing can create the chance to participate in the conversation and to contribute to it although the required words are not accessible.

7. Laughter and humour

7.1 Introduction

The textual orientation within linguistics regards conversation as an act of information transmission between people via the means of language. This view has resulted in the neglect of several recurrent features in speech and conversation, for instance pauses, hesitations, repetitions and laughing. In this chapter, I will focus on the use of laughter and humour in aphasic conversations. Although it has been emphasized that laughter is part of social communication, few empirical studies have been conducted on the role of laughter in conversation (Adelswärd 1989:108).

Although laughter has been understood to be a spontaneous phenomenon, several studies recognize that laughter is a socially organized activity (Jefferson 1985, Mulkay 1988, Adelswärd 1989), therefore systematic, and can thus be studied as an interactional resource. According to Jefferson et al. (1987:156), laughter has the status of an 'official' conversational activity and as such it can be a relevant, consequential next action. Sacks (1992b:571) establishes an important notion when he suggests that laughing is one of the few things in conversation which can be shared and which often occurs in unison. He even claims that speakers prefer simultaneous laughing.

Jefferson (1979) introduced the idea of invited laughter in conversation. Laughter can be handled as a sequence in which the speaker of an utterance invites the recipient to laugh, and the recipient accepts the invitation. Jefferson has also analysed patterns of laughter in 'troubles telling' (Jefferson 1984). A typical pattern is that a troubles-teller engages in laughter while expressing troubles, but the recipient does not.

Laughter and humour are usually seen as being tightly interconnected. Mulkay (1988) suggests that laughter is one sign of humour. Besides humour, laughter may also have other functions in conversation; for instance, Adelswärd (1989:129) claims that in dialogue, participants often laugh alone and not always at things considered particularly funny. Adelswärd argues that the functions of such unilateral laughter (a person laughing alone) may be used to modify verbal expressions or attitudes. Mutual laughter, on the other hand, can be interpreted as a sign of rapport and consensus.

One crucial question concerns the definition of humour in interaction. Sacks (1972) offers the concept of membership categories. One of the central members of Sacks' categories is the serious/joke pair. Mulkay (1988) has also formulated the principles and practices of humorous and serious discourse,

Conversation as an
achievement in aphasics
Studia Fennica
Linguistica 6
1996.

and he regards these as radically different. One may also ask if laughing is a necessary and sufficient prerequisite for humour. Whereas humour is a very complex phenomena, laughing seems to be a critical feature of humour. Nevertheless, it is disputable whether unilateral laughing can be regarded as a sign of humour in conversation, but mutual laughing is a coordinated effort by the recipients and hence, it can be regarded as a sign of humour.

Bateson (1972:152) examines the phenomenon of 'play' in his essay *A Theory of Play and Fantasy*. He explains that play can only occur if the participant are capable of some degree of metacommunication, i.e. of exchange signals which would carry the message 'this is a play'. Mulkay (1988:46-52) uses the terms 'humorous mode' or 'play frame' and serious mode. His work reveals that participants indicate their switches back and forth from a serious mode to a humorous mode. Participants therefore signal their departure from one mode to another. Many of these signals are nonverbal, such as changing the speaker's normal voice pattern or using slight physical movements. Likewise, each humorous contribution also has to be marked by recipients in some special way. These signs may be laughter, smiling or some related token of appreciation. In the case of ironic statements, various kinds of signals are employed to suggest that the utterance is not to be taken literally. In these cases, the use of appropriate signals is especially critical to the recipients' awareness of entry into the humorous mode, the 'play frame'. This frame idea stresses the importance of the various signals for interpretation. According to Mulkay:"The recipient has to formulate some counter-text of his own which contradicts the actual utterance and which will convey the speaker's real meaning" (p. 49). The implied counter-text is usually taken to be the opposite of what is actually spoken (cf. also Adeswärd 1988:110).

For Mulkay, 'signals' seem to mean almost the same as 'contextualization cues' for Gumperz (1982). Gumperz proposes that the interpretation of any utterance is based on conventionalized congruence expectations between content and surface style. According to him, contextualization cues are constellations of surface features by which speakers signal and receivers interpret the utterances. He defines a contextualization cue as "any feature of linguistic form that contributes to the signalling of contextual presuppositions". Such cues may include the code, the dialect, style switching or prosodic phenomena. Unlike words, the meanings of contextualization cues are implicit. Gumperz also describes other less readily-noticed phonetic and rhythmic signs that enter into the contextualization process. He refers to Birdwhistell's study where it was shown that information was conveyed with eyes, face, limbs and torso in the act of talking. He also stresses that these nonverbal signs are language-like in the sense that they are learned through interaction, they are culturally specific, and they are analysable in terms of underlying processes. Furthermore, nonverbal signals are also coordinated with verbal signs both at the micro-level of syllables and at the level of longer discourse segments (ibid, p. 131–141). In fact, laughter is not mentioned in Gumperz's list as a contextualization cue, but clearly laughter can be regarded as the same type of cue as those he lists.

Within current aphasic literature, no mention of aphasic speakers' humour and its occurrence is found in actual communicative situations.

The focus of this chapter is on laughter and humour and their social organization in aphasic conversation. My intention is to investigate whether aphasic speakers use the same signs and contextualization cues of humour as do 'normal' speakers. My starting point is Sacks' idea of membership categories (1972), where one of the central members of categories is the serious/joke - pair, and Mulkay's (1988) distinction between humorous and serious discourse. As mutual laughing is regarded here as a central sign of humour, my objective is to find out and to analyse the following:

1. Whether mutual laughter occurs in these conversations and whether conversational sequences with mutual laughter can be regarded as humour sequences between aphasics.

2. Another aim here is to investigate the aphasic speakers' means of entering and inviting other participants to engage humorous discourse, and hence, of making a distinction between two basic categories mentioned previously.

In the study, laughter occurs during spontaneous conversations and as a consequence, it is not connected to standardized jokes which have a more or less stable content and can be passed from person to person for retelling at some other time (cf. Mulkay 1988). This analysis has focused on the sequences initiated by aphasic speakers that lead to mutual smiling or to laughing. In the present data, this kind of laughter sequence was mainly observed in the first discussion. Laughter also occurred in the fourth discussion, but in most cases the examples were either of unilateral laughter or of the therapist's initiated laughing. Thus, because these occurrences did not lead to mutual laughter, they were excluded from the analysis. In the following pages, I will concentrate on analysing two types of sequences containing aphasics' initiated laughing. I will present examples and analyse them, paying special attention to the features which, according to Mulkay (1988), form the humour frame.

Sacks' (1992b) suggestion that laughing can be done together and at the same time places special demands on the transcription system especially when studying group discussions with several participants. Due to these special demands, I have adopted the transcription system in partiture form (a syncWRITER transcript) for analysing this data (see p. 46), which could better handle simultaneous acts in interaction than does a conventional transcript system of conversation analysis in vertical form.

7.2 Analysis

I will start with the conversational sequences from the conversation number 1 in which mutual laughter occurs. These sequences are similar in terms of their structure, and they are also connected to a particular topic, namely the problems of speaking, or the illness which led to aphasia in general. The first conversation contains several examples which are analysed in the following pages.

The first excerpt is a typical example.

Example 1

Mgaze	GJ..
M	minä(.)edistyly(.)koko ajaln. NAURAA
	I progress-3 all time-ACC
	I (.)progress (.)all the time. LAUGHS
Mgesture	***LH stepwise↑, Onod***
t	mm.mm.
	DM
Jgaze	Gpaper..........
J	(0.6)aha.(1.7)
	(0.6) oh. (1.7)
Jgesture	***Onod***

Mgaze	GJ........................
M	NAURAA$hyvä juttu.$NAURAA
	great thing
	LAUGHS$ great thing.$LAUGHS
J	hyvä juttu.	o-oikein.NAURAHTAA
	great thing	rigth
Jgesture	***Onod,EB↑***	***T to M,Onod***
E		NAURAA/LAUGHS

Mgaze	GJ...
M	hmm.
	hmm.
Mgesture	***X..............***

Maija previously told the others about her continuing progress during her long illness (she had become aphasic 12 years earlier). In the beginning of this excerpt she returns to her recovery, uttering I(.)progress(.)all the time. gazing at Jaakko and laughing briefly. During her laughing, the therapist gives two acknowledgement tokens and points to Maija. Jaakko also utters a short acknowledgement token oh. (aha. in Finnish) and nods his head, gazing at the table. Then, after a pause (1.7 sec) he says great thing.. His nonverbal behaviour is characteristic while uttering his contribution; he raises his head and eyebrows slightly and looks directly at Maija. Jaakko's short statement provokes a burst of laughter from Maija. Maija's gaze is directed at Jaakko and she repeats Jaakko's contribution with a laughing voice and continues laughing, whereby Elina joins her laughter. Jaakko turns to Maija and again acknowledges her, uttering r-right., and laughs. The mutual laughter ends when Maija throws her pen on the table and gives a short acknowledgement token to Jaakko.

This excerpt is an interesting piece of conversation. Maija has been a troubles-teller (Jefferson 1984) when talking about her illness, but at the same time she turns the positive side up and makes an upgraded self-assessment (cf. Pomeranz 1984) of her recovery; she tells about her continuing recovery, laughing and looking at Jaakko. Jaakko then gives an acknowledgement token, and after a pause, continues with a short second assessment which prompts mutual laughter.

The second, comparable excerpt immediately follows the first:

Example 2

J	ei puhu mitään.
	NEG speak anything
	not speak anything.
t	mm.
	mm.

Mgaze	GJxxxxxxxxxxxxxxxxxxxxxxxxxxxxxxxxxxxxxxGJ
M	minä oleØ1,.(1.4)neljä vuot|ta,.(0.2)puhumaton.
	I beØ1 four year-PAR mute
	I beØ1,.(1.4)four years,.(0.2)unable to speak.
Mgesture	*B->............ Dself.............. openLH↑,B<-*
Jgesture	*T to t*

Mgesture	*(0.7)LH↑¤*
Jgaze	GM........
J	(1.2)aha..hhh
	(1.2)oh..hhh
Jgesture	*RH¤*
t	*mm.mm.*(0.7)no niin
	PRT PRT
	***mm.mm.*(0.7)well then**
tgesture	*DJ*

J	$si|lä
	that-ADE way-ADE
	$like that.$
Jgesture	*OnodM*
t	Jaakkoheh-heh-heh$että ei ei nyt,.$NAURAA
	1name M NEG speak anything
	Jaakkoheh-heh heh$that no no now,.$LAUGHS

115

Mgaze	GJxxxxxxxx		G↓,,Gt........	
M	$si‖llä lai‖lla.$NAURAA$si‖llä lai‖lla.$			
	that-AD way-ADE that-ADE way-ADE			
	$like that.$LAUGHS$like that.$			
Mgesture	*B->J*	*LH->J B<-X..............*		
Jgaze	GMxxxxxxxxx			
J	lai‖lla.$	NAURAA		
		LAUGHS		
t	Maija(.)Maija,			hmm.
	1name F 1name F			
	Maija(.)Maija,			**hmm.**
E		NAURAA/LAUGHS		

The beginning of this excerpt contains Jaakko's and Maija's self-assessments of their speech abilities. The talk begins with Jaakko's aphasic problems when he explains that [he can] not speak anything. and nods at the same time. Literally taken, Jaakko's self-assessment is contradictory because he claims that he [can] not speak anything. but he expresses this with speech. The therapist gives an acknowledgement token and Maija also continues giving a self-assessment, leaning slightly towards Jaakko and saying I be,.(1.4)four years,.(0.2)unable to speak.. The nonverbal behaviour connected to her verbal expression is revealing; Jaakko and Maija have a shared gaze, Maija then points to herself, and at the end of her turn, she uses a hand shrug stretching her arm to Jaakko and opening her palm, a movement which has been paraphrased as meaning "what else could I do" (Ekman & Friesen 1972, Bavelas & al. 1992). Although Maija's contribution is in a present tense, it is evident that she is referring to the past, when she became ill. Thus, instead of commenting on Jaakko's self-assessment, Maija shifts the topic to her own speech problems, adding the length of the speechless time for her own self-assessment.

After the above-mentioned speech, Jaakko again gives a short acknowledgement token oh. (aha. in Finnish) and looks at Maija. Subsequently, Maija makes a highly emotional gesture, raising her hand in front of her mouth. The therapist seems to have interpreted their assessments as somehow competitive, because she acknowledges the contributions with a soft voice and utters elliptically well then Jaakkoheh heh heh$ that no no now,.$ and laughs. Jaakko's subsequent reaction is very laconic. He grasps his nose, nods his head towards Maija and says like that.. Maija again leans forward to Jaakko and bursts into laughter and repeats twice Jaakko's statement $like that.$(LAUGHS)$like that.$, and even stretches her hand to Jaakko. Both Jaakko and Elina join in Maija's laughing. The sequence ends with Maija's second repetition, after which she leans backwards and puts her pencil on the table.

The same elements occur in this excerpt as in the previous example. In both cases, speaker Maija utters a self-assessment concerning her illness or specifically her speech, and Jaakko gives an acknowledgement token and a second assessment of Maija's self-assessment. The structure of Jaakko's assessments is similar in both cases; at first he produces a dialogue particle *oh* (*aha*) and after a pause, he adds a short phrase-type assessment without any obvious prosodic sign. Maija's hilarious laughter, which also invites others to laugh, occurs after (or even overlapped with) Jaakko's second assessment.

The third excerpt again contains Maija's bursts of laughter as the prominent feature

Example 3

t	no Maija.(.)kerro|ppa sinä.		
	PRT 1name F tell-CLI you		
	well Maija(.)you tell.		
tgesture	***LHDM***		
M			°kaksitoista vuotlta,
			twelve year-PAR
			°twelve years,(0.9)paralyzed°(7.6)
Mgesture			***LH↓***

M	(0.9)halvaantunut°(7.6)	
	paralyzed	
Mgesture		***LH↑¤***
Jgaze	GM,,..	

t	h-mm?h-mm?		
	h-mm?h-mm?		
Mgaze	Gt	G↓	GJ........G,,,,,,E......G↓.....
M			$keksiNAURAA°keksi°$
			$thinkLAUGHS°think°
Mgesture	***(5.2)SMILES***		
Jgaze		GM.......G,,E........	
J		°keksi,(.)keksi,°	hmm
		think think	
		°think,(.)think,°	**hmm**
All			***LAUGH***

117

Jgaze	GE.............,,,GM..
J	$nii joo joo joo$NAURAA
	PRT PRT PRT PRT
	$yeah right right right$LAUGHS
Jgesture	**RH scratch O RH↑¤**
E	NAURAA/LAUGHS
Egesture	**RH scratch Ear**

In the above example, the therapist asks Maija to tell about herself. In response, Maija explains that she has been paralysed for 12 years. After her turn, Maija uses the same type of hand shrug as in the previous example. In reality, Maija's paralysis has been very mild from the onset of the illness, making only her right hand clumsy, but it is probable that she was referring to the whole syndrome, aphasia and paralysis. A longish pause (7.6 seconds) follows during which Maija raises her hand near her chin, as if in front of her mouth. This gesture was also seen in the previous excerpt (ex. 2) in the same type of context, after the very emotional contribution I be,.(1.4)four years,. (0.2) unable to speak.. In response, the therapist gives only two acknowledgement tokens with rising intonation. Although there is a clear space and expectation for Maija's next turn, she does not take the turn. Afterwards, another longish pause (5.2) occurs, during which Maija only directs her gaze towards the therapist with a faint smile, and then turns her gaze downwards. As Maija clearly refuses the turn, the right to acquire it is transferred to any first-starter. At this point, Jaakko gazes at Maija and says in a soft voice think,(.)think,, gazing at the end of the turn at Elina and smiling. Maija bursts into laughter and repeats Jaakko's contribution. This is followed by mutual laughter which breaks down with Jaakko's laughing affirmations $yeah right right right$. During this contribution, he also scratches his head and, while laughing, he covers his mouth with his right hand. At the end of the excerpt one can also observe interesting synchronized movements, 'mirror movements', between Jaakko and Elina; during his last laughing contribution, Jaakko gazes at Elina who has joined in the laughter earlier. Jaakko scratches his head, and Elina immediately raises her hand and touches her ear.

The fourth excerpt also comes from the first discussion; now the topic has turned to Elina and her illness.

Example 4

E	(.)$puhumista ja,. (.) nyt siltä tulee kuulemma liikaaki
	speech and now it-PAR comes I hear too much-CLI
	(.)$speech and,.(.)now there is they say too much (of it),.(.)

E	sano|o,.(.)lapset joskus,$=
	say-3 child-PL sometimes
	children say sometimes,$=
Mgaze	GE......................
M	=eh-heh-heh-
	=eh-heh-heh-

Egaze	G,,,,t.........	
E	$puhe\|tta$heh-heh heh-heh	
	speech-PAR	
	$speech$heh-heh heh-heh	
Egesture	*RH↑¤*	
Mgaze	.,,,Gt.............	GE.................G,,↓.............
M	heh-heh-heh	$hyvä juttu.(.)hyvä juttu.$
		good thing good thing
	heh-heh-heh	**$great thing.(.)great thing.$**
Mgesture		*LHDE* *B<-*
t	$ai jaah.$heh-heh	
	$oh I see.$heh-heh	

In this case the laughter and humour occurs in Elina's, Maija's and the therapist's interaction. The development of this excerpt is a little different from that found in the earlier examples. Example 4 is from the end of Elina's story where she tells about her illness and describes her speech problems and speech exercises. Even before the end of her story, her voice acquires a laughing tone, and at the end of her turn she says laughingly, (.)$speech and,.(.)now there is they say too much (of it),.(.)children say sometimes,$ referring to her own speech. Maija begins to laugh and the therapist joins in the laughter and says oh I see., during which speaker Elina completes her previous elliptic utterance, saying speech between the bursts of laughter. During this mutual laughing, Maija states $great thing.(.)great thing.$ pointing to Elina and laughing. The sequence ends with Maija's second repetition. The laughing stops and Maija turns her gaze downwards and changes her body position, at the same time drawing her chair a little bit forward.

These four examples show a fascinating behavioural system between the interactants which in the first three cases led to mutual laughter between Jaakko, Maija and the others and in the fourth case between Elina, Maija and the therapist.

The structures of the first two laughter examples have similar features, although the latter example is more complicated. In both cases, Maija utters a self-assessment concerning her illness – or specifically her speech – and Jaakko gives acknowledgement and a second assessment of Maija's self-assessment. The mutual laughter arises after Jaakko's subsequent assessments. In the third example, Maija again makes a self-assessment. A long pause

follows after Maija's contribution. The therapist then gives an acknowledgement token to her but not a second assessment to the first one. Another pause
follows, which may indicate Maija's unwillingness to take the turn. Finally,
Jaakko contributes to the conversation with a soft-toned invitation
think,(.)think,. This causes the hilarious repetition by Maija, and the ensuing
mutual laughter. The fourth excerpt is somewhat different than the earlier
ones; it is exceptional in the sense that only the three women participate in the
laughter, and in this case, the laughter begins immediately in the first
contribution and continues until the end of the excerpt.

When observing Jaakko's contributions, we notice that the verbal part of
his second assessment is in each case a short stereotypical phrase. Jaakko's
laconic-sounding contributions form a sharp contrast to the delicate,
emotional self-assessments of Maija.

This raises the question of what makes Maija behave in the same way in
each of these excerpts? Because Maija's prominent laughter turns occurred
after Jaakko's turns, it is reasonable to focus the analysis on those of Jaakko's
turns which followed Maija's self-assessments. In excerpts 1 and 2, Jaakko's
turns are agreements – second assessments – although in the second excerpt
his turn was delayed until after the therapist's turn. There are also certain
elements in Jaakko's agreement turns which make them different from typical
agreement turns. I will discuss these differences below.

One important issue in conversation is preference organization (Levinson
1983: 332-337, Atkinson & Heritage 1984:53-56). The central idea of this
preference organization is that not all the potential second parts are of equal
standing to the first part of an adjacency pair; thus, preferred and dispreferred
response categories occur. Here preference is not a psychological claim but is
close to the linguistic concept of markedness. Preferred second turns are
unmarked and are structurally simpler turns, whereas dispreferred seconds are
structurally more complex and are marked by various features. One
characteristic of a dispreferred turn is a delay, for instance, a pause before
delivery. Prefaces also may be used as a sign of dispreference (Levinson
1983:334).

According to Pomerantz (1984:65), agreement turns are filled with turn
components that serve to imply agreement. These are usually explicitly stated
and performed with a minimum gap between the completion of the prior turn
and the initiation of the agreement turn.

Returning now to the first excerpt, the two subsequent agreements for
Maija are different. In the first agreement, the therapist quickly gives her
acknowledgement token, even overlapping with Maija's laughter and pointing
to Maija at the same time. However, Jaakko's agreement has some peculiar
features: the first part of his agreement is only a simple acknowledgement oh.
(aha.) uttered with a falling intonation contour, looking at the paper on the
table. In Finnish, aha is a typical dialogue particle which can be used to mark
new information (cf. Hakulinen & Sorjonen 1986). A 1.7 second pause
follows, and only then does Jaakko give his second assessment great thing.,
still looking at the paper. This is clearly an agreement turn but it is peculiar
that the structure of the turn is that of a dispreferred turn because of the long
pause before the utterance. In addition, his agreement can be regarded as a
slight downgrading because Maija had focused on her progress in the

recovery. Maija bursts subsequently into laughter and repeats Jaakko's contribution $great thing.$, and Elina then joins in the hilarious laughter. During this laughter, Jaakko turns to Maija and again gives Maija an assessment-type acknowledgement accompanied by a laugh.

In example 2, Jaakko gives the first self-assessment and Maija provides the next one. Jaakko gives an acknowledgement token oh. (aha) to Maija after a short pause. Later, after the therapist's interrupted turn (with a laugh), Jaakko states his second assessment to Maija like that.. Thus, although Jaakko's second assessment has the content of an agreement turn, the structural features of this assessment resemble a dispreferred turn.

In example 3, Jaakko does not give a second assessment to Maija's turn, although there is an obvious space for a second assessment. Only the therapist's short acknowledgement tokens and a rather long pause occur, after which speaker Jaakko produces a non-topical turn that tempts Maija to say more. Mulkay (1988:26) reports that, in contrast to the unitary character of serious discourse, humour occurs when there is a surprising movement between, or unexpected combination of, distinct interpretative frames. This notion fits well with Jaakko's contradictory contributions.

Example 4 is different from the previous excerpt in that Elina already begins to laugh in her self-assessment turn, and Maija joins in her laughter. The therapist also enters into laughter, giving a short acknowledgement token oh I see. (ai jaah.) which is a typical way to acknowledge new information. Elina repeats the word speech with a laugh and Maija joins in, uttering a similar type of second assessment as she herself had received in the earlier conversation from Jaakko, $great thing.(.) great thing.$. In this excerpt, the laughter continues, and it can be interpreted as an open invitation to which Maija and the therapist adjoined.

In these examples, other nonverbal behaviour arises that is related to laughter and is significant for interaction. In the first example, Maija laughs immediately at the end of her self-assessment. Jaakko's short comment oh.(1.7) great thing. (aha.(1.7)hyvä juttu.) does not contain laughter, but his facial expressions, head tilting and raising of eyebrows are revealing. In the second and third examples, Maija explains a delicate issue, but with a serious face. She also uses a gesture, raising her hand in front of or near her mouth, which increases the emotional import of her expressions. In the first example, Maija herself laughs in the first contribution, but in the second and third examples, on the contrary, her face is serious from the onset. But also in this case, Jaakko manages to invite Maija to join in the laughter.

What then are Jaakko's detailed invitation devices for transforming Maija's seriousness into laughter? In the second and third excerpts, Jaakko's behavioural pattern consists of a series of nonverbal movements. In the second excerpt, Jaakko and Maija have a shared gaze. Also, Jaakko grasps his nose, utters his contribution with a smiling voice and then nods his head. In the third excerpt, his nonverbal behaviour is even more clearly marked; he gazes at Maija and uses a low and soft voice-quality when urging Maija to tell more. Evidently this behaviour, connected with his verbal contributions, has the same function as in the first sequence. In connection with his verbal contribution this can be regarded to form a 'play frame' and signals for Maija the shift to the humour mode (Mulkay 1988) and thus, it is invitation-behaviour for Maija to join the humour mode (Jefferson 1979).

Comparing the four examples, the invitation behaviour is more transparent in examples 1 and 4 than in examples 2 and 3. In the first example, Maija's laughing is open, and in the fourth example, Elina's voice quality turns to laughing, but also the verbal part of her turn contains specific invitational features (.)$speech and,.(.)now there is they say too much (of it),.(.)children say sometimes,$. Thus, there are two types of humorous examples: those which begin with the teller's laughter and the others join in (examples 1 and 4), and those where the laughter is initiated by the recipient, in both cases by Jaakko (examples 2 and 3).

A notable feature, which has been mentioned above, is that the topic of these excerpts is always the same: the aphasics' speech problems or illness. This promotes the hypothesis that speaking about speech and its disorders is a special topic in aphasic conversation, and this needs some special sensitivity to handle it. Furthermore, Mulkay (1988:79-84) has pointed out the connection between laughter and difficult topics and Adelswärd (1989) explains that unilateral laughter, in these cases a teller's initiated laughter, is often used to modify verbal expressions or attitudes and helps speakers in handling ambiguities and tension.

The following is an excerpt where humour is used in a different way than it has been in the previous examples. Even when the means of creating humour are the same, however, the structure of the sequence may not be as simple as above. Again, the most rich verbal and nonverbal behaviour is displayed by Jaakko with laughter, face expressions and prosody, and these lead to mutual laughter. I will show a specific way to use the nonverbal resources in conversation to modify the verbal part of an utterance. The fifth example, presented below, is part of a conversation where Elina interviews Jaakko.

Example 5

Egaze	GJxxxxxxxxxxxxxxxG↓............
E	mi│tä sä te│i│t siellä Venäjä│llä heh-heh
	what-PAR you do-PST-2 there Russia-ADE
	what did you do there in Russia heh-heh
Egesture	***LHDpaper***
Mgaze	GJ..........
M	NAURAA
	LAUGHS
J	$ka-katt│e│li│n vaan$.
	look-FRE-PST-1 only
	$I just lo-looked around.$
Jgesture	***O↑EYB↑***

Egaze	GJ...
E	$katt\|el\|i\|t vaan maisemi\|a$heh-heh-heh-heh
	look-FRE-PST-2 only scenery-PAR
	$you just looked at the scenery$heh-heh-heh-heh
Egesture	**LH¤** **B->**
Mgaze	GJ.........................
M	katt|el|i|t heh-heh
	look-FRE-PST-2
	looked heh-heh
Jgaze	,,GM...
J	joo jooNAURAA
	yes yes LAUGHS
Pgesture	**B->**

Egaze	GJ..........
E	hmm nii
	hmm yes
Egesture	**Onod**
Mgaze	GJ........................
M	hirveesti tö|i|tä.
	lots of work-PRT
	a lot of work.
Mgesture	**Oshake**
Jgaze	GM...........,,G↓......
J	ei(.) TÖ|l|tä (.)TÖ|l|tä joo.
	NEG work-PL-PAR work-PL-PAR
	well no(.)WOrk(.)WOrk yes.
Jgesture	**OshakeOshake**

The conversation above begins with the interlocutors agreeing that they interview Jaakko. Thus, the conversation proceeds with a question-answer structure. Elina has already posed several questions to Jaakko who has responded with short answers. Jaakko reveals that he has worked in Russia. The next sequence begins with Elina's question <u>what did you do there in Russia.</u> The intonation contour of Elina's contribution fluctuates and she smiles during her question. Her body position indicates uneasiness. When she has agreed to interview Jaakko, she has also been forced to accept the responsibility for interactional work. Perhaps she was a bit ashamed when asking such 'intimate' questions of another participant, and her smiling may suggest uneasiness (e.g. Gumperz 1982). Maija also begins to laugh at the end of Elina's turn. Thus, the female participants on both sides of Jaakko laugh right from the beginning.

Jaakko's reply to Elina is interesting; with a smiling expression and raising his eyebrows he answers I just lo-looked around.. This reply cannot be taken literally. Thus, some signs must show that the interpretation of the contribution is be based on something other than the literal meaning. Elina shows that she has understood Jaakko's humour and continues the joking, adding a demonstration of understanding $you just looked at the scenery.$ with a laugh, which provokes the others to continue laughing.

Jaakko's faint smile may be interpreted as a sign or as a contextualization cue (Gumperz 1982:131, Adelswärd 1989:124) to shift to a humour mode, and thus to give the recipient instructions or assistance in her/his attempts to reach mutual understanding within the humour frame. Elina's verbal contribution and her cheerful laughter provokes the mutual laughing. Almost simultaneously, Jaakko and Maija give acknowledgement tokens, although in different ways. Jaakko gives two acceptances and smiles after uttering them, and Maija repeats the first word of Elina's previous contribution and laughs. In addition, Jaakko's smile changes to laughter.

This joking sequence comes to a close, however, in the next turn when Jaakko takes his words back and his face turns serious while he is explaining well no (.) WOrk. (.) WOrk., and he shakes his head. In this utterance, Jaakko's head shake and the lexical repetition seem to support each other and they are interpreted by Maija as an expression of hard work. Also, noteworthy is Maija's seriousness and the voice quality in her turn, which also underlines her interpretation.

One important question that arises is, what are the initiative contextualization cues which move the conversation to the humour mode? In this example, Elina's question have such cues, which seem to be important for the further development of the conversation. Her modified tone and smile seem to function as a trigger for moving to the play frame. In the next step, Jaakko's reply has some more contextualizing cues, of which head position and facial expression seem to be important. He raises his head and eyebrows, smiles and turns his gaze to Elina. In the third turn the joke climaxes with the punchline. Elina repeats Jaakko's contribution and joins the joking, adding her own joke to the conversation, $you just looked at the **scenery**.$ and laughs cheerfully. This example shows a very sophisticated use of nonverbal means to modify the verbal part of the utterance.

Later in the same conversation there is another excerpt (example 6 which is presented below) that shows a similar use of laughter, facial expressions and other nonverbal signs in conversation.

Example 6

Egaze	GJ...............................GJxxxxxxxx	
E	puhu|t|+sä? (.)hyvi?(.)venäjä|ä.	
	speak-2+you well russian-PAR	
	do you speak?(.)well?(.)Russian.	
Egesture	*SMILE...*	
Jgaze		„GE..........
J		eli puhu.
		NEG-3 speak
		not speak.
Jgesture		*Oshake,EYB↑,Onod*

Egaze	G↓.............
E	(0.3)°aha°
	(0.3)°oh°
Egesture	*Onod,SMILE*
Jgaze	GP.......
Jgesture	*SMILE...*
Pgaze	GJ..
P	e|m pu-puhu yhtään
	NEG-1 speak at all
	{I notch}spe-speak anything

Jgaze	GP..	Gt and M
J	hmm e|i e|i e|i pu:hu mitään.	e|i puhu(--)
	NEG-3 NEG-3 NEG-3 speak anything	NEG-3 speak
	hmm no no not spe:ak anything.	**not speak(--)**
Jgesture	*Onod,RHopen*	*Onod*
Pgaze		GJ,,G↓..
P		e-heh
	so LAUGHS	
Mgaze		GJ........
M		heh-heh
		heh-heh

```
Egaze                                              GJ........................
E                                                  $NIIH$NAURAA
                                                   PRT
                                                   $YEAH$LAUGHS
J                                                  aikai-  jaah

                                                   ear-  yeah
Mgaze                          GJ....................................
M                              aikaise|mmin  NAURAA
                               early-COM
                               earlier LAUGHS
t                    mutta AIkaise|mmin  NAURAA
                     but    early-COM
                     but EArlier LAUGHS
```

```
Egaze                          GJ................
E                              $puhu|i|t|ko$
                               speak-PST-2-Q
                               $did you speak$
Jgaze              GE..........................    GE...
J                  AIkaise|mmin                    no:h
                   early-COM                       PRT
                   EARlier                         we:ll
Jgesture           Onod      Onod                  RH↑,Onod
Mgaze                                              GJ...
M                                                  mi|tä(5.3)
                                                   what-PAR
                                                   what(5.3)LAUGHS
```

```
Egaze          GJ..GJxxxxxxxxxxxxxx     GJ.........
E                 $rehellisesti  vaa$(4.6)NAURAA
                  honestly just
                  $frankly$(4.6)         LAUGHS
Jgaze          G↓.............           GJ,,t............
               LAUGHS                    LAUGHS
Pgaze          GJ...
Mgaze          GE and P                  GE.........
                                         LAUGHS
```

Egaze	GJ............................	GJ..
E	se+o vaikee kieli kyllä(--)	
	it+is difficult language yes	
	it is difficult language yeah(--)	
Jgaze		G↓... (7.1)
Pgaze		GJ..
Mgaze		GJ...GJ..
		hmm
t		mikä mikä tei|
		what what you-
		what what

t	jän(.)mikä suomalais|t|en tehtävä siellä ol|i
	GEN what finnish-PL-GEN task there be-PST then
	your(.)what was the job of you Finns there then(.)in the

t	sitten.(.)siellä tehtaa|ssa.
	there factory-INE
	factory.

This conversational sequence begins with Elina's information-seeking question do+you speak?(.)well?(.) Russian. and Jaakko replies agrammatically not speak. Again, this adjacency pair has some specific features which attract one's attention. First, the attention is fixed on the glottal stops in Elina's utterance. As in the previous excerpt (example 5), as well as in Elina's earlier questions, we can detect some features which are characteristic. Also in this case there seem to be some interactional problems in posing the question that become evident due to the glottal stops and smiling. This may be the reason for Jaakko's peculiar reply and it contains several characteristics which evidently became noticed. As before, Jaakko's reply is contrary to expectations because Elina's question has presupposed that Jaakko speaks Russian (do you speak well Russian). First, he shakes his head and utters not speak. with raising his eyebrows and nodding his head. Elina's acknowledgement token aha. (oh.) is very quiet, nearly a whisper and she smiles.

Paavo's next contribution is dysarthric and very inaccurately articulated but the semantic content clearly indicates that speaking is difficult and his turn ends with laughter. The crucial point is Jaakko's interpretation of Paavo's turn, and Jaakko's subsequent contribution where he says hmm no no not spea:k anything. which makes Paavo laugh. In this case Jaakko's nonverbal behaviour is also very prominent. He nods his head, smiles and even shrugs his right shoulder (hand) as if to express "what else could I do" (Bavelas & al. 1992). His joking is now so evident that both Paavo and Maija laugh aloud. Once again Jaakko offers a confirmation not speak. and he leans back as if to close the topic. The point is that Jaakko's and Paavo's statements cannot be regarded as true, because all the participants have independently noticed that Jaakko can speak but, of course, he has aphasic disorders. This means that these statements cannot be taken literally, which is why these specific signs have to be given for the interpretation. There is already laughter in Jaakko's turn. Speaker Paavo must have noticed Jaakko's smiling voice and he continues the game which Jaakko has started, saying something that should not be taken literally because it has been said with certain contextualizing cues. Paavo even underlines the signs for interpretation with laughter.

The preceeding excerpt continues with the therapist's emphatic turn in which she strongly stresses the word but EARlier and Maija repeats this part of her contribution while laughing. These contributions again promote laughter, which indicates that the participants have paid attention to the prominence of the intonation. The therapist's and Maija's inquiring tones are clear but Jaakko does not give a clear reply. He only partly repeats the earlier contribution, stressing the same word earl yeah EARlier while nodding and laughing. Jaakko again uses the same cues as before, and thus he shows that he is going on with 'the game'. Nevertheless, Jaakko gives no sign of an unambiguous reply, and Elina asks again $did you speak.$ and smiles. It is surprising that Jaakko does not respond verbally but only laughs, even though Elina clearly tries to persuade him to reply with her next contribution $frankly$. From the point of view of turn-taking (Sacks et al. 1974:704), Elina has selected Jaakko as the next speaker, but Jaakko shows no sign of accepting the turn. Consequently, Elina again takes the turn and only states that Russian is a difficult language, whereby Maija closes the sequence with an acknowledgement token, gazing at Jaakko who only looks down at the table.

Laughing and other nonverbal behaviour also carry specific meanings in this excerpt. In fact, the entire sequence is a very good example of the use of laughing, prosody and nonverbal behaviour as resources in conversation, and even the very skilful use of them.

This excerpt likewise raises some questions. The first observation concerns the smiles in the adjacency pair at the beginning of the sequence, and Elina's response to Jaakko's reply. Both Elina and Jaakko smile. Jaakko remarks that he not speak. and subsequently smiles. Elina acknowledges this utterance with oh. (aha.), also accompanied with a smile. Why do both speakers smile at the beginning of this excerpt? One possible explanation could be that speaker Elina's uneasiness was observed by Jaakko who seized the opportunity to change the mode of speaking. An open question is whether or not Elina noticed this change. It is nevertheless obvious that Paavo interpreted the nonverbal behaviour as a contextualizing cue and thus made humour even more prominent in his contribution. If this is true, one could also interpret Jaakko's contribution as 'joke first' behaviour (Schegloff 1987) when uttering not speak. which Paavo recognized and continues. Jaakko's agrammatic utterance can actually be interpreted in two ways, either literally "I don't speak Russian" or as a strongly dramatized "I don't speak anything" as Paavo seemed to have interpreted it.

Another important question concerns turn allocation (Sacks et al. 1974). As the current speaker, Elina selects Jaakko as the next speaker. Jaakko accepts taking the next turn and replies to Elina, but in a rather unexpected way.

Hence, his reply was contrary to the expectations of the recipients. This fifth example also suits the 'joke-first' behaviour. At first Jaakko shifts to a humour mode but immediately after the joke, he returns back to a serious mode. However, in example 6 the shift to the serious mode is gradual, and although Elina again selects Jaakko as the next speaker and continues asking his ability to speak Russian, Jaakko rejects the turn. As a result, participants do not get a clear answer to Elina's question. Instead he only gives a laughing reply to the questions posed to him. In this case the laughter is a very ambiguous sign, leaving the interpretation open to the recipients. Although Jaakko had accepted the idea to be interviewed by the other interlocutors, he was able to maintain his autonomy in conversation to accept or reject the next turn.

7.3 Discussion

The aim of this chapter was to focus on aphasic speakers' initiated laughter and humour which leads to mutual laughter in the conversations. The starting point for the analysis of these sequences is based on the observations of conversation analysis which make the basic distiction between serious and joke categories (Sacks 1992b).

Mulkay (1988) and Gumperz (1985) introduce the important notion of 'marked discourse'. The previous sequences are good examples of using the same signs and contextualization cues of humour in aphasic conversation as in 'normal' conversations. The signs and cues used include modification of voice, facial expressions, prosodical cues, laughing, etc., which implicitly convey, "this is a joke".

There is no doubt that the aphasic participants accepted the invitation into the humorous category, which was revealed by mutual laughter. The examples show that the aphasic speakers were able to receive, interpret and express humour in these conversations as any 'normal' speakers do in conversation. The sequences of mutual laughter presented above are proof of the existence of humour in these conversations. As already mentioned in the introduction, little mention of laughter and humour is found in aphasic literature and thus there is no possibility to evaluate and compare the results in the broader aphasiological context.

The most fascinating matter is that the most severe aphasic (according to the WAB test) in this group, Jaakko, was often the initiator of the humour sequences. Due to aphasia his verbal means are limited, and in fact the verbal part of his humour turns was often a short phrase typical for everyday language use. However, in order to get interaction to work effectively, participants need to know and to be able to inform each other which conversational mode is in progress. In Jaakko's case his ability to use very discrete nonverbal means to express his entry to the humour mode is striking. Actually, in all of the sequences presented here, he did not once use open laughter as a sign of entering or inviting others into the humour mode. Rather, he used facial expressions, slight head movements and mutual gaze in order to show the shift to the humour mode and at the same time inviting others to join in.

The second issue which turned out to be an important conceptual means in analysing these excerpts was the preference organization in conversation. In addition to nonverbal means in examples 1 and 2, the structure of the second assessments expressed by Jaakko subsequent to the first self-assessments expressed by Maija, was an important sign of 'marked discourse'. Jaakko's second assessments had the features of dispreferred turns, delays and prefaces, although the contents of Jaakko's contributions were that of preferred ones. The specific features of the second assessments were interpreted to be clear invitation devices for the humour mode. Also in examples 5 and 6, Jaakko changed to the humour mode. Thus, he was no longer bound to normal codes of behaviour and he could answer unexpectedly against the preference expectation.

The two laughter excerpts initiated by the women, Maija and Elina, were in a certain sense different (examples 1 and 4). In these cases, the inviting turns already contained open laughter, which is easy to join in. Adelswärd (1989:123) has discussed laughter also from the perspective of gender and she suggests that men and women tend to use different laughter strategies. According to her, one of the functions of female laughter may be to regulate the interactive climate. Also in this aphasia group, the laughter occurrences were often initiated by the women participants although they did not always lead to mutual laughter. It is possible that in interactionally complex conversations, as aphasic conversations are, women in particular use laughter in order to create an informal and collaborative conversational climate.

As a joint activity, laughter can be regarded as instrumental in establishing and demonstrating a relationship. Adelswärd (1989) has regarded laughter as a sign of rapport and consensus. For these reasons, it was perhaps possible in this group to talk about speaking and its difficulties, which could otherwise be a difficult and rejected topic. Hence, laughter and humour can be regarded as interactional resources also in aphasic conversation, showing mutual understanding between the interactants, expressed by laughing. In addition, the humour sequences are fine examples of cooperation, even collaborative achievements (cf. Haakana 1993). This notion is extremely interesting and important in view of aphasic conversation. Although the aphasics have problems in verbal communication they may be able to communicate in a sophisticated way with other modes and means in interaction. They also seem to have the ability to shift fluently from a serious mode to a humourous mode and to invite the others to join in. Thus, laughter is one of the interactional resources which aphasic speakers may be able to resort to.

The notions here, for their part, may have some important consequences for aphasia therapy, especially for severe aphasics. As they have lost their usual conversational means – language – opportunities should be provided for communication and interaction. However, this poses some demands for creating such opportunities; there should be space for laughing and joking.

8. Collaborative repair initiated by aphasic speakers

8.1 Introduction

The notion of repair is extremely relevant for aphasic communication. The phenomenon of repair has been studied mainly from a psycholinguistic perspective (e.g. Schlenck et al. 1987) and the research has been focused on the process of self-repair. The methodology of conversation analysis has contributed to the research of the repair process by examining the role of the co-participant, and the concept of other-initiated repair (Schegloff et al. 1977, Schegloff 1992). This view has led to the notion of collaborative repair in aphasic conversation (e.g. Milroy et Perkins 1992, Perkins 1993).

From the interactive perspective, the occurrence of repair has no self-evident relationship with the occurrence of 'error'. Repair can be observed without an audible error or mistake and it may be either self-initiated or other-initiated. Conversely, there may be a clearly audible error in an utterance without any type of repair (Schegloff et al. 1977:363). For this reason, the process of repair is a very complex phenomenon and the details of the interaction may be decisive in the onset of the repair.

A principal question in aphasic conversation is how to deal with recurrent 'errors', whether they are performed by an aphasic speaker or by a 'healthy' speaker. The typical problem situations are caused by various aphasic 'errors' like disordered articulation and morpho-syntactic problems (e.g. in Broca's aphasia), word-finding difficulties (e.g. in anomic aphasia), using verbal or literal paraphasias (e.g. in Wernicke's and conduction aphasia), or in general, a very limited oral expression (e.g. in global aphasia) (cf. Damasio 1981, Benson 1988, Albert & Helm-Estabrooks 1988). At the same time, even 'healthy' speakers' speech contains various slips of the tongue (Dufva 1993). The picture becomes more complicated when the comprehension problems of either party in a conversation are taken into account. Various comprehension problems of different degrees arise in most aphasic speakers during the acute stage of aphasia (e.g. Damasio 1981, Benson 1988, Albert & Helm-Estabrooks 1988) becoming milder over time with recovery, or even disappearing. On the other hand, an aphasic speaker's impaired speech can cause problems in comprehension for the 'healthy' interlocutor.

The notions of intersubjectivity, sequential implicativeness and conditional relevance are central concepts within conversation analysis (cf. p. 29–32),

Conversation as an achievement in aphasics
Studia Fennica
Linguistica 6
1996.

linked to the sequential development of conversation. In 1992, Schegloff published his research on 'repair after an intervening turn'. In this article he analyses the grounding in the sequential organization of conversation. According to him, speakers ordinarily address themselves to the immediately preceding conversation, and thus, reveal their understanding of the prior talk to which their own speech is addressed. The notion of sequential implicativeness (Schegloff & Sacks 1973:296) suggests that by an adjacently positioned second, a speaker can show that s/he has understood what a prior speaker aimed at, and that s/he is willing to go along with it. Conversely, the first speaker can, by inspecting the second pair part, see if the first part has been understood. Thus the second pair part may display either the understanding or the failure to understand. In the same way, each successive turn provides a locus for the display of many understandings by its speaker – understandings of what has immediately preceded. Furthermore, a speaker can also reveal understandings of what s/he regards as misunderstandings. Misunderstandings can occur, for instance, in what is being referred to, or in the serious/nonserious dimension, such as taking a joke seriously (Schegloff 1992). In such cases, either the next speaker can initiate repair work (a next turn repair initiation, NTRI), or a speaker her/himself can initiate repair work after a 'problematic understanding'. The latter repair is called 'third position repair'.

Schegloff et al. (1977) propose two main distinctions within repair: first, there is a distinction between the initiator and the performer of the repair process, and second, there is self-initiated versus other-initiated repair (see p. 32–33). A self-repair refers to a speaker's own turn and is initiated by the speaker her/himself. An other-repair refers to an interlocutor's turn and is initiated by her/him. Hence, the four possibilities for handling the trouble in conversation are the following: self-initiated self-repair, other-initiated self-repair, self-initiated other-repair and other-initiated other-repair (Table 7). Other-initiated repairs are also called 'next turn repair initiations' (NTRIs).

Table 7. Distinctions within repair

REPAIR	SELF	OTHER
INITIATION	self-initiation	other-initiation
OUTCOME	self-repair	other-repair

According to Schegloff et al. (ibid. 367–368), self- and other-initiations of repair are performed using regular and different initiator techniques. Self-repair initiations within the same turn use a variety of means, for instance cut-offs, sound prolongations, "uh's", etc. Other-repair initiations use various types of turn-constructional devices to initiate repair. Table 8 shows the positions of different repair types in a conversational sequence.

Table 8. Possible repair-initiations and their positions in a conversational sequence (compiled from Schegloff et al. 1977)

Turn 1	cut-off, sound stretch, "uh", repetition, etc.
Transition space between T1 and T2	"I mean..."
Turn 2	"huh?", Wh-questions, partial repetition of the trouble-source turn plus a question word, partial repetition of the trouble-source turn, "y'mean" plus a possible understanding of prior turn
Turn 3	"I don't mean...I mean", "no, I mean..."

T = turn

Schegloff et al. (1977) also suggest that the other-repair initiations have a natural ordering based on their relative 'strength' or capacity to locate a trouble source. The order of the initiators, from the weakest to the strongest, is the following:
1. "huh", "what"
2. question words like "who", "where" and "when".
3. partial repetition of the trouble-source turn with a question word
4. partial repetition of the trouble-source turn
5. y'mean" plus a possible understanding of prior turn

Schegloff et al. (1977) further propose that there is a preference for stronger over weaker initiators and if more than one other-initiated sequence is needed, the other initiators are used to increase strength. A possible implication of the strength-idea is that an initiator technique used in repair may have consequences for the length of the repair sequence. For instance, a possible understanding of a prior turn is a stronger technique in interaction than a general question "what", which is why its use may lead to a quicker resolution of the repair sequence. Clark & Schaefer (1987, 1989) have adopted the idea in their model of contributions to conversation and they call this notion 'the principle of least collaborative effort'. They maintain that an addressee minimizes collaborative effort by quickly and informatively indicating what is needed for mutual acceptance.

Some studies on adult-child interaction have analysed various other-repair initiation techniques, generally referred to as 'requests for clarifications', a term which has been used for several types of other-repair initiations. According to Gallagher (1981), requests for clarification are examples of discourse sequences requiring both interactants to attend to the prior discourse in their production of successive utterances. This request may occur anywhere in a conversation when a recipient indicates that the speaker's meaning has not been understood or that it cannot be interpreted without clarification. Hence, this is a means by which one party to a conversation is able to acquire information needed to respond appropriately to a co-participant. Gallagher presents three major types of requests for clarification: request for confirmation (e.g. A: "Puppy in it." B:"Puppy?"), neutral requests for repetition (e.g. "What?", "Uh?", "Pardon?", "I didn't understand you.") and request for specific constituent repetition (e.g. A: "After came a knock at the door." B: "After came what?" (with rising intonation)). Gallagher's use of the term 'request for clarification' seems to cover the categories 1-4 in Schegloff et al's list of other-repair initiators.

Donahue et al. (1980) have reported that disabled children appear to be deficient in the production of clarification questions even when they have the necessary linguistic skills. In the earlier-mentioned study, Gallagher (1981) explored adult-child conversations (aged 1;11-3;0 years), and found that requests for clarification appeared less frequently in children's speech than in adult conversation, and children used requests for confirmation most frequently. Further, Brinton & Fujiki (1982) and Brinton et al. (1986, 1988) have explored the use of the three clarification requests in order to observe children's abilities in progressively adapting conversational needs. The clarification requests they observed were questions like "huh?" (rising intonation), "what?" (rising intonation) and "I didn't understand that". These studies indicated differences in the repair strategies used by normal and language-impaired children. Moreover, it seems that the use of clarification requests is a rather advanced means of maintaining a conversation because these requests are rarely found in small children's conversations (e.g. Gallagher 1981, Shatz & Watson O'Reilly 1990). In addition, younger children and linguistically-impaired children had greater difficulty responding appropriately to requests for clarification (Brinton & al. 1986).

Literature dealing with the use and organization of repair in aphasic conversations is still scarce. Lubinski et al. (1980) compared aphasic-spouse and aphasic-therapist dyads and noticed that both partners, the spouse and the therapist, offered guesses like "Is it X?" or "Is it Y?" and Wh-questions. Also, Gurland & al. (1982), when studying conversation in aphasic-spouse and aphasic-therapist dyads, noticed that the spouse and the therapist used a large number of clarification requests. When studying aphasic-therapist dyads, Laakso (1992) reported that the therapists used significantly more requests for clarification than did the aphasic speakers. In fact, in her study, only one aphasic speaker (the most severe one) used clarification requests in the case of severe miscomprehensions. Perkins (1993) provides several examples of the repair sequences in aphasic conversation, and in her data also the other-initiations of the healthy speaker seemed to be the most common ones. These results suggest that other-repair initiations are typically used by a healthy interactant.

The focus of these studies was healthy speakers' other-repair initiations. Most of the studies did not even mention the other-repair initiations (for instance, requests for clarification) made by aphasics. Possibly this is connected with the data used. Previous studies indicate that the therapist-aphasic dyads are mostly organized by adjacency pairs of a therapist's questions and an aphasic's answers (cf. Edwards 1987, Laakso 1992). In such conversations, aphasic speakers appear to make self-repair initiations and the therapists make other-repair initiations. As aphasic speakers' other-repair initiations seem to be exceptions in these dyads, a systematic study of them has not been undertaken.

Even though other-repair initiations have not served as objects of study, they are especially important for aphasic speakers in conversation, particularly for those who have comprehension problems. As Schegloff et al. remark (1977), other-repair initiations offer a possibility for the recipient to return to the previous context to try to locate and clarify the trouble source. With various types of next turn repair initiations (NTRIs), an aphasic speaker needs an opportunity to handle her/his comprehension problems that are due to aphasia, such as asking various questions or asking for clarification. On the other hand, aphasic speakers' contributions may be severely impaired so that recipients may have problems in understanding them. In these cases, especially in group discussions, other aphasic recipients also can initiate a repair.

In this chapter, I will provide an in-depth look at aphasic speakers' other-repair initiations that lead to collaborative repair. First, the other-repair initiations due to an aphasic speaker's comprehension problems (or hearing problems) will be studied, and next, the other-repair initiations connected to an anomalous turn of the aphasic speaker with insufficient information. Schegloff et al's (1977) observations of healthy speakers' other-repair initiations serve as the basis for this analysis. Additionally, I will explore the relevance of Clark & Schaefer's (1987, 1989) idea of the principle of least collaborative effort in aphasic conversation based on Schegloff et al's (1977) suggestion of strength in other-repair initiations.

The specific questions studied here are:
1. What kinds of aphasic speakers' other-repair initiations (NTRIs) combined with comprehension problems (or hearing problems) can be found in aphasia group conversations?
2. How can an aphasic speaker specify her/his trouble with the help of different other-repair initiators?
3. What kind of consequences do the aphasic speakers' different other-repair initiators have for the development of the conversation?

8.2 Other-repair initiations related to comprehension (or hearing) problems

In the following pages I will analyse sequences with aphasic speakers' other-repair initiations in evident cases of hearing or comprehension problems. The data will be presented according to the various techniques of other-repair initiations.

8.2.1 What-questions

I will begin with the *what*-questions contributed by Jaakko in the fourth conversation. An example of the use of a *what*-question (line 5) in connection to a hearing or a comprehension problem is presented below.

Example 1

```
1   t:no mut haastatel|ka|a vaikka Jaakko|a.(.)minu|st se ol|is
       PRT but      interview-IMP-2PL for instance 1name M-PAR   I-ELA   it   be-CON
    well but go ahead and interview Jaakko(.)I think it would be

2   ihan(0.8)°hyvä°,
    PRT         good
    all(0.8)°right°,

    (2.8)

3   M:h.*$ehe|i oshaa$[san-*
         NEG3    can      {say}
      h.*$channot $[sa-*

4   E:                [missä sä ol|i|t tö|i|ssä.
                       what-INE   you be-PST-2   work-PL-INE
                      [where were you working.

    (1.3)

5   J:°mitä.°=
       what-PAR
      °what.°=

6   E: =°mi|ssä sä ol|i|t,.°
          what-INE     you be-PST-2
       °where were you,.°

    (0.6)

7   J: Lemminkäinen.{Ø INE}
       company name-NOM
       Lemminkäinen.{Ø INE}

8   E: Lemminkäinen.{Ø INE}
       company name-NOM
       Lemminkäinen.{Ø INE}
```

In this example, it is justified to presume that Jaakko's *what*-question is a sign of a hearing problem rather than to interpret it as a comprehension problem, because the initial part of Elina's question is overlapped with the previous turn. In addition, Jaakko's orientation is towards Maija who is on his right-hand side whereas Elina is on his left. However, Jaakko evidently notices that Elina directed the contribution to him because he turns his gaze to Elina and initiates the repair work. Another observation confirms this interpretation; Elina's subsequent turn remains syntactically and prosodically incomplete as Jaakko hastens to answer her. The repetition of the initial part of the trouble turn seems to be sufficient for Jaakko's problem, and he manages to give his answer to Elina.

The next excerpt also contains a repair-initiator with a *what*-question.

Example 2

```
1   J:on vaan. (0.4) on vaan. (2.4)[koo oo pee.]
       is  just          is  just        K  O  P
    it is just. (0.4) it is just.(2.4)[K O P]

2   E:                              [°sairastu|i|t]+sä si-siellä
                                      get ill-PST-2 +you    there
                                    [°did you get ill]when being the-

3   ol|le|ssa.°
      be-INF-INE
    there.°

    (0.8)

4   J:*mi|tä.*=
       what-PAR
      *what.*=
                        *G,,,,E *

5   E:=ol|i|t+sä siellä(.)kun(.)sairastu|i|t.
        be-PST-2+you   there    when    get ill-PST-2
      =where you there(.)when(.)you get ill.

    (0.5)

6   J:ei ei ei ei ei(2.7)hhhhh.
      NEG NEG NEG NEG NEG
      no no no no no(2.7)hhhhh.
```

In this example, there is no clear distinctive sign whether Jaakko's other-repair initiator is caused by a hearing or by a comprehension problem. Example 2 also contains a small overlap in the beginning of Elina's question (line 2) which may have caused problems in hearing for Jaakko. However, it is noteworthy that after Jaakko's repair turn (line 4) Elina changes the syntax of the question from the participial phrase (*olle-ssa; in-being*) to the subordinate clause (*kun; when*) (line 5). A possible interpretation is that Elina suspects Jaakko has not understood her question and she begins to facilitate the collaboration by reformulating her question in an easier syntactic format.

"What" is a nonspecific repair-initiator often used in normal conversation. In this data there were five examples of using *what*-type of repair-initiators; Jaakko had four and Maija one of them. In all cases, the use of it led to the repetition of the previous turn (in example 2 with a slight modification) which also shows similarity with normal conversation. In these examples the trouble was solved after the repetition of the trouble turn. Behaviourally, aphasic speakers rather often display problems in processing auditory verbal signals, necessitating repetition of a previous turn. The use of *what*-initiators may reflect this type of problem of an aphasic speaker and in such case a *what*-initiator functions principally as a hearing check.

8.2.2 I don't understand

One possibility for handling comprehension problems in conversation is to inform the interlocutor explicitly of such problems. Gallagher (1981) and Brinton & Fujiki (1982) have regarded *I don't understand*-type of repair initiations as a request for clarification. Kalin (1995:153) reports that in her data – in conversations between native and non-native speakers – one speaker used that explicit indication of non-understanding. Schegloff et al. (1977) do not mention this type of repair initiation. The present data contains only one example of such a repair-initiator, which is presented below.

Example 3

```
1   M: hmm(.)*ede,*(0.4)*minä edisTY|Y?*=
                                |      progress-3
       hmm(.)*progr,*(0.4)*I progRESS?*=
       *LHDherself,Onod**LH upwards.*

2   t:=ni-I?=
       =mm-hm?=

3   M:=*edisTY|Y?*
           progress-3
       =*progRESS?*
        *B->*,LHmakes fist*

4   t:=ni-I?=
          PRT
       =mm-hm?=

5   M:=kaksitoista vuot|ta,(.) edisTY|Y.(1.0)mm.
       twelve            year-PAR     progress-3
       =twelve years,(.) progRESS.(1.0)mm.

           GM
6   J: *e|i ymmärrä.*
        NEG-3 understand
       *not understand.*
        *O->M,B-> *

    (0.8)

           GJ
7   M:mi|tä.
       what-PAR
       what.

           GM
8   J:*e|i ymmärrä.*
       NEG-3 understand
       *not understand.*
        * O->M*

    (2.0)
```

```
          Gt
 9  M: e|i.
       NEG-3F
       no.

    (2.0)

10  t:mm

11  (3.5 M:*chuckles, Gt*)

12  t:hmm sano vaan.
            say   just
       hmm just say what.

13  J:[*strokes cheak*

14  M:[kaksitoista vuot|ta.=
          twelve          year-PAR
       [twelve years.=

          GM
15  J:=*e|i ymmärrä.*(2.3) kaksitoista [*vuot|ta.*]
       NEG-3 understand            twelve          year-PAR
       =*notØ understand.*(2.3) twelve [*years.*]
          *RHopens*                      *Onod*

16  M:                              [*vuot|ta.]halvaantunut.*
                                     year-PAR     paralyzed
                                    [*years]paralysed.*
                                    *Onod,B->,LHDherself*

    (0.6)

          Gdownwards      GM
17  J:kakhi,.(*3.2 *)*pane paperi|lle.*
                         put      paper-ALL
       {two},.(*3.2 *)*put it on paper.*
                      *RHmoves,B and O->*

    (1.0)

18  t:ahaa.=
       I see.=

19  M:=e|i [ymm-]
       NEG-3
       =not [und-]

20  J:    [mm]

21  t:    [Jaakko]haluaa,=
           1name M     wants
          [Jaakko]wants,=

22  J:=hmm=
```

23   t:=*Jaakko haluu näh|dä paperi|lla* numero|t koska hän ymmärtää
         1name M   wants   see-INF   paper-ADE   number-PL   because he   understands
         =*Jaakko wants to see numbers* on the paper because he understands
              passes paper to M

24   ne paremmin jos sä laita|t paperi|lle ne.=
         they better   if   you put-2   paper-ALL   they
         them better if you put them on paper.=

25   M:=jaah
             PRT
         =oh yeah

26   J:=mm=

27   M:=°jaah° (7.1, KIRJOITTAA) kaksitoista. (0.9) kaksitoista.
           PRT   twelve   twelve
         =°yeah° (7.1, WRITES)   twelve.   (0.9)twelve.

28   (1.3***J stretches forward and makes a mark on the paper***)

29   **t: m-m?=**

30   M:=*jo-o*=
         =*yea-yeah*=
          Onod

31   J:=on|ko se,=
          is-Q   it
         =is it,=

32   M:***Onod***

33   J:[jaaha.]
         [I see.]

34   M:=[joo]=
         =[yes]=

33   **t:=mm=**

34   M:=ole|n.=
          be-1
         =I have.=

35   **t:=[mm]**

36   M:=[minä]ole|n(.)sairastu|nut.(.)hmm
         I   be-1   get ill-PPC
         =[I] have (.)become ill.(.)hmm

This is a long and complex example. At the beginning of the excerpt, Jaakko's
not understand-type of repair-initiator (line 6) leads to another repair initiator
by Maija (line 7). Maija's general interrogative <u>what.</u>, her gaze towards Jaakko,
and a silent voice, all reveal that the location of Jaakko's trouble is unclear to
Maija. Possibly Jaakko interprets *what* as a hearing check and repeats his
previous repair-initiation <u>not understand.</u> in line 8. Jaakko shifts his gaze to the

therapist, followed by two long pauses in between which Maija utters no and the therapist gives a short acknowledgement token. Maija laughs briefly and looks rather confused. In spite of these difficulties, the therapist does not participate in the repair work but instead urges the others to continue (line 12; because the therapist is sitting with her back towards the camera it is impossible to say to whom she is allocating the turn). Jaakko remains silent and wipes his chin. At this point, Maija goes on by uttering twelve years. (line 14), to which Jaakko responds and repeats for a third time not understand., shifting his gaze to Maija and adding immediately, twelve years. (line 15). However, Jaakko's expression is so slow that when he starts to say the word years, Maija joins with him, and they utter it together while nodding their heads and exchanging gazes. Maija continues, adding the word paralysed.. One can assume that she is still unaware of Jaakko's precise trouble. As a result, when repeating the word years and continuing with the word paralysed., Maija is again initiating collaborative work with a demonstration of the trouble place in understanding Jaakko.

Nevertheless, Jaakko does not give an acceptance to Maija, and while looking at her, he mumbles the word two, (possibly an attempt to repeat "twelve") and then points to Maija, demanding put it on paper. (line 17). This attempt at repetition reveals the precise trouble to the therapist and she consequently breaks into the conversation exclaiming I see. (ahaa in Finnish which is typically used in Finnish as a function of a piece of new information). Maija begins, interestingly enough, to utter not und- (pro not understand) (line 19) but the therapist interrupts her and initiates collaborative work. This collaboration takes the form of an other-initiated other-repair by the therapist while pointing out that Jaakko has to see the numbers on the paper before he is able to understand the meaning of the numeral twelve. This also clarifies the problem for Maija, and so she begins to repeat oh yeah(.)yeah and writes the number on the paper (line 27).

Although a resolution was reached in this interaction, a confirmation of the resolution is also added. To accomplish this, Jaakko points to the number written by Maija and makes a self-initiated other-repair is it, while gazing at Maija (line 31). The therapist and Maija both give overlapping acceptances with the therapist offering only short acknowledgement tokens, while Maija gives verbal affirmation that she really has become ill so long ago. Finally, Jaakko gives his final acknowledgements with nods.

This extended, and rather complex, repair sequence has as its focus the repair work which turned out to discover the meaning of the word *twelve*. In this exchange, Jaakko did not understand what Maija said and thus he initiated the collaborative work to reach a mutual understanding and also began an exposed correction sequence (Jefferson 1987), which interrupted the treatment of the current topic and focused on the repair work aimed at resolving his problem. Jaakko's *not understand*-type repair initiator turned out to be rather weak because it could not specifically locate his trouble source. Moreover, Jaakko was not at first able to change it to the stronger repair-initiator because he kept using the same initiator three times (lines 6, 8 and 15). Only later, after repeating not understand. a third time, was Jaakko able to change his unspecified repair-initiation for the repetition of the trouble spot and he repeated it twice. In fact, the problem was solved only after the therapist contributed the other-initiated other-repair which has been regarded as the strongest repair-initiator (Schegloff et al. 1977). In sum, the unspecified comprehension trouble led to Jaakko's several other-repair initiators: three *not understand*-contributions, two repetitions of the trouble source, and finally a request for action which resulted in the therapist's other-initiated other-repair. Although the development of the repair sequence was slow and repetitive, it confirms the 'strength' idea of repair suggested by Schegloff et al. (1977), as well as supporting Clark & Schaefer's (1987, 1989) notion of the principle of least collaborative effort; both ideas propose that if more than one other-initiated sequence is needed, the other-initiators are used in increasing order of strength.

Jaakko's repetitive use of *not understand* repair-initiators and the length of the previous repair sequence demonstrated that the exchange of the repair-initiator for a stronger one was not an easy task for Jaakko. On the other hand, the striking characteristic of this sequence is that it was Jaakko who began the collaborative repair work and he kept it going until reaching resolution of the trouble. Although his devices for the repair work were rather weak, he nevertheless invited the other speakers to collaborate with him so that his efforts were rewarded with the help of Maija and the therapist. This is also a nice example of negotiation of the repair. After the trouble spot was identified, Jaakko himself was able to offer a resolution strategy for his problem, and he subsequently asked Maija to write down the problematic number. Mutual understanding was finally reached which was marked by the acceptance by the co-participants and the conversation could go on.

8.2.3 General questions

One strategy used to clarify comprehension problems is to ask general questions referring to the previous context. In the following I will analyse an example where the aphasic participant, Kalle, asks several successive questions which refer to the preceding conversation. His repair initiations reveal that he has had problems in comprehending what was said previously. The topic in this example is the trip which two of the group members, Jaakko and Paavo, had taken. The conversation has proceeded for some time concerning several subtopics, such as the number of participants, the weather during the boat trip and the dates of the trip. Kalle takes a turn and explains that there is something that he cannot remember; he poses several other-repair initiations concerning Jaakko's participation in the trip. Kalle begins with a declarative sentence but interrupts it and changes it to the question form. However, he still continues with formulating his utterance as a rather general candidate understanding.

Example 4

```
1   K:*kuule mä oo* *(-)nyt anteeks jos mä[(-)]*
       listen  I          now   sorry      if   I
      *listen I'v* *(-)now sorry      if I[(-)]*
       *GJ, DJ*      *Gt, ODt*

2   t:                                    [juu juu]
                                           PRT PRT
                                          [yes yes]
```

3 K:mä e|n muista.(0.3)*sä ol|i|t(.)kesä|llä*(.)
    I NEG-1 remember   you be-PST-2   summer-ADE
   I don't remember.(0.3)*you were(.)in the summer*
                      GJ,DJ

4 *käv|i|t|kö Ruotsi|n puole|lla siellä vai.*
   go-PST-2-Q   Sweden-GEN side-ADE   there   or
   (.)*did you go over to Sweden there or.*
     GJ,Dleft.

5 (1.4)*sinä ol|i|t,.*(0.3)*nyt jossain meno|ssa vai.*
        you be-PST-2   now somewhere go-INE or
   (1.4)*you were,.*(0.3)*now somewhere going or.*
     GJ,DJ   *GJ,Dforward.*

   (1.4)

6 J: juu juu.
   yes yes.

   (0.2)

7 K:*ahaa.*
   I see.*
   GJ,Onod

   (0.5)

8 t:nyt,.
   now
   now,.

   (1.0)

9 J:* *nyt,.
      now
   * *now,.
   *GP,DP*GP->GK*

   (0.5)

10 M:nyt,.=
   now
   now,.=

11 P: =me ol|ti|i|n.
     we be-PASS-PST-4
   =we were.

12 t: ihan   [viime (.) [viime viiko|lla
    just   last   last   week-ADE
   just   [last (.) [last week

13 K: *AI[te ol|i|tte [no nii*
         PRT you(PL) be-PST-2PL PRT PRT
       OH[you were [oh yeah*
        GP,Onod

```
14  J:                        [joo joo.
                               PRT  PRT
                              [yes yes.

15  P:nii niim+me viiko|lla.=
       PRT          week-ADE
       yeah {last} week.=

16  t:=°mm°=

17  K:*a-ahaa nyt.(.)no se o [varmaan,.*
         PRT     now   PRT it is  surely
       *I-I see now(.)well it is[surely,.*
             *GP*

18  J:                        [just just kohta kato.
                               just just soon  look
                              [right right soon you see.

19  P:°nii°
       PRT
       °yeah°

20  K:*joo joo*ahaa.=
       PRT  PRT PRT
       *yes yes*I see.=
       *GJ,Onod*

21  P:=°äskettäin.°
         recently
       =°recently.°

22  K:no se[|hän] on kiva|a siellä et oo|tte (.)käy|ny|t kats|ele|ma|ssa
       PRT it-CLI    is  nice-PAR there PRT be-2PL    go-PPC-2    look-FRE-INF-INE
       well [nice]it's nice that you have(.)looked look around a

23  vähän
    little
    little

24  t:      [se ol|i,.]
             it  be-PST
           [it was,.]

25  K:maa-(.)[mu|i|ta|ki.
              other-PL-PAR-CLI
       ot-(.) [others.

26  t:       [se ol|i(.)afasiayhdistykse|n järjestä|mä,
             it  be-PST aphasia association-GEN organize-INF
            [it was(.)organized by the aphasics association,

27  M:mm

28  t:[risteily.]
       cruise
      [a cruising.]

29  K:[ahaa.](3.4) nii.( 0.4) .hjoo
       PRT          PRT         PRT
       [I see.](3.4) yeah.( 0.4) .yes
```

Because the conversation had just handled Jaakko's participation in the trip, Kalle's questions show that there was no question about Kalle's problems in remembering, but rather his problem was to follow and comprehend the conversation. In any cases, his utterance showed that he had noticed his problem and he began the repair work to clear the trouble. It is important to note that although his requests for clarification were directed to Jaakko, other participants – Maija, Paavo and the therapist – joined in the repair work which led to the collaborative negotiation of the repair.

After Jaakko's affirmative reply (line 6) and Kalle's acknowledgement token ahaa. (I see.) (line 7), the therapist continues the sequence by adding now,. with a head nod (line 8) confirming that the trip had taken place only recently and Jaakko and Maija repeat it. In addition, Jaakko supports his speech with a pointing gesture to the left. The therapist's contribution now,. can be regarded as a direct other-initiated other-repair because it is subsequent to Jaakko's affirmative reply, and it further clarifies Kalle's evident misunderstanding of the time of the trip. Next, Paavo continues with the further explanation we were. (line 11) possibly referring to Kalle's clarification requests which had only referred to Jaakko. This turn also can be regarded as a direct other-initiated other-repair, used to explain that both Paavo and Jaakko participated in the trip. The therapist then completes his turn, uttering just last(.)last week. (line 12), which again can be regarded as an other-initiated other-repair. This is a fine example of a joint sentence production (Sacks 1992a, Fall 1967; lecture 4) or a collaborative-turn sequence (Lerner 1987) where the participants jointly formulate an other-initiated other-repair which clarifies Kalle's troubles. Subsequently, Kalle gives his acceptance with a longer turn, with a preface "ai" ("oh" in English; line 13). The beginning of the acceptance turn, "ai" also confirms that he only now reaches the understanding; in Finnish, the expression "ai" is typically used in connection with the receipt of new information (cf. Hakulinen & Sorjonen 1986). Next, Jaakko gives affirmations (line 14) and Paavo confirms this strongly, beginning with a *nii*-particle and once more clarifying "last week" (niimme viikolla pro viime viikolla) with a literal paraphasia (line 15).

In line 17, Kalle begins the turn but Jaakko overlaps him and contributes to the conversation with an ambiguous turn right right soon you see. This turn could again refer to the time of the trip which Kalle once more acknowledges, but this time with two yes's and he even adds an ahaa. (I see) -particle. Paavo seemed to have interpreted Jaakko uttered a paraphasia using the word soon and he makes a direct other-initiated other-repair uttering recently.. The sequence ends with Kalle's assessment of the trip and the therapist's explanation that the trip was organized by the Aphasics Association.

This sequence has many interesting features, among them the astonishing number of repairs and confirmations in the sequence. One could ask what it is that creates a need for so many other-repair initiations and such a long exposed correction sequence? Kalle's repair initiations which motivated the repair sequence offer a possible explanation. Although Kalle's requests for clarification (lines 3-5) are somehow contradictory, they reveal at least two issues which had remained unclear for him from the earlier conversation. First, the time of the trip was unclear because in the first question he referred to *last summer* but in the third question (line 5) he uses the word *now* which refers to the present time or the immediate past. Second, he had possibly understood that only Jaakko participated in the trip because he directs his questions to Jaakko only. Jaakko's general affirmative answer yes yes. (line 6) was not sufficient to correct both misunderstandings and the therapist began the collaborative work in which the other speakers participated, in order to give more information about the trip. The repair turns offered by the co-participants developed into a fascinating collaborative clarification for Kalle's problems and the fine co-operation between the participants of the group.

Another interesting thing is that, in this case, contrary to the earlier examples (1, 2 and 3), the other-repair initiations appeared with a delay. In the first examples, the other-repair initiations were contributed immediately after the trouble-turn. In this example, the issues related to the requests for clarification had been handled earlier and they were not taken up in the repair process until later. This may indicate that Kalle had more general comprehension problems within the present topic, not only related to a specific trouble spot.

The following excerpt shows a more specified request for clarification, posed by Jaakko:

Example 5

```
1   t:niin kerro|ppa vähän mi|tä sä nyt tä|llä hetke|llä,=
        PRT    tell-CLI         little   what-PAR you now this-ADE  moment-ADE
        well go ahead and tell us a bit about what you now at this moment,=

2   M:=minä meneØ1,(1.5)k-koulu|u.
        I      go Ø1            school-ADE
        =I goØ1,(1.5)to s-school.

    (0.4)

3   t:mm-m?

    (1.7)

4   M:joka päivä.
        every   day
        every day.

    (0.3)

5   t:mm-m?

    (0.4)

6   M:koulu|uh, (0.5)puhe|tta oppi|ma|a.
        school-ILL         speech-PAR   learn-INF-ILL
        to school, (0.5)to learn speech.

7   t:sä oot järjestä|ny ittelle|s semmose|n ohjelma|n et [su|l+o
        you be-2 organize-PST-PPC  youself-2  such-ACC      program-ACC PRT you-ADE+is
        you have organized  for yourself such  a programme that [you'v
```

```
 8   M                                              [jooh
                                                    PRT
                                                    [yeah


 9   t:joka päivä jotain [puuha|a.
       every   day    some     task-PAR
       every day something[to do.

10   M:                        [jooh jooh
                               [yeah yeah

11   t:hm-m.=

12   M:=jooh=
       =yeah=

13   t:=mm=

14   M:=puhe|tta.
       speech-PAR
       =speech.

15   t:mm

     (1.9)

16   J:koko päiväØQ.
       whole   day
       whole dayØQ.

     (0.4)

17   M:eei ei &puolitoista puo&
       NEG  NEG  one and a half
       no: no $ one and a half an ha-$

18   puolitoista,.(2.9)ähh.(1.3)puolitoista,.
     one and a half                one and a half
     one and a half an,.(2.9)uhh.(1.3)one and a half an,.

     (8.3)

19   t:tunti|a?
       hour-PAR
       hour?

20   M:tunti|a.(0.3)tunti|a.(0.3)tunti|a.
       hour-PAR       hour-PAR       hour-PAR
       hour.(0.3) hour.(0.3) hour.
```

In this example Maija tells the group that she works with her speech every day. Evidently, the word "school" (line 2) is a semantic paraphasia here or perhaps a generalized noun because she attended no school but she daily practised reading with her neighbour. The therapist offers a demonstration of understanding, a direct other-initiated other-repair, interpreting Maija having some programme every day (line 7), which Maija accepts. The therapist acknowledges Maija's contribution, after which Jaakko utters <u>whole day.</u> (line 16). The surface structure of his utterance is agrammatic [<u>koko päivä</u> pro "koko päivä+n+(kö)"; a case marker and a question particle are missing)] but Maija clearly interprets it as a question because she rejects it with laughter. Also, in this excerpt, Jaakko's repair-initiator occurs slightly delayed. This repair-initiation resembles a third position repair which may be termed 'specification' (cf. Schegloff 1992).

The following excerpt is a very complicated one because there are several instances of other-repair initiations, the first one contributed by the therapist and the following ones consecutively by Maija. The speakers began their repair-initiations with Wh-questions, but the first question and the following ones were not connected to each other, as we will see later. The conversation deals with the length of the chipboards produced by the factory which Jaakko had been building in Russia. The ongoing problem in this excerpt is the length of the chipboards. In earlier turns Jaakko introduced the idea of two kilometres and in the beginning of this excerpt, Jaakko connects the length of two kilometres with the chipboards.

Example 6

```
1   t:kaks kilometri|a.=
       two      kilometre-PAR
    two kilometres.=

2   J:=nii.
        PRT
       right.

    (1.2)

3   E:mi|tä.(0.7)kaks kilometri|a,.=
       what-PAR        two      kilometrePAR
    what.(0.7)two kilometres,.=

4   J:=ö-ö-lastulevy|ä.
            chipboard-PAR
    uh-uh- of chipboard.

5   E:°aha m°
         PRT
    °I see m°

6   Y:.hjoo
    .yeah

7   J: hmm.

    (2.5)

8   E:kaks kilometri|a lastulevy|ä.=
       two     kilometre-PAR   chipboard-PAR
    two kilometres of chipboard.=

9   J:=on VALtava.
       is   enormous
    =it is eNORmous.
```

```
     (0.6)

10  t:mi|ssä aja|s    [(-)
        what-INE  time-INE
      in which time[(period)

11  E:                [NII
                      [YEAH

     (0.7)

12  M:missä °on°
        where    is
      where is (it).

13  J:mi|tä.
        what-PAR
      what.

     (0.3)

14  M:missä on.
        where   is
      where is (it).

15  E:niih,.(0.9) niin pit pitk|i|ä la- öö tai kaks kilometri|a
        PRT           PRT      long-PL-PAR      or  two  kilometre-PAR
      yeah,.(0.9)so lo-long chi- er or two kilometres

16  lastu(-) si
      chip
    chip(-){si-}

     (0.6)

17  M:missä on.
        where   is
      where is (it).

     (1.8)

18  J:kaks kyl-,(0.5)hmm(4.7)*missä on.*
        two                    where  is
      two, {?} (0.5) hmm(4.7)*where is (it).*
                                  *G->M*

     (0.3)

19  M:*mm.*
       *GJ*

     (1.7)

20  J:hhh.

     (4.0)

21  M:*Helsinki|sä.*
        place name-INE
      *in Helsinki.*
         *GJ*
```

```
       (0.7)

22  J:*ei ei ei kato|s,*
        NEG NEG NEG look-CLI
        *no no no look,*
              *GM*


       (0.5)

23  E:*siellä,*=
        there
        *there,*=
         *GM*

24  J=*Venäjä|llä.*
         Russia-ADE
        *in Russia.*
          *GM*

25  E:[°Venäjä|llä siellä°
          Russia-ADE     there
        [°in Russia there°

26  M:[JOO.°Venäjä joo joo hyvä° hyvä on=
         PRT  Russia  PRT PRT good   good  is
        [YES.°Russia yes yes right° all right=

27  J:=mm=

28  M:=heh-heh-,hh

       (2.1)

29  t:mm=

30  E:=mi|tä toi( )kilometri|a lastulevy|ä, ö-ö(1.2)tarkottaa.
         what-PAR that    kilometre-PAR   chipboard-PAR           means
        =what does this( )kilometres chipboard, er-er(1.2)mean.

31  (3.2)k[aks,(3.9) kilometri|ä.
            two           kilometre-PAR
        (3.2)t[wo, (3.9) kilometres.

32  P:    [(RYKÄISEE)
           [(CLEARS HIS THROAT)

33  J:kaks kilometri|ä.(2.2) lastulevy|ä.(5.5) HUOKAISEE
         two    kilometre-PAR        chipboard-PAR
        two kilometres.(2.2) of chipboard.(5.5)SIGHS

34  M:hirvee (0.8) i[so
         terribly         big
        terribly (0.8) b[ig

35  J:                [joo joo
                       PRT  PRT
                      [yes yes
```

The first other-repair initiation, a Wh-initiated question, is from Elina asking to what *two kilometres* refers (line 3). Jaakko's reply uh-uh of chipboard. is clearly a surprise for Elina because she gives an acknowledgement token with a particle "aha" ("oh" in English). After Jaakko's acknowledgement token she makes another other-repair initiation gazing, at Jaakko and repeating the two previous issues two kilometres of chipboard. (line 8). There is clearly a conflict in the conversation; Elina's turn and face show doubt and seemingly this leads Jaakko to assure it is ENORmous. (line 9). The therapist offers the next other-repair initiation referring to the manufacturing of the chipboards (line 10). The content of her question possibly remains a little unclear because of the overlap. Anyway, she uses the Wh-question word ("missä" in Finnish, although in English the direct translation is in which time(period)) in the beginning of the turn but the end of the turn is overlapped by Elina's acknowledgement token.

Maija formulates the next other-repair initiation (line 12) using the same question word *missä* as the previous speaker but the meaning of her general request for clarification is quite different from the previous turn; she asks where is (it).(missä on.). Her sudden question-turn shifts the topic. This question-turn might have been due to a mishearing or a misunderstanding of the therapist's previous turn which she apparently intends to repeat. Furthermore, this topical shift causes evident trouble for Jaakko either to hear or understand Maija's question and he makes an other-repair initiation and asks for a repetition (line 13). Maija repeats her *where is*-question in a soft and hesitant voice, and lifts her hand to her mouth. Subsequently, Elina continues talking about the length of chipboards (line 15). This turn is an elliptical one, and it is difficult to interpret whether or not it is an other-repair initiation or just a surprised assessment (Pomeranz 1984) of the lengths of the chipboards. At this point, Maija continues and repeats her previous question for the third time (line 17). Jaakko then directs his gaze to Elina and begins to speak about two {?} but suddenly interrupts himself, and then directs his gaze first to the paper on the table, and next to Maija, and repeating her question (line 18) which Maija subsequently acknowledges. It seems that only now, after repeating the turn himself, Jaakko realizes the content of Maija's question. There follows a rather long pause (4 sec.) and Jaakko looks at the paper with a confused expression. Finally, Maija makes her fourth other-repair initiation, which at last shows her aim with her previous questions. She changes for a stronger repair-initiator and offers a candidate interpretation by asking in Helsinki. [in fact she offers an agrammatic form Helsinkisä (root+incomplete inessive -sä) instead of "Helsingissä(kö)" (root+inessive -ssä+(clitic -kö=question form)] which, however, displayed her trouble (line 21). In response, Jaakko strongly rejects Maija's interpretation, gazing firmly at Maija. Also, Maija's repeated questions provide the necessary clarity for Elina and she offers a direct other-initiated other-repair, stating there, and gazing at Maija. At last, Jaakko is able to give the expected second part to Maija's repeated first part of the adjacency pair, replying in Russia.. Line 25 reveals that Elina is not yet ready to close down the repair sequence but still confirms in Russia there which combines Jaakko's and her own previous turns together. At this point Maija provides acceptance with several verbal and nonverbal acknowledgement tokens by repeating Russia, admitting yes yes, nodding her head, and even by laughing briefly. Her behaviour is in accordance with Perkins' (1993) suggestion that the longer the misunderstanding, the more the acknowledgement tokens needed to demonstrate mutual understanding. Thus, the participants were able to resolve Maija's misunderstanding and close down this collaborative negotiation of repair sequence. Finally, the conversation returned to the handling of the first trouble at the beginning of the excerpt that is, to the lengths of the chipboards.

The previous sequence is a possible and somewhat typical excerpt from an aphasic conversation, where an embedded repair sequence occurs (cf. Lesser & Milroy 1993:197-201) within a longer repair sequence. The first problem concerns the length of the chipboards, and the conversation is centred around it. However, another misunderstanding arises (Maija's turn 12) which is perhaps based on a mishearing of the therapist's turn. Maija begins to introduce *where is*-questions to the conversation and, on the other hand, Elina continues with the chipboard topic. As a result, there are two competitive topics and two various other-repair initiations related to the different topics directed to Jaakko. This produces a heavy demand for Jaakko's verbal processing capability and his problems in handling them become public during his turn, in line 18. Here he first begins to offer a contribution to Elina, but stops and turns to Maija's side, repeating her question. This offers a possibility to Maija to reformulate her other-repair initiation which clears the meaning of her questions, and the embedded repair-sequence initiated by her is resolved.

Although it is probable that Maija's repair initiation was due to a mishearing of the therapist's turn (2), her repair-initiation seemed to be a relevant issue for her. This confirms the hypothesis that there also must have been some misunderstanding in the previous conversation which led her to formulate the first other-repair initiation in this sequence. The previous excerpt demonstrates particularly clearly how Maija initiates an other-repair and continues it. Although she was not able to offer the strongest repair initiation, a candidate interpretation at the beginning of the sequence, she did use Wh-questions to keep the repair in progress. To accomplish this, she had to repeat her first question twice before Jaakko realized the meaning of her repair initiators. Thus, Maija had an opportunity to offer a demonstration of understanding (an other-initiated other-repair), and this gave Jaakko the possibility to reply to Maija's first request for clarification, which ultimately led to the outcome of the repair.

8.2.4 Discussion

Even though some researchers have analysed behaviour related to aphasic speakers' self-repair patterns (Laakso 1993b, Perkins 1993, Ferguson 1994) and healthy speakers' other-repair patterns in aphasic conversation (Lubinski et al. 1980, Gurland et al. 1982, Laakso 1992, Perkins 1993, Ferguson 1994) there is generally a lack of literature concerning aphasic speakers' other-repair initiations. This seems to be connected to the materials studied. The few studies concerning aphasic conversations are collected from aphasic-therapist dyads and/or aphasic-spouse dyads. In these contexts, the linguistically 'better' speaker often carries the greater burden of the conversation.

As mentioned earlier, Lubinski et al. (1980) found that while conversing with an aphasic, a spouse and a therapist used many clarification requests and later Gurland & al. (1982) confirmed this result. In Laakso's (1992) study, only one aphasic speaker used various types of requests for clarification to facilitate his comprehension problems. Moreover, in my material the therapist used a large number of the other-repair initiations, such as Wh-type of requests for clarification. Often, these were meant to clarify the problems which were caused by the insufficient information contributed by the aphasic speakers (cf. chapter 9). In a recent study, Ferguson (1994) found that normal subjects tended to increase their frequency of interactive trouble-indicating behaviour when conversing with aphasic partners, as compared with normal partners.

In the present study, my aim has been to analyse the relevance of other-repair initiations contributed by aphasic speakers connected to their comprehension or hearing problems. Because aphasic speakers often have comprehension problems, at least in the acute state of their illness, this repair-type should be extremely important for them, as it gives them an opportunity to grasp problems in conversation, and to begin repair work to solve them. One principle notion of Schegloff et al (1977) is the preference-organization of the self- and other-initiation of repair. They suggest that both self- and other-repair initiations induce self-correction, and thus there is a clear preference for self-repair over other-repair. The organization of these examples follows this principle. In these cases, an aphasic participant begins a repair sequence because of a mishearing or a misunderstanding. Jaakko initiated the repair sequence on several occasions, whereas Maija and Kalle had only one such sequence per speaker. However, Maija and Kalle made the least contributions to the conversations over all as well.

Other-repair initiations are capable of locating the trouble-source and thus they provide the speaker of the trouble-source with another opportunity to repair the trouble (Schegloff et al. 1977). In the above excerpts, the troubles in comprehension were, in some cases, general, and in some examples they were not connected directly to the previous turn nor could they be linked with a specific trouble spot there. Furthermore, the other interlocutors did not have problems in the earlier context. Therefore, one could conclude that the problems which were taken under repair were related to Jaakko's, Maija's and Kalle's individual problems, that is, related to aphasia and to the processing problems caused by it.

According to the Western Aphasia Battery, Jaakko, Maija and Kalle had some problems with auditory verbal comprehension. Jaakko had the lowest score in auditory verbal comprehension, with a total of 157/200 points. He scored 56 out of 60 points in yes/no questions, and 55 correct responses out of 60 possible points in auditory word recognition and 46/80 points in the sequential commands. Clearly, he had problems in understanding sequential commands, based probably on his morpho-syntactic decoding problems. For instance, in commands point with the pen to the book and point to the pen with the book (osoittakaa kynällä kirjaa ja osoittakaa kynää kirjalla in Finnish) he was only able to point to the pen and the book and say what's the difference(.)don't know. His behaviour also indicated that he suffered from delayed auditory processing. For example, he often asked an interlocutor to wait in order to get more time for processing a previous turn.

Maija scored 51 out of 60 points on the yes/no questions, 59 out of 60 points on the auditory word recognition and 64 out of 80 points on the sequential commands, for a sum 174 out of 200 points in auditory verbal comprehension. According to my clinical observations, miscomprehensions were seldom found in dyadic conversation with Maija, but some problems were observed in quick shifts from one topic to another.

Kalle also displayed problems with comprehension. He had 58 out of 60 points in yes/no questions, 57 out of 60 points in auditory word recognition and 64 out of 80 points in the sequential commands. Clinically, he had various problems in concentrating on the rehabilitation tasks, in following the requests of the therapist, and also he showed impulsiveness and sometimes uncritical behaviour. However, it is difficult to judge whether his problems are really due to a specific linguistic disorder or if they reflect a more general disorder connected to his problems in regulating his executive behaviour (e.g. Luria 1976).

The above excerpts show that speakers recognized their comprehension troubles in conversation, located them at least on a general level, and were able to begin to solve the problem. Kalle's case is particularly noteworthy, as he had a rather acute posterior type of aphasia (according to the WAB, he had anomic aphasia) and he had difficulties in understanding longer verbal sequences. Also, a common symptom connected to posterior aphasia is often said to reflect an unawareness of the disorders (e.g. Lhermitte & Gautier 1969). Kalle showed anosognosia in the clinical assessment of his aphasia, especially concerning his problems with verbal memory, but it seems that at least on some occasions he was able to return to the previous conversation and to ask for clarification for his comprehension problems.

In addition, the excerpts indicate that aphasic speakers use similar types of other-repair initiations as do 'normal' speakers when handling problems of hearing or understanding. On the other hand, some typical features can be observed in the repair sequences that were initiated by the aphasic speakers. The first notion concerns the length of these sequences. Schegloff et al. (1977) suggest that the repair in normal conversation is principally organized in four consecutive turns. Churchill (1978) also presents procedural problems in request-response sequences, and his examples show that the repair sequences are short in normal conversation. However, Milroy and Perkins (1992) have noticed that the aphasic repair sequences span over a large number of turns. My data supports this observation. Especially when an aphasic initiates the other-repair sequences that are associated with the comprehension problems, these sequences may be very long, as the examples above display. Also, Laakso (1993a) has reported that the self-repair initiations by aphasic speakers may lead to lengthy repair sequences. The second notion concerns the intensive collaboration between the speakers. The long repair sequences always contained several collaborators. In this sense, the long repair sequences can be called collaborative negotiation of the repair (Milroy and Perkins ibid.).

Schegloff et al. (1977) proposed that there is a preference for stronger over weaker repair initiators, and if more than one other-initiated sequence is needed, the other-initiators are utilized in the order of increasing strength. The principle of the least collaborative effort (Clark & Schaefer 1986 and 1989) is based on this idea, which is highly relevant from the point of view of aphasic conversation. According to this principle, the use of the strongest possible option in other-repair initiations should lead to a quicker solution of the repair sequence than does the use of a weaker initiator. If we look at the above examples from this perspective, we notice that in the long and complex repair sequences (examples 3, 4, 7) the initiator of the repair indeed had a tendency to develop the other-repair initiators of the stronger type. For instance in example 3, Jaakko first used a general repair-initiator *not understand* three times. However, this was evidently too general for locating the problem and so he later replaced it with a repetition of the trouble spot. He also requested an action; he asked Maija to write down the problematic number. At this point, the therapist joined the repair process and offered an other-initiated other-repair. Through these steps the trouble was resolved. Example 7 is an excellent example because Maija first offered three repair-initiators *where is*, but finally replaced these with the stronger initiator, a candidate understanding. This led to the outcome of the repair sequence. In example 5, Kalle offered three other-repair initiations in the same turn. The first such initiation was general, stating that he could not remember. Then, he began a candidate understanding which he transformed to question-form. The last one was in the form of a candidate understanding. Using this means, he also modified the formulations of his questions of which the last one was the strongest.

In order to resolve conversational comprehension/hearing problems, a speaker should recognize when and in what way her/his comprehension is inadequate, and recognize the procedures that are needed to repair the problem. The use of the other-repair initiations by aphasic speakers displays preserved pragmatic knowledge of conversational management procedures in the case of hearing or comprehension problems. On the other hand, a speaker needs linguistic abilities to be able to formulate other-repair initiations, such as Wh-questions or open questions. The more specified the repair-questions are, the more sophisticated the linguistic structure required. My data indicates that aphasics are able to make use of the basic sequential organization of repair, but special difficulties in formulating repair initiations may arise due to word retrieval and syntactic problems from aphasia. The agrammatic formulations (examples 3 and 5) and the repetitiveness (examples 3 and 6) indicate that Jaakko and Maija had specific problems at least in formulating open questions. However, in these examples they managed, with collaboration of the co-participants, to lead the repair sequences, which they had initiated, to their conclusion.

From the clinical point of view, it would be very relevant to know about the other-repair initiation procedures of aphasic speakers. An important question is whether the type or the stage of aphasia have some specific influence on the mastering of the other-repair initiation procedure. Also, more specific knowledge is needed of the linguistic ability required for using the different other-repair initiators.

8.3 Other-repair initiations connected to the speaker's word-finding difficulties

As was previously mentioned, a distinctive character is found in the sequential organization of some repair sequences in this data. They span over a large number of turns, which seems to be different from the repair sequences seen in normal conversation. A typical feature in aphasic repair sequences is that different repair initiator techniques such as questions, repetitions or candidate understandings, follow each other, and there may also occur several embedded repair sequences. Thus, an adjacency pair structure is too limited to describe this kind of sequence, and it may be insufficient for analysing them. In the following, I will analyse an extended repair sequence connected to Jaakko's word-finding difficulties, which contains various other-repair initiations contributed by the participants. The collaborative negotiation of repair is well attested in this sequence.

The following excerpt is a typical example of an extended repair sequence in these data. The repair is initiated with Jaakko's agrammatic turn with word-finding difficulty. There were actually two problems in the sequence; the first problem concerned a new item which Jaakko introduced in the conversation. Later it turned out to be the name of a place where Jaakko had worked previously. The second problem concerned the geographical location of that place. I will now present the whole excerpt, focusing especially on various other-repair initiations and on the collaborative repair work. In addition, the strategies utilized in order to resolve the problems will be analysed.

During the conversation, the speakers are sitting around the table. The figure 14 below demonstrates the order in which they are seated.

Figure 14. The seats of the participants in example 7.

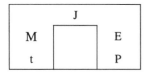

Only one camera was used in the video recording, and thus it is difficult to reconstruct all gazes between the participants, and because the body of the therapist is often outside the frame, we can only follow her hand movements.

Example 7

```
          GM              GM              GM
1  J:  on Sarja,(2.1)*sinneh.(.)sin[ne.]*
        is    name          there+to      there+to
       Sarja is,(2.1)*thereh.(.)the[re.]*
                   *Onod,RHDL↑       RHDL↑  *

                                GJ            GJ
2  M:                        [jooh](0.7)°joo°
                              PRT           PRT
                             [°ye:s°](0.7)°yes°
```

```
                              Gpaper              ,,GM
3  J: hhh.(KIRJOITTAA 7.2) [on|k|s oikein(2.3)Sae-Sarja
                            be-Q-CLI  right            name
   hhh.(WRITES 7.2)       [is it alright(2.3)Sae-Sarja


4  M:                         [*G paper LHDpaper*

   (0.9)

                   GM......,,Gt
5  P: se paika|n se [nime|ltä] Sarja
      it  place-GEN it  name-ELA    name
   it of the place [called] Sarja

                         GP
6  M:                    [joo]
                         [yes]


7  E: *Onod*

8  t: hmm


9  J:*t[änne]*
          here+to
     *the[re]*
       *RHDL↑ *


           GP
10  M:   [°Sarja°]
          name
        [°Sarja°]

         GM
11  J: juuh=
       ye:ah=

12  t: =ahaa=
       =I see=
        *Onod*

       Gpaper
13  M: =joo
       =yes
        *Onod*

   (1.1)

       GM            G↑              G↑
14 J:*tonne.(.)  tonne.*(2.4) [hhhhh.3.8]
        there+to     there+to
     *over there.(.)  over there.*(2.4) [hhhhh.3.8]
       *RHDL↑          RHDL↑ *

15  t:                   [*takes a map*]

                         GJ  ,,Gt
16  P:             [ei se löyd|y sieltä.=]
                    NEG it find-REF there+from
                   [cannot find there.=]
```

17 t: =ei löyd|y.=
      NEG find+REF
     =cannot find.=

                           Gmap
18 P: =ei varmasti.[°e|m+mä us(-)°]
      NEG for sure   NEG-1 +I
     =surely not.[°I don't beli(-)°]

19 t: [löyty|y|kö suunta kuitenki.]
                     find-REF-Q   direction   anyway
                [is the direction found at least.]

     Gmap
20 J kato|ta|an.
    look-PASS-4
    let's look.
    RH->

    (0.4)

21 t:missä PÄin suurin piirtein.&täs+on niin& täs+on to:ta,(.)
    where   roughly   here+is so   here+is PRT
    which Direction approximately.&it's so& it's well,(.)

22 on siinä Neuvostoliitto [mut+se on tommose|na piene|nä=
   is   there   Soviet Union   but+it is like that-ESS little-ESS
   there is Soviet Union [but it's such a small=

23   ***[* J takes a map***

24 t:=läntti|nä siinä että (.) mutta että suuntah,
    spot-ESS   there PRT   but   PRT   direction
    =area there that(.) but the direction,

25 J:**hh.**

26 t:on|k|+se Euroopa|n puoleise|ssa osa|ssa vai
    is-Q+it Europe-GEN   side-INE   part-INE or
  is it in European or

27 Aasia|n puoleise|ssa osa|ssa.
   Asia-GEN side-INE   part-INE
  Asian side.

                       G↓   G↓
28 J: *asettaa silmälasit* just(1.0)just(7.9)(hhhh. 1.1)
                       PRT   PRT
    ***puts his glasses on* just(1.0)just(7.9)(hhhh. 1.1)**

     Gmap
29 E: on|ko lähellä Tsernob?
      be-Q near   place name
    is it near Tsernob?
               o↓

    (1.1)

```
          Gmap
30  J:  .hh ei.=
              NEG
        .hh no.=
        *Oshake*


          Gmap
31   E:  =ei
             NEG
         =no

    (4.2)

32   t:  *°mu|n täytyy ihan tul|la katso|ma|an kans.°*
             I-GEN   must   quite  come-INF  look-INF-ILL    too
         *°I have to come and look too.°*
                 *goes behind J*


          Gmap
33   J:*tässä.*
           here
         *here.*
         *RHDmap*


    (3.0)

          Gmap
34   E:  °ahaa.°
            PRT
          °aha.°

    (2.4)

          Gmap
35   J:*tässä.*
           here
         *here.*
         *RHmap*

    (0.6)

          Gmap
36   t:  näytä|ppä to|lle Paavolle|kin.
            show-CL⁓      that-ADE  1name M-CLI
         please show also to Paavo.

37   J:*tuossa.*(1.5) suurin piirtein.
           there                 roughly
         *there.*(1.5) approximately.
         *RHDmap.*


          Gmap
38   P:joo joo.
          PRT  PRT
         yes yes.

39   M:  [mm.]
```

40 t: [mi]ten pitkä matka Moskova|sta.
        how   long   way   Moscow-ELA
        [ho]w far from Moskow.

    (1.5)

            Gmap   *,,Gt*   *,,Gpaper*   *,,Gt*
41 J:(hhh. 4.3) ö-ö (1.6)*kato.(.) tossa.*=
                            look   there
        (hhh. 4.3) uh-uh(1.6)*look.(.) there.*=
                        RHmoves paper,RHDpaper

42 M:=°kaheksan kymmentä°=
         eight   hundred
        =°eighty°=

            Gmap
43 t: =kaheksan sataa.=
         eight   hundred
        =eight hundred.=

                Gmap
44 M: =   [joo]
        =   [yes]

45 E: [°kaheksan sataa°]
                eight   hundred
        [°eight hundred°]

        Gt
46 J: jooh [joh]
        ye:s [yes]

47 t: [kah]eksansataa kilometri|ä Mosko[va|sta.
                eighthundred   kilometre-PAR   Moscow-ELA
        [ei]ght hundred kilometres from Mos[cow.

                                                    Gt
48 M: [mm

                                                    Gt
49 J: [jooh
                                                    [ye:s

                            GJ
50 t:hmm-mm.(0.4)elikkä se (0.8)ol|i|k+se*sinne POHjose|en
                  that means it   be-PST-Q+it   there+to north-ILL
      hmm-mm.(0.4)in other words it(0.8)was it*to the NOrth
                      RHD↑

51 #päin vai.#*
       wards or
       #wards or.#*

    (0.8)

                Gmap
52 J: ei kun,=
        NEG PRT
        no but,=
        RHDmap

53 t=eei
        NEG
        no:

54 P: itä|än.[et(-)]
        east-ILL
    to the east.[sou(-)]

55 J: [*RHmoves his pen DR↑ *

    (0.7)

56 t:*HETkinen.*
        moment
        just a MOment.
        *RHD↑ *

        Gt
57 J:*ylös.*
        up+to
        up.
        *RHD↑ *

    (1.5)

58 t:*koillise|en.*
        north-east-ILL
        north-east.
        *RHD↑ *

        Gmap
59 J:[joo]
    [yes]

        GJ
60 P: [hmm.]
    [hmm.]

61 t: koillise|en.
        north-east-ILL
        north-east.
        *RHD↑ *

62 (5.6 J:*G↓*)

        GM
63 J: entä sitten.
        and   then
        and then.

The first problem concerns the name of the place *Sarja* (lines 1-13). This sequence begins with Jaakko's turn <u>Sarja is,</u>, with which he quite suddenly introduces a new topic to the conversation. There is a longish pause (2.1) and Jaakko, gazing at Maija, continues the conversation while pointing diagonally leftwards with his pen and says <u>thereh.(.)the[re.]</u>. Maija gives two silent acknowledgement tokens, the first one overlapping with the end of Jaakko's preceding turn. Jaakko sighs loudly and begins to write down the word *Sarja* while looking at the paper. Jaakko then turns his gaze to Maija, makes a self-initiated other-repair initiation, and asks <u>is it all right(2.3)Sae-Sarja.</u>. With this act he begins a repair concerning the word *Sarja*, especially referring to its written form. Evidently, this is not sufficient information for Maija, because she gazes and points to the paper, but does not give a verbal acceptance. Subsequently, Paavo offers a demonstration of understanding (a direct other-initiated other repair), stating that the place where Jaakko had been was called *Sarja* (line 5). Several acknowledgements follow which were contributed by Elina, Maija and the therapist. Jaakko returns to the direction, and points again to the left, uttering <u>the[re]</u> (line 9). However, Maija repeats <u>Sarja</u> in a whispering voice which Jaakko accepts. In response, the therapist gives an acknowledgement with <u>ahaa</u> (<u>I see</u>) and Maija then gives an extra acknowledgement token with <u>joo</u> (<u>yes</u>) and nods.

After a one-second pause, the talk returns to the geographical location of Sarja (line 14). Jaakko had already vaguely referred to the site of Sarja in his first turn (line 1). In line 14, after the acceptance of the name of the place, Jaakko returns to the issue of the site of Sarja, pointing to the same direction as before. However, he can only add to his turn the repetitions <u>over there.(.)over there.</u> and sighing again loudly. At this point, the therapist takes a calendar with a map, and this nonverbal act has immediate consequences for the conversation. There follows a side-sequence (Jefferson 1972) between the therapist and Paavo concerning the possibility of finding such a small place on the map (lines 15-19). In response, Jaakko wants to have a look at the map and so the repair sequence continues.

Reacting to Jaakko's interest, the therapist passes the calendar to him and contributes to the conversation with two requests for clarification (other-repair initiations). The first of these is quite general (line 21), but after noticing that the map is very small, she clarifies her question by asking whether it (Sarja) is on the European or Asian side of the Soviet Union (lines 26-27). Jaakko puts on his glasses (line 28) and concentrates on examining the map. His turn displays an interesting turn-keeping behaviour; he has a pen in hand, and he puts the point of his pen on the map uttering <u>just (1.0) just</u> and gazes intensively at the map. A 7.9-second pause follows, during which all participants lean forward towards the map and gaze at it. At last, Jaakko sighs and immediately Elina makes the next request for clarification <u>is it near Tsernob?</u> which, however, Jaakko rejects. This simple question-answer pair explicitly shows that the negotiation has to go on because Jaakko did not give an affirmative reply for Elina's question. C. Goodwin (1995) has analysed an aphasic conversation where simple question-answer adjacency pairs are used in such a way that a healthy speaker poses questions (guesses) concerning the topic and an aphasic speaker gives *yes* or *no* answers. An aphasic speaker's *yes* answer provided an exit from the guessing sequence whereas a *no* answer

162

led to the recycling of another round with a new guess. In this excerpt, Jaakko continues the searching for Sarja on the map, and the entire orientation of the participants is focused on Jaakko's pen movements on the map. Their concentration on this activity is so total that even the therapist moves from her place behind Jaakko to have a look at the map. Finally, Jaakko finds the approximate situation of the place (line 33), and while gazing and pointing at the map he shows it by saying here.. Elina gives an acknowledgement token aha. (oh.) which reveals the receipt of new knowledge. After a while Jaakko repeats the contribution here. (line 35), again pointing to the map. The following turn, contributed by the therapist, is again a non-topical one, also requesting Jaakko to show the place to Paavo, and he repeats for the third time there (1.5) approximately. which Paavo acknowledges.

This sequence is a good example of how important acknowledgement tokens are for the development of conversation. In this occurrence, Elina gives the first acknowledgement token, clearly marking the new knowledge, but afterward a longish pause follows without other acknowledgements. Because there has been a rather long negotiation and all interlocutors have contributed to it, Elina's acknowledgement is evidently insufficient for Jaakko and he repeats his previous contribution. The therapist's next turn can be regarded both as an acknowledgement token and as a request for Jaakko to once again show the place, especially to Paavo who also adds his acknowledgement token, even two of them, to the conversation. After this Maija also adds a short acknowledgement token. Thus, all the participants have given an acknowledgement token which shows that they have reached an understanding for current purposes.

Even so, the issue is not yet quite clear. The therapist's next question, how far from Moscow. refers anaphorically to the preceding conversation (it instead of Sarja), and can thus be regarded as a request for clarification rather than a topical question. The therapist's question forms the first part of an adjacency pair which creates an expectation of an answer of the second part of the adjacency pair. The sigh at the beginning of Jaakko's turn indicates that he is in trouble again. He turns his gaze to the therapist and tries to begin the vocalization. However, it is beyond his verbal abilities and he turns his gaze to the paper and points to it uttering look.(.)there. (line 41). So, he repeatedly relies on an external aid and shows the paper on the table where he had previously written numbers down. At this point a typical incidence occur in the conversation: Maija reads the numeral aloud, but incorrectly; she offers a demonstration of understanding by whispering eighty instead of "800". The therapist makes an immediate other-initiated other-repair, correcting it to eight hundred., which Maija, Elina and Jaakko accept in overlap with each other. So this correction is left as an embedded correction (Jefferson 1987). However, the therapist continues making yet another other-initiated other-repair to make sure that it is 800 kilometres from Moscow, which Jaakko and Maija both confirm.

The fourth and the last subsequence concerns the direction of Sarja's location (lines 50-61). The therapist begins with an elliptical request for clarification (an other-repair initiation), referring anaphorically to the earlier conversation, by saying the typical other-repair initiation in other words, but changes the structure of her contribution and formulates a request for clarification <u>was it to the NOrth#wards or.#</u>, which Jaakko rejects. The therapist then repeats the rejection and Paavo responds by offering a display of understanding (an other-initiated other-repair) suggesting at first <u>to the east.</u> but later interrupting himself. Jaakko starts to search for the direction by turning his pen to point rightwards. At his point the therapist asks for a moment and raises her hand imitating Jaakko's gesture. Jaakko himself presents a contribution <u>up.</u> (line 57), now pointing his pen diagonally upwards to the right. At last the therapist presents a demonstration of understanding (an other-initiated other-repair), uttering <u>to the north-east.</u> (line 58) which both Jaakko and Paavo accept simultaneously with acknowledgement tokens. The sequence is closed only after the therapist has repeated her accepted interpretation and pointed to the north-east. A 5.6-second pause follows and since they had agreed earlier on that the other participants should interview Jaakko, his subsequent contribution is orientated to the next question, and he says <u>and then..</u>

8.4   Discussion

The sequence in example 7 is a fascinating excerpt of the collaborative repair sequence in aphasic conversation. In this example, the length of the repair sequence is very different from those in 'normal' conversations, and the interlocutors used several interesting strategies to overcome the problems caused by Jaakko's aphasic difficulties. This handling of troubles demonstrates interestingly the complex development of the repair, as it can be divided into four subsequences which handle one issue at a time.

Jaakko's agrammatic opening turn introduced two issues, seeking the referent for the name *Sarja* and its location. In fact, his opening turn revealed the restricted verbal behaviour typical for him (cf. chapter 9) but it is not clear whether it is his conscious strategy to deal with lexical and syntactic problems. As the participants received two clearly insufficient formulations to decipher, they had a choice: either to gloss over Jaakko's contribution or to begin the repair work. On this occasion, the collaboration began and continued until both issues were resolved.

Already in the first subsequence Jaakko employed two facilitating strategies, the gestural strategy and writing which, however, turned out to be insufficient in that context. Paavo's repair strategy, his candidate understanding, was the resolution of the current problem, that is, seeking the reference for the name *Sarja*. As Schegloff et al. (1977) have suggested, a candidate understanding is the strongest technique of the other-repair initiations and leads to the most efficient resolution, and in this case it also worked efficiently.

The second issue, Sarja's geographical site, was more problematic. The first part of this issue concerned its location on the map. In this excerpt, the repair was only partly based on the verbal repair work, as using the map offered another strategy for resolving the problem. Jaakko initiated the subsequence with the turn containing two repetitive deictic proadverbs <u>over there.(.)over there.</u> and a pointing movement leftwards. The therapist took the map, which can be regarded as an other-repair initiation, as an act of resorting to an external aid. However, this act immediately led to a side-sequence initiated by Paavo's doubt that the map can be of help in this issue. Even so, the side-sequence ended with Jaakko's willingness to look at the map. Consequently, the therapist introduces two subsequent other-repair initiations, requests for clarification, for the motivation to use the map. The first other-repair initiation is general and the second one is more specific, giving two alternatives for an answer (lines 21 and 26-27). As the search process from the map was rather slow, Elina had the possibility to introduce a third other-repair initiation, a request for clarification, with the possibility to answer with a *yes/ no* answer. Goodwin (1995) has regarded this as a guess-sequence, and Lubinski et al. (1980) speak about a 'hint and guess' sequence. It is impossible to say if the requests for clarification offered any help for Jaakko in his search process, but in the end he was able to show the approximate location of the place.

The third subsequence handled the distance of Sarja from Moscow, and it was initiated by the therapist with a Wh-question. Again in this sequence, the external aid, the paper and the numbers on it, was needed before the participants understood the reply. The use of an externalization strategy was initiated by Jaakko. The fourth and last subsequence dealt with the direction of the place. In this sequence, Jaakko employed the gestural strategy to overcome his speech problems; he was able to show the direction and the therapist verbalized Jaakko's meaning.

In analysing the previous sequence, it was my aim to focus on the extended repair sequences which seemed to be representative of this data. Several noteworthy points arose in this sequence. I have focused my attention on the structure of the sequence, the other-repair initiations and the strategies used in order to clarify the troubles. The most fascinating issue in this sequence is that all the speakers in the group participated in the repair work offering various repair initiations. Paavo offered displays of understanding, Elina and the therapist asked questions, or requests for clarification, and Maija acted as the 'voice' of Jaakko when he used a paper and a pen in order to write down numbers. This collaborative activity can be seen as a manifestation of a joint process in which all participants' cognitive resources are brought into work (cf. Hutchins 1993). Thus, participants can contribute to the repair process with different means: somebody produces repair initiations verbally, somebody uses gestures, somebody draws, etc. The participants' repair-behaviour seems to be in accordance with the speakers' general way of resolving conversational breakdowns in these conversations. It is possible that the speakers had individual styles of collaborating that reflected their own styles of speaking or those of their aphasic disorder. The other possibility is that the speakers adopt certain roles in the group and behave according to their assigned roles.

Another prominent characteristic of this repair sequence is Jaakko's reliance on the nonverbal responding strategies. This suggests that his linguistic capabilities to modify his responses according to the other-repair initiations of the interlocutors were limited. On the other hand, he was sensitive to the interlocutors' need for more information, and managed to offer it with the help of the external aids (the map, the paper and the pen) and with nonverbal behaviour. These aids served as compensatory strategies for

Jaakko. Thus, this sequence is an excellent example of the importance of not only analysing the linguistic behaviour, but also taking into account the other behaviour, in conversation.

Some problems did arise in the analysis. The first problem concerns the function of questions contributed by the therapist and Elina: line 21 (the therapist), line 26-27 (the therapist), line 29 (Elina), line 40 (the therapist) and line 50 (the therapist). Are these other-repair initiations, or just topical questions used to develop the conversation? My interpretation is that these are other-repair initiations because they are closely connected to the problems in conversation, although the sequential location of the other-repair initiations was far away from the trouble source. Perhaps the most problematic question in this respect is found in line 40 [ho]w far from Moscow. There is no particular sign that it is connected to a definite trouble source. However, the question is connected to the general trouble of locating the site of Sarja and for the reason these questions are regarded as other-repair initiations. Also, this sequence clearly can be considered as a whole entity, although it can be divided into subsequences. Thus, the repair questions contributed by the other interlocutors can be regarded as collaborative repair work aimed at bringing clarity to Jaakko's incomplete opening turn.

As it turned out, the first contributions expressed by Jaakko in this sequence needed extended repair work before the problems were resolved, the interlocutors had reached mutual understanding, and the sequence could be closed down. The entire sequence contained various repair-initiators contributed by the interlocutors. Although the therapist initiated the repair work, the other interlocutors joined the repair process. However, the most prominent and characteristic feature in this sequence is the determination to communicate, employing various means available and relying on the support of interlocutors (cf. Lesser & Milroy 1993:214), which at last led to the successful outcome of the repair work.

8.5   Summary

This chapter has dealt with the various types of repair sequences related to the handling of aphasic disorders in conversation. I have presented trouble sequences caused by aphasic participants' comprehension/hearing problems, and by an aphasic speaker's restricted ability to express meanings. These problems in turn led to different repair sequences initiated by the aphasic speakers.

Some characteristic features arising in these repair sequences can be compared to the findings of repair in 'normal' conversation. First, the typical, but not necessary, feature was the length of the repair sequences in aphasic conversation. In several cases the sequences were long and there was a need for numerous repair-initiations before the trouble was resolved. Second, dealing with the trouble often led to collaborative repair work in which all the interlocutors participated. This indicates that the participants made use of distributed cognition; everyone contributed conversation with their available means (cf. Hutchins 1993). Furthermore, in group aphasic speakers have possibilities to practice handling troubles in conversation and to make other-repair initiations. This may be an important notion, as we have some evidence that in dyadic conversation the 'better' speaker usually makes other-repair initiations (Lubinski et al. 1980, Gurland et al. 1982, Laakso 1992, Perkins 1993). Perhaps this is one advantage of group discussion compared with dyadic conversation.

Another important observation is that all aphasic speakers used various other-repair initiators even though all speakers did not use all initiator types. The mastering of the various initiator-techniques is a major question because they yield the possibility to specify a trouble in conversation and subsequently lead to repair work. This is especially significant in the case of comprehension problems, as other participants do not necessarily notice them. Examples from this material indicate that aphasia type and the severity of aphasia may influence the mastery of using various repair techniques. For example, the speakers with Broca's aphasia had problems in formulating other-repair initiations, for instance, requests for clarification. This may lead to problems of using the different other-repair initiators, as many of them are in the form of an interrogative clause. In addition, the more capable other-repair initiators are of locating troubles, the more complex interrogative syntax they usually have. There were also indications that the flexible replacement of one other-repair initiator for another was not easy. However, a larger database would be needed to make a thorough study of the variations. In short, further study is needed to address this question.

9. Uninflected single-word turns

9.1 Introduction

In this chapter I will focus on a phenomenon that can occasionally be over-emphasized in aphasic communication, namely communicating with uninflected single-word turns. It is a symptom that is usually related to Broca's aphasia. In the aphasia group in question two of the speakers, Maija and Jaakko, had Broca's aphasia (see also chapter 4, p. 37–38). As was mentioned above, both speakers were chronic aphasics: Maija had been aphasic for twelve years and Jaakko for three years. Their acute stages of the aphasia were, however, different. For example, after her illness Maija had been virtually speechless, and when her speech recovered, it was highly agrammatic. Jaakko had a short period of jargon speech after which he ceased speaking altogether and subsequently began to communicate only with single-word turns and short phrases. During the group meetings both speakers still had marked syntactic and lexico-semantic problems. These were realized in different ways in their speech: Maija aimed at producing syntactically correct speech which was very time-consuming, whereas Jaakko seemed willing to accept more imperfectly formed utterances and often used single-word utterances.

A central question of conversation is intersubjectivity, how the participating individuals can reach a shared interpretation of the conversation's constituent activities. The answer to this question is complex even between 'normal' interactants, and still more complicated when involving an interlocutor who for some reason is incapable of using the linguistic code. This occurs, for instance, with a child in the initial stage of speech development, with a speaker of a foreign language with incompetent language ability, or with an aphasic speaker.

Goodwin & Heritage (1990) maintain that intersubjective understanding is actively achieved as the outcome of concrete interactive processes. Schegloff & Sacks (1973:296) have suggested the assumption of sequential implicativeness (sequential relevance), which also links with the concept of conditional relevance (e.g. Schegloff 1972). 'Conditional relevance' means that the first part of an adjacency pair builds a context for the next turn. Schegloff & Sacks (1973) suggest that by an adjacently positioned second, a speaker can show that s/he understood what the prior speaker aimed at, and that s/he is willing to go along with that. The first speaker can, by inspecting the second pair part, see if the first part has been understood. This notion has

Conversation as an achievement in aphasics
Studia Fennica
Linguistica 6
1996.

been a starting point for the analysis of this chapter, how meaning is constructed in aphasic conversation from such minimalistic utterances as uninflected single word utterances are.

According to Clark & Schaefer (1987, 1989), people speak for the benefit of all the participants in conversation. They contribute to the social process they are all engaged in, and in order to do this they must make themselves understood to everyone. Speakers thus act according to two requirements. First, a speaker needs to assure her/himself that the interlocutors are currently attending to, hearing, and trying to understand what s/he is saying. Second, a speaker needs to assure her/himself that the others have actually understood what is meant with her/his utterance before going on to the next utterance. Speakers need help from their interlocutors in both of these assurances, and so conversation requires the coordinated involvement of all parties concerned. Clark & Schaefer (ibid.) refer to the ideas of Sacks, Schegloff and Goffman and state: "Together, the participants bear the mutual responsibility of assuring that what is said has been heard and understood before the conversation goes on".

Conversation analysis operates with a concept called a turn constructional unit (see p. 27). Conversational turns are constructed from turn constructional units. The unit types are sentential, clausal, phrasal, and lexical constructions (Sack, Schegloff & Jefferson 1974). They are identified as turn-units partly by prosodic, and especially by intonational, means. Initially, a speaker is allowed to use just one of these turn-constructional units. The end of the unit is a possible transition relevance place, a point at which a speaker change may occur.

The classical explanation of Broca's aphasia has been that a speaker has problems in constructing larger units than words because of the syntactic problems caused by the aphasia, and the syntactic problem leads, in the extreme case, to the use of single words. As mentioned earlier (p. 47), Finnish is a synthetic language and words are morphologically complex and longer than words in English. The basic principle of word formation in Finnish is the addition of endings to stems. The nominals can take four kinds of endings: plural marker, fourteen morphological case endings, possessive, possessive suffixes and clitic particles. The verbs inflect for four tenses, four moods, six persons and one impersonal ("passive") form, and finally clitic particles may be added. Finnish is usually classified as an agglutinative language, but because of several morphophonemic alternations, however, the stems often do not occur as free allomorphs. Hence the singular nominative form of nouns and the present singular third person form of verbs can be regarded as unmarked and hence uninflected forms. In Finnish, also most adverbs and particles are uninflected or opaque inflected forms (for a more detailed description of Finnish morphology see, e.g., Karlsson 1987).

In Finnish the endings have the same function as the grammatical words (especially pronouns and prepositions) do in English, and hence morphological formations are very important in the study of agrammatism in Finnish. In this study, single-word turns are defined as those turn constructional units which consist of a single uninflected word. This may be a whole conversational turn, or one turn may be constructed from two repetitive single-word utterances, for instance bank. or mixer.(.)mixer.. In some occurrences, a speaker begins a turn with a discourse particle, for instance well, or some kind of conjunction like then or and, but is unable to go on. Then there is often a pause, and only after this pause does the speaker utter a single uninflected word. Here the terminal intonation contour is falling, for example and then, (PAUSE) chipboard..

Excluded from this phenomenon are simple affirmative answers (for instance "yes" or "right") and negative answers ("no"). Also, turn-taking or turn-keeping phrases like see and mere conjunctions like "then" were excluded. Finally, single-word interrogatives were excluded. All these form a natural turn in 'normal' conversation as well.

The general aim of this chapter, then, is to investigate uninflected single-word turns in my data. More specifically, the objective is to examine their sequential position in conversation and the consequences of their appearance for the conversation, in other words, how the meanings of uninflected single-word turns are understood in aphasic conversation. Specifically, this chapter is designed to address the following questions:

1. The frequency of uninflected single-word turns in the data.
2. The sequential position of uninflected single-word turns in aphasic conversation.
3. The consequences of the appearance of uninflected single-word turns for conversation.

9.2 Analysis

First, I will report on the results of simple quantification, this is the frequency of uninflected single-word turns per speaker.

In the four group conversations there were 89 cases of uninflected single-word turns. All speakers including the therapist, used some uninflected single-word turns in their communication at least in some occurrences (Table 9).

Table 9. The number of uninflected single-word utterances and distribution of word categories

	Nouns	Adjectives	Numerals	Verbs	Pronouns	Particles	TOTAL
Jaakko	22 (48%)	1	5	1	5	8	42 (47%)
Maija	10 (21%)	1	7	2	0	2	22 (25%)
Kalle	1 (2%)	0	0	0	0	0	1 (1%)
Elina	3 (6%)	0	1	0	0	0	4 (4%)
Paavo	2 (4%)	2	1	2	0	1	8 (9%)
therapist	8 (17%)	0	2	0	0	2	12 (13%)
TOTAL	46 (52%)	4 (4%)	16 (18%)	5 (6%)	5 (6%)	13 (15%)	89 (100%)

As indicated in Table 9, 72% of uninflected single words were produced by the Broca's aphasics, Jaakko and Maija; of their cases, 36% (32/89) were uninflected single-word nouns. Jaakko used 42 uninflected single-word which was 47% of the total by all speakers. Maija had a smaller amount of uninflected single-word turns (22 cases), accounting for 25% of all cases. The other aphasic speakers and the therapist together used 28% of the uninflected single-word turns (25 remaining cases), and of these, the therapist used 12 cases, or 13% of the total.

Of all the expressions, 52% were nouns, 18% were numerals and 15% were particles. Adjectives, verbs and pronouns were minor groups, about 5% each.

These frequencies give us some basic data on their appearance in these conversations. However, they do not reveal how these utterances are used and handled in conversation. As one of the aims of this chapter was to analyse the consequences of the occurrence of uninflected single-word turns for conversation, sequential analysis was the means for analysing the positions of uninflected single-word turns in the conversational sequence.

Uninflected single-word turns were classified into topic initial turns (initiative turns) and topic-continuing turns (responsive turns). Tentatively, initiative turns were defined as being prospectively loaded setting up constraints on possible types of responses, while topic-continuing turns are retrospectively loaded in that they are only analysable in relation to what has gone before (cf. Lesser & Milroy 1993:163). Thus, initiative turns introduce a new topic or a new subtopic to conversation, and topic-continuing turns may, for instance, comment on or even close the topic.

Topic-continuing turns can be divided into various categories and in this data the following categories were observed: replies, expanding turns, repetitive turns and turns involved with some nonverbal activity (drawing, handing, etc.) and other turns. The categorization of uninflected single-word utterances is presented below:

A. INITIATIVE TURNS:
The participant introduces a new topic or a subtopic and opens a new sequence.
Example: *"Clause"*
    "what is it?"

B. ANSWERS:
Responsive turns, the second pair part in an adjacency pair where the first part has been interpreted as a question.
Example: "Where were you working?"
    "Lemminkäinen"
In this example, the response has been given in nominative case (uninflected) whereas it should be in the adessive case, *Lemminkäi+sellä* (company name+ADESS)

C. EXPANDING TURNS:
Responsive turns which expand the topic with a narrative turn, with a comment, with an assessment, etc.
Example: "It costs five hundred and well was it thirty or something"
    "expensive"

D. REPETITIVE TURNS:
Responsive turns which repeat the previous turn.
Example: "con-conveyor"
    "conveyor"

E. TURNS IN CONNECTION WITH ACTIVITY:
Turns which are connected with some activity, for instance drawing or handing something.
Example: "well no (.) cannot speak anything"
    "paper" (the speaker passes an empty paper for drawing or
    writing to the first speaker)

F. OTHERS
Procedural or unclassified uninflected single-word turns.
Example: "a moment"

The frequencies of respective categories are seen in Table 10. As we see, most cases occurred in a responding position, as topic continuation turns in a conversational sequence, in expanding turns (33 cases) and in repetitive turns (30 cases). Jaakko had the largest number of expanding turns (17 cases), which is 40% of all his single-word turns, whereas Maija mainly used the repetitive cases (13 cases), which is over half of all her single-word turns. A single-word turn in an initiative position, as a topic-initial turn, was used very rarely – only three times – and all were contributed by Jaakko.

    In the following, I will analyse qualitatively the conversational sequences containing an uninflected single-word turn from the point of view of their status in the development of talk. My purpose is to examine how the participants are able to construct the meaning of an uninflected single-word turn from the previous talk. First I will concentrate on analysing the conversational sequences where the participants expressed trouble.

Table 10. The number of uninflected single-word utterances according to their conversational position.

	Initiative	Answer	Expanding	Repetitive	Activity	Others	TOTAL
Jaakko	3	8	17	6	7	1	42
Maija	0	0	8	13	1	0	22
Kalle	0	0	0	1	0	0	1
Elina	0	0	1	3	0	0	4
Paavo	0	2	5	1	0	0	8
therapist	0	0	2	6	0	4	12
TOTAL	3	10	33	30	8	5	89

9.2.1 Topic-initiating single-word turns

First, I will analyse the cases where an uninflected single word is used in an initiative position, as a topic-initial turn to introduce a new topic or a new subtopic. In this instance the single word is in the position of the first pair part of an adjacency pair. According to the principle of sequential implicativeness (Schegloff & Sacks 1973:296) the first part of the pair sets up an expectation which the second pair part is expected to meet, and also the speaker of the first pair part can examine whether the first part has been understood. If we now look at a conversational sequence (an adjacency pair) where the first turn is expressed with an uninflected single word by an aphasic speaker, we will understand how the conversation will develop after that.

Example 1

```
1   P:kakkos kori ja kolmos kori ja mi|tä siinä.
      number two basket and  number three basket and  what-PAR  there
      second basket and third basket and what there.

2   t:nii jo[o.
      PRT  PRT
      yeah ye[s.

3   P:        [mi|täi sirontaa sirontai pitää tapahtu|u.
               what-PAR                 must    happen-INF
               [what kind of {evaluation} has to happen.

    (0.3)

4   J:klausuuli kuule.
      clause        listen
      clause listen.

    (0.2)

5   P:mikä se on.
      what  it is
      what is it.

6   t:&niihh&
      PRT
      $yeahh$

7   J:[*klausuuli.*]
         clause
      [*clause.*]
      *RHswings,GP*

8   P:[okei]nii*noh.*
      PRT   PRT PRT
      [okay]well*then.*
              *LHswings,GJ*

    (1.0)
```

173

```
 9  t:nii=
       PRT
       yeah

10  P:=[me mittään mi|tä teh|dä|än.
       we              what-PAR   do-PASS-4
    =[we nothing what shall be done.
          *J G->M, smiles*

11  J:=[jooh
    =[yeah

    (0.7)

12  t:joo se on ilmeisesti semmos|ta(.)sii|t paljon kirjoi[te|ta|an ja
       PRT it is  obviously     like that-PAR  it-PAR  a lot    write-PASS-4    and
       yes it is obviously like that(.)they wri[te a lot about it and
```

In this example, the main topic concerns the European security conference. The previous speaker, Paavo, has introduced the terms 'the second basket' and 'the third basket' to the conversation, and he then wonders what kind of {evaluation} has to happen. In the next turn (line 4) the focus of the conversation changes and Jaakko introduces a term clause listen. to the conversation, *listen* being a discourse particle (Hakulinen 1993). This phenomenon has been described as topic shading (e.g. Goodenough & Wiener 1978, Schegloff & Sacks 1973). Jaakko's turn evidently refers to the general topic (European Security Conference), but it is not self-evident as to how it is connected to the previously mentioned 'the second and third baskets'. For this reason it has been regarded as an initial turn which introduces a new subtopic.

Jaakko's contribution seems to come too unexpectedly and this leads straight into the next turn repair initiation by Paavo (line 5). Paavo gets some support from the therapist who gives an acknowledgement token. Jaakko repeats the term clause. but is clearly unable to explicate his meaning further. Paavo says, rather laconically, [okay] well then.. Apparently, neither Paavo nor anyone else begins to collaborate and help Jaakko to express his meaning more clearly. Thus, Jaakko gives up (line 11) and the conversation develops with the therapist's following turn.

In this excerpt, there are two possible explanations for Paavo's behaviour: first, Paavo was perhaps unable to find the connection between Jaakko's single-word turn and the previous conversation, and as Jaakko was unable to give further clarification on the issue, he ignores Jaakko's contribution. The second explanation may be that although Paavo possibly caught the meaning of Jaakko's turn, he was not willing to continue it. One can consider Jaakko's topic-initial turn to have the status of candidate topic initiation which requires the next speaker to upgrade it (e.g. Button 1987:115). However, neither Paavo nor anyone else upgraded the offered topic and so it faded.

In example 2, Jaakko uttered three letters, which were interpreted by the next recipient as an abbreviation for the name of a well-known Finnish bank:

Example 2

```
1  E:mi|tä siellä teh|dä|än #sii(0.7)# tuo,.
     what-PAR  there   do-PASS-4         that
   what is done there #well(0.7)# that,.=

2  P:=mikä [tehdas ol|i
     what    factory  be-PST
   what[was the factory

3  E:        [mikä (.) nii mi|tä tuota,=
             what      PRT  what-PAR well
            [which (.)yeah what well,=

4  J:=lastulevy.
      chipboard
   =chipboard.

5  E:ai lastulevy.
     PRT  chipboard
   oh chipboard.

6  J:mm.

7  t:m-hm.

   (7.3)

8  J:koo,(0.2)koo oo pee.(0.8)on|k+se.
     K        K   O   P          is-Q-it
   K,(0.2) K O P.(0.8) is it.

9  t:mm-m

10 J: koo oo,
       K   O
     K O,

   (0.5)

11 M:pankki.
     bank
   bank.

12 E:°pank-°
     °ban-°

   (0.8)

13 J: koo oo pee joo.
       K   O   P   PRT
     K O P     yes.

   (0.7)

14 t:°hm-m?°

15 J:e|m+mää tierä.(3.0) mikä vai|ko ei(0.4) e|n sano|ttu,
     NEG-1+I  know         what  or-CLI NEG    NEG-1 say-PPC
   I don't know.(3.0)what or not(0.4) I no said,
```

```
16  Y:hm-m

    (0.6)

17  J:on vaan. (0.4) on vaan. (2.4)[koo oo pee.]
       is  just       is  just        K  O  P
      it is just. (0.4) it is just.(2.4)[K O P]

18  E:                        [°sairastu|i|t]+sä si-siellä
                               get ill-PST-2 +you    there
                          [°did you get ill]when being the-

19  ol|le|ssa.°
    be-INF-INE
    there.°

    (0.8)

20  J:*mitä.*=
       what
      *what.*=
      *G,,,E *

21  E:=ol|i|t+sä siellä(.)kun(.)sairastu|i|t.
       be-PST-2+you there   when  get ill-PST-2
      =where you there(.)when(.)you get ill.

    (0.5)

22  J:ei ei ei ei ei(2.7)hhhhh.
       NEG NEG NEG NEG NEG
      no no no no no(2.7)hhhhh.
```

The preceding conversation has dealt with working life and, quite unexpectedly, Jaakko introduces the letters (KOP) to the conversation (line 8). However, Jaakko is evidently uncertain of the letters because after a short pause he begins a self-initiated repair appealing for other participants for help requesting is it.. The therapist gives a short acknowledgement token, and Jaakko repeats the two first letters (line 10). Jaakko still keeps his intonation steady but nevertheless Maija offers a candidate understanding bank. giving an other-initiated other-repair (line 11). Jaakko does not give a sign of acceptance, but repeats again KOP yes. Afterwards, the therapist offers a short acknowledgement token, and Jaakko continues his turn with several short phrases accompanied by rich nonverbal behaviour. However, no one continues collaboration in the handling of the topic. One possibility is that Jaakko's turn may not have provided sufficient hints for the recipients to begin the collaboration. In the next turn (line 18), Elina makes a topical transition and brings the conversation back to Jaakko's illness. In this case, Maija offered a candidate understanding as the second pair part, but Jaakko ignored it.

There is a third excerpt which displays Jaakko's way of using a single-word turn in an initiative position of the sequence (cf. Klippi 1990, Leiwo & Klippi forthcoming). Before this excerpt the conversation had dealt with Jaakko, who had told that he had worked in Russia, and there had been a discussion of the number of Finnish workers in Russia. In the following example, Jaakko returns to speak of his own work in Russia where he was a foreman supervising the workers.

Example 3

```
1   J:kontrolli.
      control
      control.

    (3.8)

2   E:°sinä lu|i|t laki|a nii|lle°.
      you    read-PST-2 law-PAR  they-ALL
      °you laid down the law to them°.

    (0.4)

3   M:hh.hh.

4   J:mi|tä.=
      what-PAR
      what.=

5   E:=sinä lu|i|t laki|a nii|lle.
      you    read-PAR-2  law-PAR  they-ADE
      =you laid down the law to them.

6   J:°mm°
```

In this excerpt, Jaakko introduces the word <u>control.</u> to the conversation after the closing of the previous sequence. So, he placed word <u>control.</u> in a position to initiate a new topic. As in the earlier cases, the single word appears without any explanation as to why it has been introduced. In this case, Elina gives a candidate understanding, a paraphrase (line 5), of Jaakko's single word. It is evident that Elina had to infer her interpretation from the preceding conversation and she suggested that Jaakko had to control the workers, to *lay down the law* to them. This is in accordance with the central idea of conversation analysis of the contextuality, which suggests that an communicative action is context-shaped as its contribution to an ongoing sequence of action cannot be adequately understood without a reference to the context in which it participates. In this case, however, Elina's paraphrase is also too unexpected and sophisticated for Jaakko, and he thus makes an other-repair initiation – a request to repeat – which is a mark of misunderstanding or mishearing. Elina repeats her previous contribution, which then seems to be sufficient for Jaakko, as he gives an acknowledgement token and the discussion can proceed. Another possibility is that Jaakko had misunderstood Elina's paraphrase, leading to further negotiation for mutual understanding. Even so, the most important point is that Elina begins the collaboration by giving her interpretation for Jaakko's single word, which Jaakko accepts. Only after that could the conversation continue.

Jaakko was the only speaker to use the uninflected single word utterances as the first part of the adjacency pair or as an initiative turn of a sequence, introducing a new topic to the conversation. Nevertheless, these occurrences were few (three occurrences). Each of these sequences had problems. In two cases out of three, the meaning of Jaakko's single word turn possibly remained unclear. In this data, Jaakko was the only participant to initiate the 'unsuccessful' sequences; all began with a single-word turn. In these instances, Jaakko was unable to expand or elaborate on the topic in his next contributions and the interactants were neither competent nor willing to co-operate. Another characteristic of these 'unsuccessful' sequences is that the topic handling ended without passing turns (Schegloff & Sacks 1973) or without closing components (Button 1987), both of which represent a collaboration by the participants in closing the topic (Goodenough & Wiener 1978, Schegloff & Sacks 1973, Clark & Schaefer 1987, Button 1987). These 'unsuccessful' sequences could be interpreted as having failed in collaboration. One way to resolve the problem is to move to another topic. Hence, the sequences with this kind of single-word initiations seem to have high risk of failure in conversations.

9.2.2 Single-word turns in a responsive position

9.2.2.1 Answers

In the previous cases, uninflected single words were topic-initial turns, in initiative positions of a sequence. Conversation looks rather different if an uninflected single word appears as a topic-continuer in a responsive position, for instance as an immediate answer. Here, an uninflected single word occurs as the second part in an adjacency pair where the first part has been interpreted as a question. These kind of examples were found mostly in Jaakko's contributions and also in two cases by Paavo. The form of the question itself effects the answer so that after an open question there are many more possibilities for answers than after a more specific question. In the next example the question which was posed restricted the possibilities for an answer.

Example 4
___

```
1   t:no mut haastatel|ka|a vaikka Jaakko|a.(.)minu|st se ol|is
      PRT but   interview-IMP-2PL   for instance 1name M-PAR  I-ELA    it   be-CON
    well but go ahead and interview Jaakko(.)I think it would be

2   ihan(0.8)°hyvä°,
      PRT           good
    all(0.8)°right°,

    (2.8)

3   M:h.*$ehei oshaa$[san-*
        NEG3     can      {say}
      h.*$ channot $[sa-*

4   E:              [missä sä ol|i|t tö|i|ssä.
                    what-INE   you be-PST-2  work-PL-INE
                    [where were you working.

    (1.3)
```

```
5   J:°mi│tä.°=
        what-PAR
        °what.°=
```

```
6   E:  =°missä sä ol│i│t,.°
           what-INE  you  be-PST-2
        °where were you,.°
```

```
    (0.6)
```

```
7   J:  Lemminkäinen.{Ø  INE}
            company name-NOM
        Lemminkäinen.{Ø  INE}
```

```
8   E:  Lemminkäinen.{Ø  INE}
            company name-NOM
        Lemminkäinen.{Ø  INE}
```

Elina asked Jaakko where he has worked. After an other-initiated self-repair, she got the answer and she immediately acknowledged it. Although Jaakko's answer was agrammatic (there was no case marker), its interpretation was easy for several reasons: first, the answer, the name of the company where Jaakko had worked, is well known; second, the syntactic function of the uninflected single word is self-evident and the answer uses ellipsis in an acceptable way. Moreover, Jaakko's answer was given with a clear, falling terminal intonation contour, and thus there was no sign that he wanted to continue his turn after uttering the name.

The following example is complex because there is a need for repair work before the participants are able to co-construct the meaning for Jaakko's answer (cf. Goodwin 1995). In this excerpt, the general topic concerns Jaakko's earlier working place, which was a chipboard factory in the former Soviet Union.

Example 5

```
1   t:mi│tä,(.)mi│tä tapahtu siis *tä│nä,(.) seiskytkuus viiva
       what-PAR   what-PAR happen-(PST) PRT  this-ESS   seventy-six      clash
       what,(.)so what happened *this,(.)seventy-six dash
                                    *Dnumbers*
```

```
2      [kahdeksankymmentä.*
        eighty
       [eighty.*
```

```
3   J:[hhhhh.
```

```
4   t:nyt+mä e│n ihan(.)tarkkaan pääs│sy,.
       now+I  NEG-1  quite      clearly      get-PPC
       now I didn't quite(.)clearly get,.
```

```
    (1.9)
```

```
 5   J:*lastulevy.*
        chipboard
      *chipboard.*
       *Dpaper*


     (0.6)

 6   t: aha.(0.3)sillon|ko sä ol|i|t juuri siellä,.=
         PRT         then-Q    you be-PST-2  just   there
       oh.(0.3)were you there just at that time,.=

 7   J:=juu=
       =yeah=

 8   t:=Neuvostoliito|ssa.=
          Soviet Union-INE
       =in the Soviet Union.=

 9   J:=jooh=
       =yeah=

10   M =jooh=
       =yeah=

11   E:=hmm
```

This example is part of a larger repair sequence which aims to clarify the meaning of the years 1976 and 1980, which Jaakko had written down. The question in line 1 is already a repair initiation, a clarification request for Jaakko. He replies with a single word <u>chipboard.</u> ("lastulevy" in Finnish) and the therapist offers two further candidate understandings concerning the place where Jaakko worked (lines 4 and 6). Again, the therapist's interpretations are possible because the single word refers anaphorically to the preceding conversation, and thus she is able to infer the meaning of the single word from the context.

The following example also shows the collaboration in the occurrence of a single word.

Example 6

```
 1   P:[(-)]tää iso kasa[on|k|se]tukki|a mi|tä.
             this big  pile  is-Q-it    stock-PAR  what-PAR
       [(-)]this big pile[is it]is it stock or.

     (0.5)

 2   J:ei|kun,(0.3)°köi-°(0.2)
        NEG-PRT
       no but,(0.3)°{?}°(0.2)

 3   P:ku tää iso ka[sa
        PRT this big  pile
       well this big pi[le

 4   E:              [tä|tä lastulevy|ä
                      this-PAR  chipboard-PAR
                     [this chipboard
```

180

```
 5  P:nii
       PRT
       yeah

 6  J:kato .hh lastu. hh.
       look      chip
       look .hh chip. hh.

 7  E:°levy|ä°
         board-PAR
        °board°

    (0.3)

 8  J:la-lastu *koputtaa neljä kertaa pöytään*
       chip
       chi-chip*taps four times on the table*

 9  t:lastu|a=
       chip-PAR
       chip=

10  E:=[lastu|a
          chip-PAR
        =[chip

11  P:[lastu|j|a lastu|j|a
       chip-PL-PAR   chip-PL-PAR
       [chips chips

12  J:[lastu|a
       chip-PAR
       [chips chips

13  t:[hmm.

14  P:=joo aa joo=
       =yeah oh yeah=

15  J:=juu
       =yes
```

Jaakko had drawn a scheme of the chipboard factory and was able to explain the main phases of the production process. However, the other participants want to get further knowledge and in line 1 Paavo makes a repair initiation, a request for clarification, pointing to Jaakko's scheme and asking [(–)this big pile [is it] is it stock or. Jaakko denies this request and points to the paper. Paavo then continues well this big pile, again pointing to the paper. Subsequently, Elina continues with another other-repair initiation, a request for clarification, and inquires this chipboard. (line 4). Jaakko gives the answer look .hh chip. hh., where the word *chip* is in an uninflected form. Elina immediately offers a completion for Jaakko's initiation word board (line 7). However, Jaakko still utters his previous uninflected contribution with a slight hesitation ch-chip., tapping the table. In the next turn, the therapist gives an other-initiated other-repair uttering the word *chip* (*lastu* in Finnish) in its partitive case, *lastua* interpretating that the pile is full of chips. Evidently this small correction clarifies the problem and three speakers, Elina, Paavo and Jaakko simultaneously repeat the inflected word, Elina and Jaakko in its partitive form "lastu+a" and Paavo in its plural form "lastu+ja". Paavo explicitly closes this repair sequence by saying <u>yeah oh yeah</u>. In this excerpt, Jaakko offers an uninflected single-word answer as a second pair part for the first pair part. Thus, repair work was needed before the meaning of Jaakko's single word answer was established.

A total of ten single-word answers (as second parts of an adjacency pair) were observed in the data. Jaakko had eight uninflected single-word answers and Paavo had two. Paavo's answers were syntactically adequate, and no trouble was detected in the ensuing conversation. In addition, no problems were observed in four of Jaakko's single-word answer turns in the conversation that followed. After three other single-word answers, some negotiation and co-operation with the co-participants was needed before the sequences were closed and the conversation could go on. Jaakko's answers could lead to an interesting conclusion. Although he had severe limitations in expressing his meanings verbally, he used his few conversational means very economically, for instance to refer to the preceding conversation and thus make his meaning known. In this respect, from an interactional perspective, we can regard Jaakko's verbal behaviour as very skilful. On the other hand, the co-operation of the recipients was also needed, so that co-construct meanings could be created for his single-word answers. Trouble spots required co-operative actions, such as using requests for clarification and/or offering candidate understandings. In short, this interaction shows that there are risks in using single-word answers.

9.2.2.2 *Expanding turns*

Single uninflected words were most often – in 33 cases out of 89 – used in the expanding turns, which were topic-continuing, such as assessments or additions to a story. Most of these could also be regarded as a second pair part of an adjacency pair, for instance in an assessment-assessment pair (cf. Pomeranz 1984). In general, using an expanding turn was an instance of 'elliptical' use of language, typical of everyday speech. There were no signs of problems for any of the sequences containing uninflected single-word turns in these contexts. The next sequence represents a typical case:

Example 7

```
1  E:se loppujen lopuksi ol|i,.(0.6) mi|tä nyt on kuul|lu nois|ta
      it     in the end     be-PST        what-PAR now is hear-PPC those-ELA
   it was after all,.(0.6)now what I have heard about those

2  puhe|i|sta niin aika kallis.(0.4)ku+otta|a huomio|on että se
   talk-PL-ELA  so  quite expensive      PRT+take-3 consideration-ILL PRT it
   talks well rather expensive.(0.4)if one takes into consideration
   that

3  on(1.3) ↑eläkeläis|t|en [tai
   is        pensioner-PL-GEN    or
   it is(1.3) ↑pensioners' [or

4  M:                          [mm
```

5 E:se ol|i [maks|o viissataa ja,(1.0)°ol|i|k|+se
    it   be-PST cost-PST five hundred and be-PST-Q-it
    it was [costs fivehundred and,(1.0)°well was

6 K: [(RYKÄISEE)mm
        [(CLEARS THROAT)mm

7 E: nyt°kolmekymppii.(0.8) tai jotain.=
    now   thirty   or   something
    it °thirty. (0.8) or something.=

8 M:=↑kallis.
     expensive
    M:=↑expensive.

   (0.9)

9 E:↑kohtalaisen kallis.
    rather   expensive
    ↑rather expensive.

Syntactically, Maija's single-word assessment "expensive" is completely adequate (line 8). Another excerpt displays the same trend, where these types of sequences proceeded fluently and caused no difficulties (line 5):

Example 8

1 t: ketkä,(.)ketkä ol|i mukana.
    who-PL   who PL be-PST with
    who,(.)who were with (them).

   (1.6)

2 P:Jaakko ol|i.
    1name M be-PST
    Jaakko was.

   (0.3)

3 Y:(--)

   (3.8)

4 P:mu|i|ta ol|i,(0.6)*tuurin* piirtein neljäkymmentä,(0.7)°ol|i mukana.
    other-PL-PAR be-PST   approximately   forty   be-PST with
    there were others,(0.6){approximately}forty,(0.7)°were with (them).°

   (0.9)

5 M:vähä.
    little
    a few.

6 E:**joo.**
    PRT
    yes

Single words were also occasionally observed in connection some action.
Several single-word examples arise with reference to Jaakko's drawing or to
other activities (see ex. 9 below). Again, all but one case were connected to
Jaakko's contributions. Typically, these were related to Jaakko's attempts to tell
about a complex state of affairs or event. For instance, during the topic of
chipboard production, several examples arose where Jaakko facilitated his
attempts to explain the manufacturing process with drawing. These cases,
however, did not lead to repair sequences (cf. chapter 6).

9.2.2.3 Repetitive turns

34% of the uninflected single-words were used in repetitive turns. The
sequential positions of the repetitive turns varied, as did their functions in the
conversation. All speakers used repetitive uninflected single-word turns in
these discussions. The only single-word turn of Kalle was a repetitive turn.

Most of Maija's single-word utterances were repetitive (13/22), and they
were typically connected to the situations when Jaakko introduced issues
about which the other participants did not previously know. In the following
example, Jaakko draws a scheme of a chipboard factory and names the parts
of the scheme. This is a revealing example of Maija's repetitive style:

Example 9

```
1   t:niih-hih-hih-heh$mi|tä]tekee kahde|n kilometri|n pi[tui-$
                         what-PAR does  two-GEN   kilometre-PAR  {long}
    yeah-hih-hih-heh$what]does one do with a two kilometres l[on-$

2   J:                                          [*ja(.)
                                                             and
                                                [*and(.)

3   taas,.*(1.5)*kuli*-*kuljetin.*
    again            conveyer
    again,.*(1.5) *con*-*conveyer.*

    (0.5)

4   J:[*kuli-kuljetin.* * *
              conveyor?
      [*con-conveyor.* * *

5   E:[kahe|n kilometri|n,.
        two-GEN    kilometre-GEN
      [two kilometres,.

    (0.4)

6   M:°kuljetin°
        conveyor
      °conveyor°

    (0.7)
```

```
 7  J:*taas,.(1.2)pönttö.*
       again          container
    *again,.(1.2)container.*

    (0.8)

 8  M:pönt[tö.
         container
    contai[ner.

 9  J:        [pönttö.(0.6)sitten,
              container        then
              [*container.(0.6)then,*

    (1.5)

10  M:kuljetin,(0.5)VIelä [heh-heh.
       conveyor        more
       conveyor,(0.5)AGain [heh-heh.

11  K:                    [NAURUA
                          [LAUGHS
```

This excerpt is part of a longer sequence, and here Jaakko's turns are regarded as topic-continuing, whereas Maija's repetitive turns have at least two possible interpretations. The first possibility is that she simply acknowledges Jaakko's contributions and thus the turns function as acknowledgement devices. The other possibility is that she repeats turns in order to understand a word's meaning. In fact, in clinical work I have met several aphasic speakers who often repeat a co-participant's previous word or a few previous words. One possible hypothesis might be that repetition is used to catch the meaning(s) of the word(s). This explanation is also possible in Maija's case; an articulated word yields better access to a word's semantic content. If this interpretation is correct, this turn does not have a clear interactional function but is rather intended for the speaker's own processing purposes.

Laughter is also a significant factor at the end of the sequence. In the last turn by Maija (line 10), her voice reveals a tinge of laughter which can be interpreted as an invitation for laughter at the unintentional humour in the conversation (see e.g. Jefferson et al. 1987).

Repetitive single-word turns can also be used as repair initiations, in such cases beginning a repair sequence. The following excerpt illustrates such a case: the therapist offers a candidate understanding (lines 2 and 4):

Example 10

```
 1  J:ei kato(.)to to juu juu (0.3)Valmetti(.)homma|s.
       NEG look                     company name -NOM    get-PST
       no look(.){? ?}yes yes (0.3) Valmetti(.)gets.

 2  t:Valmetti,=
       company name-NOM
       Valmetti,=

 3  J:=juu
       =yes
```

185

```
 4   t:[oli rakenta|nu.
        be-PST  build-PPC
        [had built.

 5   J:[juu ol|i juu
        PRT  be-PST PRT
        [yes had yes

     (0.6)

 6   E:°jaah°
        °yeah°

 7   J:ruus truu te-(.)juu(1.2)suurtehdas.
                     PRT         large factory
        {big fa-}    (.)yes(1.2)big factory.

     (0.2)

 8   t:hmm?

     (0.5)

 9   J:valtava.
        enormous
        enormous.

10   t:hmm?hmm?
```

Also, a repetitive single-word turn may function as an acknowledgement token. This instance is found below (line 5):

Example 11

```
 1   E:              [mi|ssä sä ol|i|t tö|i|ssä.
                      what-INE  you  be-PST-2  work-PL-INE
                     [where were you working.

     (1.3)

 2   J:°mi|tä.°=
        what-PAR
        °what.°=

 3   E: =°mi|ssä sä ol|i|t,.°
           what-INE  you  be-PST-2
        °where were you,.°

     (0.6)

 4   J: Lemminkäinen.{Ø INE}
         company name-NOM
         Lemminkäinen.{Ø INE}

 5   E: Lemminkäinen.{Ø INE}
         company name-NOM
         Lemminkäinen.{Ø INE}
```

It is revealing that all speakers, and especially Maija, used repetitive single-word turns. Jaakko, who mostly used single word-turns, had only a few examples of repetitive single-word utterances (see also Leiwo & Klippi, forthcoming). The other aphasic speakers and the therapist each had one or two cases of the repetitive use of a single-word turn.

The positions and functions of the repetitive single-word turns varied. They were either acknowledgement devices, for instance to Jaakko's previous single-word contributions, or – especially in Maija's case – they were used for the speaker's own processing purposes. Sometimes single-word turns were initiations of repair sequences, in which the following speaker repeated the previous speaker's turn, using it as an other-repair initiation. The repetitive single-word turns show that, in some occurrences, speakers other than Broca's aphasics use uninflected single-word utterances. This kind of repetitive speech is also found in normal conversation (e.g. Schegloff, Jefferson & Sacks 1977).

9.2.3   Other uninflected single-word turns

Few uninflected single-word turns met the requirements posed by the previous classes. Typically, the therapist used these turns when, for example, naming the next speaker or asking for the time, such as uttering "a moment" ("hetki" in Finnish). Thus these turns can be regarded as non-topical, and were used to direct discussion. From the point of view of mutual understanding, these presented no interactional problems.

9.3   Discussion

A typical feature of Broca's aphasia is laborious, verbally-restricted speech with morphological and syntactic omissions. In more severe cases, even uninflected single-word utterances are observed. This raises the question of how the recipients are able to achieve the understanding 'for current purposes' in order to develop aphasic conversation. According to Schegloff & Sacks (1973), the sequential structure of the conversation, for instance an adjacency-pair structure, can reveal the understanding or misunderstanding of the previous turn; the adjacently-positioned second shows an understanding by the first pair part. Hence, the purpose of this chapter has been to examine the use of uninflected single-word turns in aphasic conversation. More specifically, the objective has been to examine their frequency in aphasic conversation, their sequential position in conversation, and the consequences of their appearance in conversation.

The results of the present study show that all the speakers used uninflected single words. The total amount of the cases was 89, of which speaker Jaakko had 47% of the cases (42) and Maija had 25% of the cases (22). The remaining 25 cases were distributed amongst the other speakers: for example the therapist had 13% of the cases (12). The uninflected single words were mostly nouns (52%) and numerals (18%) and particles (15%). Uninflected adjectives, verbs and pronouns were minor groups.

In conversation, the uninflected single words occurred in different sequential positions and in several functions. Within the entire data there were only three uninflected single-word turns which were in a topic initial position, as a first part of an adjacency pair, and all were contributed by Jaakko. Within the conversational sequence, 73 cases arose in a responsive position and ten of these were clearly responses to questions, and 30 were repetitive single-word turns whose functions varied. They were, for instance, repair-initiators or acknowledgement tokens. In addition, uninflected single-word turns were used eight times in connection with some activity, such as drawing.

It is noteworthy that all speakers used them, and they typically constituted adequate use of single-word utterances. The single-word turns usually were adequately used as expanding turns, for instance when giving a second assessment of the first assessment concerning some issue in conversation. Also repetitive use, such as acknowledging the previous turn, often Jaakko's single-word turns, was typical.

Using uninflected single-word turns was problematic only in some conversational contexts. Problems occurred if they were used as a topic-initial turn in the initial position of a sequence. Also, the uninflected single-word answers were sometimes problematic if the context required a more elaborate answer. In addition there were two cases in the expanding turns where some co-operation among interactants was needed before the meaning of the single word turn was constructed. In both cases they were used as a topic-continuing turn in a long repair sequence, but in both cases their content was too vague to solve the problem in conversation.

Only one Broca's aphasic, Jaakko, had problematic use of single-word turns. Maija used single-word turns mostly in repetitive positions which did not cause comprehension problems for other participants. Hence, it is possible to hypothesise that Jaakko can be characterized best as more 'syntactically' agrammatic than can Maija, who for her part may be characterized more as 'morphologically' in comparison (cf. Niemi et al. 1990). Jaakko had severe word-finding difficulties and propositional problems and he also had occasional morphological simplifications. Maija on the other hand often managed to produce longer syntactic structures but she had clear problems in using proper morphological endings in her utterances.

The analysis of the problem sequences shows that before the conversation proceed participants must reach some level of mutual understanding of the referent in the ongoing conversation. In most cases there was no sign of trouble after an uninflected single-word turn, and the conversation developed fluently. However, the problem cases led to repair work, and Jaakko's single-word turn was the starting point for the interactional work needed to develop the conversation. Thus, in problem situations, the effectiveness of the other participants' collaboration was an essential factor. In the first two examples the other participants were unable or unwilling to begin collaboration and to figure out the meaning of the single-word utterance. In such cases, the trouble may be ignored and a speaker may close the sequence her/himself, or a new topic may be introduced by another participant.

According to the sequential implicativeness, speakers link their turns to the previous talk. This notion offers one possible explanation for the results in this chapter. In cases of answers, repetitive and expanding turns, a speaker's single-word turn does not stand alone but is situated within the talk of others. Thus, the sequential context of a turn is a resource, assisting a recipient to understand it. For instance, Goodwin (1995) has analysed the interactions with an aphasic speaker who had three words ("yes", "no", "and"). He points out that an aphasic speaker's one-word utterances do not stand alone as isolated, self-sufficient utterances, but instead achieve a sense within an environment that has been constructed through the prior work of the interlocutor. He (ibid. p. 2) formulates: "This raises the possibility, that despite the extraordinary sparseness of this system, its speaker might nonetheless be able to engage in complicated language games, to say a wide range of different things while performing diverse kinds of action, by making use of resources provided by the speech of others."

As one may have expected, the single-word topic-initial turns seem to be problematic. Although the data is very restricted here, one can assume that, in such a position, the use of an uninflected single word may be troublesome. The responsive turns have an immediate link to the preceding speech, but in the case of a topic-initial turn, the link is more complex. Of course, it is possible that the recipients have presuppositions or 'word knowledge' which may help in constructing a possible meaning for the single-word utterance. Nevertheless, the collaboration of a recipient is more difficult because the possibility of making use of the immediate previous context is more limited than in topic-continuing turns.

If we observe aphasic speech of from a structural perspective, it inevitably leads to the notion of, for instance Broca's aphasics' agrammatic or telegraphic speech; in other words it involves an impairment of morpho-syntactic structures. On the other hand, if we espouse a communicative orientation, the most important question becomes how an aphasic speaker is able to use her/his limited abilities; how an aphasic speaker is able to utilize the earlier conversational context, for instance the semantic coherence and how s/he is able to utilize the physical context and even to utilize the coparticipants. The essential point is how restricted means are used in the most efficient way. Only then, can we actually speak of a pragmatic skill. The occurrences I have discussed indicate that, in most cases, the speakers were able to make their meaning public with an uninflected single-word turn, although it was an exceptional way to converse.

10. Summary and general discussion

10.1 Summary and discussion of the results of the study

The aim of speech-language therapy is to remedy and facilitate the communicative difficulties of a person suffering from speech and language problems. Traditionally, intervention has focused on the deviant features of interaction, and the clients of speech-language therapy, 'the patients', have been rehabilitated in clinical contexts. Thus, the patients' problems have been traditionally treated in a didactic way; for example, in language therapy, rehabilitation has been focused on specific elements of the language, for instance on phonological or on syntactic problems (Green 1984). Unfortunately, what has often been ignored is that speech and language are primarily interactive tools to be used for various purposes and in various contexts. Only recently, within the past fifteen years, has there been a shift in focus to pragmatics and to the study of face-to-face interaction also in speech-language pathology, and this shift has had an immensely enriching influence on it.

Due to the multidisciplinary nature of aphasiology, researchers have adapted their orientations from a number of disciplines. Thus, the study may have used, for instance, (neuro)psychological, (neuro)linguistical or neurological approaches. Yet many speech-language pathologists have followed their theoretical framework without asking themselves whether it is really worthwhile to do so. These studies have increased our knowledge of the structure of aphasic language, and of the relationship between language and the brain. However, in order to be able to rehabilitate the communication of an aphasic speaker, this is not enough. Knowledge concerning deviant language use, as in aphasia, and about its consequences for interaction, is very limited to date. The core issue is that, in order to efficiently remedy aphasic problems, one has to know exactly what to remedy. For this reason, we need detailed knowledge of aphasic face-to-face conversation and interaction.

The impetus for undertaking the present study emerged from my empirical observation of aphasics' communication and interaction while working as a speech-language therapist. It was evident that the traditional aphasia tests used in clinical work were unable to provide any information about aphasic interaction, to say nothing of the basis for communicatively oriented rehabilitation. As the pragmatic approach focused on actual speech and interaction, I decided to choose that framework and become acquainted with it.

Conversation as an achievement in aphasics
Studia Fennica
Linguistica 6
1996.

The purpose of this study was therefore to investigate aphasic conversation and interaction, and the means of interaction within a group of aphasics. As the main focus of aphasiological study has been to investigate the consequences of brain damage for linguistic ability, in this study I have analysed the conversational skills that have remained intact after aphasia and which make communication and conversation possible. In addition, some compensatory skills which were observed due to limited speech and language ability were studied. The present study contains five substudies concerning selected, clearly observed, and recurrent characteristics in aphasic conversation. The selective characteristics were nonverbal behaviour, writing and drawing, the use of humour, the use of aphasic speakers' initiated repair and the use of single words in conversation. Furthermore, the consequences of the use of these means in interaction were studied.

The three first substudies (potentially compensatory nonverbal gestures; written numbers, writing and drawing; and laughter and humour initiated by the aphasic interlocutors) aimed to analyse the function and consequences of these features for interaction.

The aim of chapter 5 was to observe and analyse the potentially compensatory use of nonverbal behaviour in aphasic conversation and its consequences for interaction. The analysis focused qualitatively and partly quantitatively on the prominent, potentially compensatory nonverbal behaviour initiated by aphasic interlocutors and on the variation in their use. The nonverbal acts were classified as emblems, illustrative gestures and pointing movements, as these nonverbal acts are, according to the literature, principally able to convey meanings in conversation, and they can replace one or two words. According to the methodology of conversation analysis, the nonverbal actions, their categorization and their interactional consequences have been investigated in their local interactive context, in conversational sequences (cf. Goodwin & Goodwin 1986).

The use of emblems was rather rare in these conversations and they did not turn out to be prominent nonverbal acts of a compensatory nature. The most frequent emblems were head nods and head shakes, usually combined with a verbal utterance by all the speakers. The other types of emblems were infrequent in these conversations. Also, the use of illustrators was rare and it was usually related to speech. Purely compensatory illustrative movements were few, although there were some interesting occurrences where illustrative movements were clearly used in the compensatory sense. Pointing movements were the most interesting ones from the compensatory point of view. They were classified into four subgroups according to their relation to the present or absent referent in the context and the concomitant verbal reference or the vague or missing verbal reference, and the frequencies of the four types of pointing movements were quantified. The result indicated that Jaakko, a Broca's aphasic, compensated for his speech disability with pointing movements.

Chapter 6 analysed the use of written numbers, writing and drawing and their interactional consequences in their local interactive context, in conversational sequences. Also, these means were clearly used as a compensatory function by Jaakko. He had a specific problem in expressing numerical information orally, and when such information was needed he took a pen and wrote down the numbers he aimed at. This alternative device worked rather well in some cases and did not stop the flow of conversation, but in some cases some collaborative repair work was needed before the conversation could go on. The use of drawing in conversation was different from that of writing numbers. Jaakko began to draw after a difficult and confusing problem in conversation. Gradually he drew a whole scheme of a chipboard plant in order to illustrate the process of manufacturing the chipboards because he was not able to explain it verbally. Evidently drawing the scheme facilitated the understanding of the recipients and they managed to get some idea of the manufacturing of the chipboards. The other speakers did not use writing or drawing on their own initiative; only Maija once used written numbers, requested by Jaakko.

The results of the two first substudies support each other; at least three clear and recurrent compensatory means utilized by Jaakko were observed: pointing movements, number writing and drawing. He used all these means in his communication in order to facilitate his speech problems. A common feature of these means was that they utilized the physical context in conversation. In this sense, one can say that Jaakko used an externalizing strategy: he made use of the contextual resources in conversation. If oral expression was hindered, he resorted to the alternative – contextual resources – and contributed to the conversation by virtue of their help (cf. Simmons-Mackie & Damico 1994).

These observations support the results of the studies which show that an aphasic speaker may use different means in order to compensate for the speech problems. Writing and drawing has been mentioned as a compensatory means in aphasic communication by many researchers (e.g. Hatfield & Zangwill 1974, Cicone 1979, Holland 1982, see also Lyon 1995). Also, according to earlier studies, it seems evident that aphasic speakers increase their use of nonverbal behaviour in comparison to normal speakers (Larkins & Webster 1981, Feyereisen 1983, Ahlsén 1985, Smith 1987a, Le May et al. 1988, Herrmann et al. 1989, Hadar 1991). The compensatory functions of nonverbal behaviour in aphasic communication have also been highlighted in some recent studies (Smith 1987 a and b, Feyereisen et al. 1988, Le May 1988, Herrmann et al. 1988, Klippi 1990, Ahlsén 1991, Hadar 1991). The results of this study support those which indicate that aphasic speakers may utilize nonverbal behaviour as a compensative means in their communication.

Hatfield & Zangwill (1974) and Cicone (1979) have associated writing and drawing with anterior types of aphasia, mainly to Broca's aphasia. With respect to the compensatory nonverbal behaviour, the picture is more controversial. There are some claims that Broca's aphasics use some types of nonverbal behaviour more than Wernicke's aphasics. However, it seems more plausible that the severity of aphasia may be more decisive in using nonverbal behaviour than the type of aphasia (e.g. Smith 1987 b). In this study, Jaakko's speech problems were very prominent and he had moderate Broca's aphasia. He had the most severe aphasic symptoms in the group, according to the WAB test. He used written numbers and drawing and nonverbal behaviour – especially pointing movements – frequently as compensatory means in these conversations.

Although there are studies which have observed the use of previously-mentioned alternative contextual resources, they have not analysed the ways in which these compensatory devices work in actual communicative situations, in their local interactional context. The sequential analysis provided to be such an investigation. The analysis of the conversational examples with nonverbal behaviour, number writing and drawing, show that the successful use of such alternative, contextual resources of communication is an extremely complex issue. In simple cases they worked well and caused no trouble in conversation. However, in more complex cases they can give rise to troubles. The information offered by writing or drawing may be too scarce or ambiguous for the recipients to find out the meaning of the signs; for instance, in this material Jaakko rather often offered numbers whose referents were unknown for the recipients. If such problems occurred, the progression of successful conversation depended heavily on the interactional factors. First of all, the interlocutor(s) had to accept working in co-operation with the speaker in order to resolve the ongoing problem. Second, the interlocutor(s) had to recruit specific resources for the cooperation as well, for instance, various types of repair initiations.

Laughter and humour in aphasic conversation were analysed in chapter 7. The third substudy was focused on laughter and humour initiated by aphasic speakers which led to mutual laughter within the conversation. The aim of this substudy was to identify and analyse mutual laughter, as well as aphasic speakers' means for entering and inviting other participants to humorous discourse, and hence to making distinctions between the humorous and serious discourse. The analysis was based on a sequential analysis and the concepts of 'serious' and 'joke' categorization (Sacks 1992a), an assessment pair (Pomeranz 1984) and preference organization (Levinson 1983, Atkinson & Heritage 1984). The results showed that the aphasic speakers were able to receive, interpret and express humour in these conversations. The turns that began the sequences with mutual laughter were characteristically marked with various nonverbal signs like modification of voice, facial expressions, prosodic cues, laughter, etc. (cf. Gumperz 1985, Mulkay 1988). Also, talented use of the signs of preference organization, delays and prefaces, was observed, especially by Jaakko who often managed to invite other participants to join in mutual laughter.

In aphasic literature, there is practically no mention of whether or to what extent various nonverbal interactional features, such as laughter and humour, exist in aphasic conversation. However, these features are very characteristic in human communication. The question of humour is very complex. I have approached this subject by analysing conversational sequences with mutual laughter, regarding them as a mutual step to the category of humour. In this data, the verbal expressions of the 'humour' turns were simple, but what was very significant was the use of various nonverbal signs in the sequences with mutual laughter. From the point of view of interaction, the crucial thing is that 'humour' sequences are carried out together with mutual laughter. With the help of laughter it is possible to express various important issues in human communication, establishing and demonstrating a relationship (Sacks 1992b), rapport and consensus (Adelswärd 1989) and cooperation and collaboration in conversation (Haakana 1993). Maybe for these reasons it was possible in this group to talk about speech and its difficulties, which otherwise could have been a difficult topic. This indicates that laughter and humour can be regarded as interactional resources also in aphasic conversation. It seems that their functions are extremely important in such complex interaction as aphasic conversations are.

The problem of recurrent 'errors' is central in aphasic conversation. One of my interests was to see how aphasic speakers were able to deal with these troubles; how were they able to handle the problems of initiating other-repairs? In chapter 8, aphasic speakers' other-repair initiations which led to collaborative repair were studied. First, an analysis was made of the other-repair initiations caused by an aphasic speaker's comprehension problems (or hearing problems), and next of the other-repair initiations connected to an aphasic speaker's anomalous turn with insufficient information. As the basis for the analysis, I adopted Schegloff et al's (1977) observations of healthy speakers' other-repair initiations, but I also took into consideration the relevance of Clark & Schaefer's (1987, 1989) idea of the principle of least collaborative effort in aphasic conversation, based on Schegloff et al's (1977) 'strength' suggestion of the other-repair initiators.

To my knowledge, there is no extant study of aphasics' other-repair initiations. This study's principal finding was that all aphasic speakers used various other-repair initiators, although all speakers did not display the use of all initiator types. Some characteristic features of these repair sequences were compared with the findings of repair in 'normal' conversation. First, the most typical feature was the length of the repair sequences. These sequences were long, and many repair-initiations were needed before the trouble was resolved. The examples indicate that aphasic speakers use similar types of other-repair initiations as do 'normal' speakers when handling the problems of hearing or understanding. Schegloff et al. (1977) suggest that there is a preference for stronger over weaker repair-initiators. If more than one other-initiated sequence is needed, the other initiators are used in order to increase strength. Clark & Schaefer (1986 and 1989) call this notion 'the principle of least collaborative effort'. If we observe the repair examples from this perspective, we notice that in the long and complex repair-sequences, the aphasic initiator of the repair actually tends to develop the other-repair initiators of the stronger type. Hence, the results indicate that aphasic speakers also aimed at developing the repair sequence towards a quicker resolution. However, the stronger other-repair initiations often required the use of more advanced syntax than did the weaker ones. The long repair sequences revealed that most severe aphasics – Maija and Jaakko – had difficulty developing the other-repair initiations of a stronger type. As a result, dealing with the trouble often led to collaborative repair work in which all the interlocutors participated (cf. Milroy & Perkins 1993). The cases observed in the present study strongly suggest that aphasic speakers are also capable of handling trouble in conversation and using other-repair initiations as a resource when conversing.

Chapter 9 was intended to study the use of uninflected, single-word turns in aphasic conversation. As this is a symptom which is usually related to Broca's aphasia, and as there were two Broca's aphasics in this group, I wanted to look at the sequential position of uninflected single-word turns in conversation, and the consequences of their appearance for conversation. The uninflected single words were found to occur in various sequential positions and in several functions in conversation. All speakers used these uninflected single words, and they typically constituted adequate use of single-word utterances. Only one Broca's aphasic, Jaakko, attested to the problematic use of uninflected single-word turns. Difficulties arose only in some conversational contexts, such as in a topic-initial turn, in the initial position of a sequence. In these cases, too little information was offered, and the interlocutors were unable to resort to the previous conversational context to infer the meaning of a single word. On the contrary, if a single word was offered as an answer, after a first pair part of an adjacency pair, they usually worked well in conversation. In some cases, if the context required a more elaborated answer, some problems were observed.

On the other hand, a single word turn may be the only verbal element to which the aphasic speaker has access at a certain moment, and s/he has to be satisfied to offer such minimalistic contribution to a conversation. In other words, a single word may be the only possible verbal resource which is available to the aphasic speaker. If we think of the issue from this perspective, the most important questions are how an aphasic speaker is able to use her/his limited resources, how an aphasic speaker can utilize the preceding conversational context, and how can s/he utilize the physical context and collaborate with the other interactants? In some cases, the use of an uninflected single word was insufficient to develop the conversational topic and the collaboration of the co-participants was needed.

To conclude, a detailed analysis of the examples in the present data revealed that these aphasic conversations contained extremely complex and fine collaboration between the interlocutors. Many researchers have stated that it is justified to call this conversation collaborative achievement. Aphasic conversation vividly shows collaboration and human adaptation in communication and interaction.

10.2 The evaluation of the method of this study

According to the prevailing tradition, one of the central features of the aphasia tests is their decontextualized nature. No methods exist where the role of the context in interaction could be analysed, for instance the role of previous conversational context, the role of the co-participants and the role of the physical context. The results of these studies which adopt a decontextual orientation offer a rather one-sided picture of aphasic interaction and communication. According to this view, the success of aphasic interaction is primarily dependent on the type and severity of aphasia. Unfortunately, this perspective has failed to explain the communication of severely aphasic individuals.

The interactional perspective to aphasia is new. Only the development of qualitative methodology, for instance the approach of conversation analysis, has yielded access to the analysis of interaction in aphasia. Few studies have applied this approach to aphasiology (Klippi 1992, Milroy & Perkins 1992, Laakso 1993a and b, Perkins 1993, Ferguson 1994, Goodwin 1995, Wilkinson

1995). However, these few studies have given a new and fresh approach to the study of aphasia.

There are several differences compared with the traditional approach to studying aphasia. First, the data of this study, the conversations of aphasia group, are analysed by the method of conversation analysis which is directed at analysing actual communication situations, everyday mundane conversations, instead of at language tests and experiments. One may question whether the aphasia group conversations are similar to everyday conversations. There has not yet been comparison between aphasic group discussions and aphasic everyday discussions. In some respect, however, the group discussions yielded information that has not been handled in aphasic - therapist dyads, such as instances of other-repair initiations by aphasic individuals. Furthermore, the collaboration between all the speakers in the group was observed in extremely rich way.

Second, the methodology of conversation analysis requires that the utterances or contributions of the interactants be examined in their local interactive context, in conversational sequences. Their analysis involves a detailed examination of how various characteristics offered by the aphasic speakers are performed, and hence it is possible to evaluate the interactional consequences of these characteristics. This opens up the chance to examine the sequential development of these conversations, not only utterances *per se*. Further, it is possible to analyse the significance of the contextual factors in aphasic conversation. This methodological approach reveals several interactional features that are extremely influential in the course of the conversations. On the other hand, it was noticed that collaborative negotiations of the meanings were often needed when such alternative conversational means were recruited. These occurrences offered a very complex picture of the collaboration between the interlocutors.

This study offered a predominantly qualitative analysis which is in contrast to the quantitative approach that typically counts various verbal constituents such as the amount of syllables, words, or mean length of utterances in aphasic expressions. In contrast, the qualitative analysis made it possible to evaluate the consequences of aphasia for communication. The World Health Organization (1980) has introduced the concepts of impairment, disability and handicap when analysing the sickness of an individual. If we apply this idea in exploring aphasia, we soon notice that the approach to study aphasia has covered the levels of impairment and disability, but not the level of handicap. However, from the point of everyday communication, consideration of the handicap resulting from aphasia is essential. The results of this study gave us some glimpses of the communicative handicap of aphasic speakers, as well as some insights into their communicative strengths. This type of knowledge cannot be obtained from the results of traditional aphasiological studies. In this study, for instance, Jaakko turned out to be far better in communication than the results of the aphasia test (WAB) had anticipated.

The obvious consequences of aphasia are various problems in speech expression and comprehension. Since the results of several studies support the hypotheses that nonverbal behaviour is increased in aphasic communication, it also was important to include the nonverbal behaviour in the transcription of the material. The question of the sufficiency of the transcription is crucial in this type of qualitative study. Heritage (1989:22) has pointed out that no detail in conversational interaction can be dismissed a priori as disorderly, accidental or interactionally irrelevant. In fact, this a serious demand for the transcription. One may question if it is even possible to prepare such a comprehensive transcription, especially in such an exceptional interaction situation as in aphasic conversation. The transcript can never be a complete description of the spoken interaction and it is always, even at best, a limited way to attempt to record actual events (e.g. Jefferson 1985:25, Nettelbladt 1994).

The choice of transcription, and its complexity, is dependent on the aims of the study. The problem is that aphasic conversations are often rich in several interactional features and these seem to play a very influential role in the development of conversation. I adopted three types of transcriptions according to the focus of the substudy. The simplest transcription was adopted in chapter 9 handling the uninflected single words, and only in such occurrences when some specific interactional feature was obvious (e.g. drawing) has it been marked in the transcript. The most complex transcription, with several 'non- or quasi-lexical speech objects' of interaction (Heritage 1989:29), was adopted in chapter 7 which dealt with laughter and humour. When evaluating the transcriptions used in this study, the third transcription turned out to be the most powerful and it yielded the possibility to describe and analyse very complex synchronous interactions. It is also possible that the more severe the aphasia the more detailed the transcription of the interaction needs to be. Hence, it is important to develop more sophisticated but also clear and illustrative transcripts for the study of aphasia.

10.3 The significance of the results for the study of aphasia, and the therapeutic implications

This study is of a basic nature. My aim has been to analyse selected conversational characteristics and their interactional consequences in one aphasia group, and the main data of study was four group conversations. With the restricted data it was not possible to study comprehensively all types of conversational resources and means; only a small amount of all the possible resources and alternative means utilized in aphasic conversation could be revealed. Also, the occurrence of some selected conversational devices was low. Hence, the results of the study are tentative, and they cannot be directly generalized in aphasic populations or to certain aphasic types.

However, the approach of this study, in addition to some earlier studies with the same methodology (Klippi 1992, Milroy & Perkins 1992, Laakso 1993a and b, Perkins 1993, Ferguson 1994, Goodwin 1995, Wilkinson 1995), has succeeded to offer a totally new perspective to the research of aphasia. A major benefit has been to introduce the interactive perspective in aphasiology where the aim is to analyse the consequences of aphasia for communication. This approach has yielded the analysis of an aphasic dyad or an aphasic group as a system, not only the analysis of an aphasic individual, and it points out the importance of utilizing actual communicative situations. Hence, the method of conversation analysis is ecologically valid compared to the traditional methods used in aphasia study.

The qualitative analysis of the previously mentioned studies and of this study have shown that there is often a discrepancy between communication and speech and language skills, especially in severe aphasia, as Holland (1977, 1991) has suggested. This view is extremely relevant from the point of view of the rehabilitation of aphasia and it has direct therapeutic applications (e.g. Leiwo 1994). The mainstream of aphasia therapy focuses on the restoration of language, for instance in strengthening the phonological, syntactic and/or semantic processes (e.g. LaPointe 1977, Shewan & Bandur 1986, in Finland Salonen 1980, see also Howard & Hatfield 1987). The problem is that there are always those aphasics who achieve only limited success with linguistic skills in spite of intensive linguistic rehabilitation, and they remain aphasic for the rest of their life. Some of them have minor aphasic problems, for instance slow auditory verbal processing, literal and/or verbal paraphasias and/or word finding difficulties, whereas some of them remain globally or severely aphasic with speech comprehension problems and severe expressive problems.

Aphasia therapy has had rather little to offer to such severely aphasic patients, although some attempts have been made to train an aphasic individual to use augmentative communication, e.g. visual symbols in conversation, for instance Bliss-symbols (e.g. Lehtihalmes 1984, Nenonen 1987), and also gestural systems, such as Makaton and Amerind, as facilitators of communication (e.g. Skelly et al. 1974). In such methods, the basis for the communication lies in the contextual extraverbal objects, pictorial or gestural symbols. On the other hand, if an aphasic has some verbal abilities left, there have been some methods for the rehabilitation of their functional communication (e.g. Aten et al. 1982). Davis & Wilcox (e.g. 1985) have developed PACE therapy (Promoting Aphasics' Communicative Effectiveness) in which the aphasic and the therapist each have a stack of cards containing information which the other does not know. The participants take turns at conveying the information to each other by various means, for instance by gesture, speech, pointing etc.

The results of the present study are relevant to aphasia therapy. In the aphasiological literature, there are already some training methods for aphasic conversation, for instance the PACE method (Davis & Wilcox 1985), a developed PACE method (Pulvermüller & Roth 1991), Audrey Holland's conversational coaching (1991), Kagan's & Gailey's techniques for training conversational partners (1993), and a group approach on the treatment of aphasics and their families (Johannsen-Horbach et al. 1993). These methods are based on the idea of conversation as interaction and they also stress the role of the interlocutor(s) in conversation. The logical consequence of this idea is that we should also train the spouses, relatives, friends to communicate with the aphasics. It also seems that aphasia therapy has to be developed toward urging aphasic speakers to take an active role in their rehabilitation instead of being passively respondent. However, it is inevitable that we need more research on specific features in aphasic conversation.

10.4 Suggestions for further research

The scope of this study has been rather broad, as I have analysed several conversational features in this material, in contrast to a study which aims to analyse one strictly focused phenomenon in conversation. It is obvious that the results of this study give only an overview of the questions studied and that every question needs a more detailed exploration. More detailed knowledge is needed of the relevant interactional features in aphasic conversation and their interactional consequences. Also, the systematic use of various interactional features is important to analyse as it yields the possibility to evaluate their conscious use in contrast to their incidental use. Based on this knowledge, we can then develop new methods for aphasia therapy.

Especially the study of 'non- and quasi-lexical' objects, e.g., nonverbal and various silent and vocal elements of communication, seems to open very relevant research questions in the study of aphasic interaction. The results of this study support some previous studies which indicate that aphasic speakers may utilize nonverbal behaviour as a compensative means in their communication. This result has two important consequences for future research. First, it seems to be worthwhile developing nonverbal therapy programmes for severely aphasic speakers and to study their possibilities to promote aphasic interaction. Conversely, the question concerning the relationship between verbal and nonverbal behaviour, as well as the question of the capacity of nonverbal behaviour to convey meanings, may be elucidated by the further study of aphasic speakers' communication and interaction.

The question of various speech turbulences such as silent and filled pauses, repetitions, hesitations, etc. is extremely interesting from the point of view of aphasic interaction. These turbulences have been traditionally regarded as errors in speech production. However, the study of conversation analysis has shown that they may have important interactional consequences and can also be utilized consciously in interaction. As these features are repeatedly and more often found in aphasic interaction than in healthy interaction, it would be important to systematically analyse the consequences of their use in aphasic interaction. It is quite reasonable to hypothesize that these features are not in all cases due to aphasia but they are also consciously utilized in developing conversation, for instance repetitions, or in regulation of the conversational turn-taking, for instance silent and filled pauses.

The use of alternative means of communicating, writing and drawing, in aphasic communication yielded some interesting results. Although there are observations that they are used in aphasic communication and interaction, there is hardly any mention of their communicative value and their interactional consequences for reaching mutual understanding in conversation. In these conversations, only one participant used them and all except one of his written contributions were numbers. Hence, it would be relevant to study various types of aphasic interactions and to analyse in more detail written contributions and their consequences for conversation.

There is already some knowledge that the structure of aphasic conversation differs from that of the normal because of the recurrent repair sequences (e.g. Milroy & Perkins 1992, Laakso 1993a). However, the results of this study indicate that the procedures to remedy the conversation are similar in normal conversations, although the linguistic means of an aphasic speaker may be rather limited for formulating the other-repair initiations. This question opens up an important research area and it would also be a relevant issue from the point of view of the rehabilitation of aphasics. The analysis of the other-repair initiations of the aphasic speakers showed also some other interesting issues related to the collaborative repair sequences in aphasic conversations. The first question relates to the length of the other-repair sequences initiated by an aphasic speaker. The examples of this study show the repair sequences may be very long. Hence, the further study of the development of the repair sequence and the principle of the least collaborative effort (Clark & Schaefer 1986 and 1989) is extremely interesting from the point of view of aphasic conversation. Another interesting finding was that the long collaborative repair sequences may have a long closing of the sequence with a large variety of discourse particles and nonverbal behaviour. From the clinical point of view, it ought to be very relevant to analyse in more detail the other-repair procedures of aphasic speakers. Important questions are whether the type of aphasia or the stage of aphasia have some specific influence on the mastering of the other-repair procedure and what kinds of linguistic ability are required to use the various other-repair initiators.

The methodological approach of this study turned out to be extremely relevant in investigating aphasia and its consequences for conversation. It is evident that this approach can be applied to the study of other speech- and communication-disordered groups, too, when the aim is to get more knowledge of deviant conversation and interaction and to develop new therapy methods in logopedics.

References

Adelswärd, V. (1989) Laughter and dialogue: the social significance of laughter in institutional discourse. *Nordic Journal of Linguistics* 12, 107–136.

Ahlsén, E. (1985) *Discourse patterns in aphasia.* Gothenburg monographs in linguistics 5. University of Göteborg. Department of Linguistics.

Ahlsén, E. (1991) Body communication as compensation for speech in a Wernicke's aphasic – a longitudinal study. *Journal of Communication Disorders* 24, 1–12.

Albert, M. & Helm-Estabrooks, N. (1988) Diagnosis and treatment of aphasia. *JAMA* 259, 1043–1210.

Armstrong, E. (1989) Conversational interaction between clinician and aphasic during treatment sessions. Paper presented at the American Speech-Language-Hearing Association Annual Convention, St. Louis, Missouri.

Aronson, M., Shatin, L. & Cook, J.C. (1956) Socio- and psychotherapeutic approach to the treatment of aphasic patients. *Journal of Speech and Hearing Disorders* 21, 352–364.

Arwood, E. L. (1983) *Pragmaticism: treatment for language disorders.* Clinical Series No. 8. Maryland: National Student Speech Language Hearing Association.

Aten, J., Caligiuri, M. & Holland, A. (1982) The efficacy of functional communication therapy for chronic aphasic patients. *Journal of Speech and Hearing Disorders* 47, 93–96.

Atkinson, J. M. & Heritage, J. (1984)(eds.) *Structures of Social Action. Studies in Conversation Analysis.* Cambridge: Cambridge University Press.

Aulanko, R. & Lehtihalmes, M. (1992)(eds.) *Studies in Logopedics and Phonetics 3.* Publications of the Department of Phonetics, University of Helsinki, Series B: Phonetics, Logopedics and Speech Communication 4.

Austin, J. L. (1962) *How to do Things with Words.* Oxford: Clarendon Press.

Bateson, G. (1972) *Steps to an Ecology of Mind.* London: Paladin Books.

Bavelas, J. B., Chovil, N., Lawrie, D. A. & Wade, A. (1992) Interactive gestures. *Discource Processes* 15, 469–489.

Behrmann, M. & Penn, C. (1984) Non-verbal communication of aphasic patients. *British Journal of Disorders of Communication* 19, 155–168.

Benson, D. F. (1988) Classical syndromes of aphasia. *Handbook of Neuropsychology, Vol. 1* (F. Boller & J. Grafman, eds.), Amsterdam: Elsevier, 267–280.

Benton, A. (1985) Visuoperceptual, visuospatial and visuoconstructive disorders. *Clinical Neuropsychology* (K. Heilman & E. Valenstein, eds.), New York: Oxford University Press, 151–185.

Blanken, G. (1991) The functional basis of speech automatisms (recurring utterances). *Aphasiology* 5, 103–127.

Bloom, L.M. (1962) A rationale for group treatment of aphasic patients. *Journal of Speech and Hearing Disorders* 27, 11–16.

Bollinger, R., Musson, N. & Holland, A. (1993) A study of group communication intervention with chronically aphasic persons. *Aphasiology* 7, 301–313.

Brinton, B. & Fujiki, M. (1982) A comparison of request-response sequences in the discourse of normal and language-disordered children. *Journal of Speech and Hearing Disorders* 47, 57–62.

Brinton, B., Fujiki, M., Winkler, E. & Frome Loeb, D. (1986) Responses to requests for clarification in linguistically normal and language-impaired children. *Journal of Speech and Hearing Disorders* 51, 370–378.

Brinton, B., Fujiki, M. & Sonnenberg, E. (1988) Responses to requests for clarification by linguistically normal and language-impaired children in conversation. *Journal of Speech and Hearing Disorders* 53, 383–391.

Button, G. & Casey, G. (1984) Generating topic: the use of topic initial elicitors. In: M. Atkinson & J. Heritage (eds.), 167–190.

Button, G. & Lee, J. R. (1987) *Talk and Social Organization*. Clevedon: Multilingual Matters.

Churchill, L. (1978) *Questioning Strategies in Sociolinguistics*. Rowley, Mass.: Newbury House Publishers.

Cicone, M., Wapner, W., Foldi, N., Zurif, E. & Gardner, H. (1979) The relation between gesture and language in aphasic communication. *Brain & Language* 8, 324–349.

Clark, H. & Schaefer, E. (1987) Collaborating on contributions to conversations. *Language and Cognitive Processes* 2, 19–41.

Clark, H. & Schaefer, E. (1989) Contributing to discourse. *Cognitive Science* 13, 259–294.

Clark, H. & Wilkes-Gibbs, D. (1986) Referring as a collaborative process. *Cognition* 22, 1–39.

Cohen, A.A. & Harrison R.P. (1973) Intentionality in the use of hand gestures in face-to-face communication situation. *Journal of Personality and Social Psychology* 10, 37–46.

Copeland, M. (1989) An assessment of natural conversation with Broca's aphasics. *Aphasiology* 3, 301–306.

Cruttenden, A. (1986) *Intonation*. Cambridge: Cambridge University Press.

Crystal, D. (1975) *The English Tone of Voice. Essays in Intonation, Prosody and Paralanguage.* Bristol: Edward Arnold.

Cutler, A. (1982)(ed.) *Slips of the Tongue and Language Production.* Amsterdam: Mouton.

Cutler, A. & Pearson, M. (1986) On the analysis of prosodic turn-taking cues. *Intonation in Discourse* (C. Johns-Lewis, ed.), London: Croom Helm, 139–155.

Damasio, A. (1981) The nature of aphasia: signs and syndromes. In: M. Taylor Sarno (ed.), 51–65.

Davis, G.A. & Wilcox, M.J. (1985) *Adult aphasia rehabilitation. Applied Pragmatics.* San Diego: College-Hill Press.

Denes, P.B. & Pinson, E. (1963) *The Speech Chain. The Physics and Biology of Spoken Language.* Bell Telephone Laboratories.

Donahue, M., Pearl, R. & Bryant, T. (1980) Learning disabled children's conversational competence: Responses to inadequate messages. *Applied Psycholinguistics* 1, 387–403.

Duffy, R. & Liles B. (1979) A translation of Finkelnburg's (1870) lecture on aphasia as "asymbolia" with commentary. *Journal of Speech and Hearing Disorders* 44, 156–168.

Dufva, H. (1992) *Slipshod Utterances: A Study of Mislanguage.* Studia Philologica Jyväskyläensia 26. University of Jyväskylä.

Easterbrook, A., Brown, B. & Perera, K. (1982) A comparison of the speech of adult aphasic subjects in spontaneous and structured interactions. *British Journal of Disorders of Communication* 17, 93–107.

Edwards, J. A. (1993) Principles and contrasting systems of discourse transcription. *Talking Data: Transcription and Coding in Discourse Research* (J.A. Edwards & M.D. Lampert, eds.), Hillsdale: Lawrence Erlbaum, 3–31.

Edwards, S. (1987) Assessment and therapeutic intervention in a case of Wernicke's aphasia. *Aphasiology* 1, 271–276.

Ekman, P. & Friesen, W. (1969) The repertoire of nonverbal behaviour: categories, origins, usage, and coding. *Semiotica* 1, 49–98.

Ekman, P. & Friesen, W. (1972) Hand movements. *Journal of Communication* 22, 353–374.

Ellis, A. & Beattie, G. (1986) *The psychology of language & communication.* London: Weidenfeld & Nicolson.

Ellis, A. W. & Young, A. W. (1988) *Human cognitive neuropsychology.* Hove: Lawrence Erlbaum.

Ferguson, A. (1994) The influence of aphasia, familiarity and activity on conversational repair. *Aphasiology* 8, 143–157.

Feyereisen, P. (1983) Manual activity during speaking in aphasic subjects. *International Journal of Psychology* 18, 545–556.

Feyereisen, P. (1987) Gestures and speech, interactions and separations: a reply to McNeill (1985). *Psychological Review* 94, 493–498.

Feyereisen, P., Barter, M., Goossens, M. & Clerebaut, N. (1988) Gestures and speech in referential communication by aphasic subjects: channel use and efficiency. *Aphasiology* 2, 21–32.

Foldi, N., Cicone, M. & Gardner H. (1983) Pragmatic aspects of communication in brain-damaged patients. *Language functions and brain organization* (S. Segalowitz, ed.), New York: Academic Press, 51–86.

Gainotti, G. (1988) Nonverbal cognitive disturbances in aphasia. *Contemporary Reviews in Neuropsychology.* (H. Whitaker, ed.) New York: Springer-Verlag, 127–158.

Gainotti, G., Silveri, M.C., Villa, G. & Caltagirone, C. (1983) Drawing objects from memory in aphasia. *Brain* 106, 613–622.

Gallagher, T.M. (1981) Contingent query sequences within adult-child discourse. *Journal of Child Language* 8, 51–62.

Gallagher, T. M. (1991)(ed.) *Pragmatics of Language. Clinical Practice Issues.* London: Chapman & Hall.

Garfinkel, H. (1967) *Studies in Ethnomethodology.* New Jersey: Prentice-Hall.

Geschwind, N. & Damasio, A. (1985) Apraxia. *Handbook of Clinical Neurology. Clinical Neuropsychology.* Revised Series 1 (P.J. Vinken, G.V. Bruyn, H. Klawans & J.A. Frederiks, eds.), Amsterdam: Elsevier, 423–432.

Glosser, G., Wiener, M. & Kaplan, E. (1986) Communicative gestures in aphasia. *Brain and Language* 27, 345–359.

Glosser, G., Wiener, M. & Kaplan, E. (1988) Variations in aphasic language behaviours. *Journal of Speech and Hearing Disorders* 53, 115–124.

Goodenough, D. & Weiner, S. (1978) The role of conversational passing moves in the management of topical transitions. *Discourse Processes* 1, 395–404.

Goodglass, H. (1993) *Understanding Aphasia.* New York: Academic Press.

Goodglass, H. & Kaplan, E. (1972) *The Assessment of Aphasia and Related Disorders.* Philadelphia: Lea and Febiger.

Goodglass, H. & Menn, L. (1985) Is agrammatism a unitary phenomenon? In M.-L. Kean, (ed.), 1–26.

Goodwin, C. (1979) The interactive construction of a sentence in natural conversation. In: G. Psathas (ed.), 97–121.

Goodwin, C. (1981) *Conversational Organization: Interaction between Speakers and hearers.* New York: Academic Press.

Goodwin, C. (1986) Gestures as a resource for the organization of mutual orientation. *Semiotica* 62, 29–49.

Goodwin, C. (1987) Restarts, pauses, and the achievement of a state of mutual gaze at turn-beginning. *Sociological Inquiry* 50, 272–302.

Goodwin, C. (1993) Recording human interaction in natural settings. *Pragmatics* 3, 181–209.

Goodwin, C. (1995) Co-constructing meaning in conversations with an aphasic man. *Research on Language and Social Interaction* 28, 233–260.

Goodwin, C. & Duranti, A. (1992) Rethinking context: an introduction. *Rethinking context. Language as an interactive phenomenon* (A. Duranti & C. Goodwin, eds.), Cambridge: Cambridge University Press, 1–42.

Goodwin, C. & Goodwin, M.H. (1987) Concurrent operations on talk: Notes on the interactive organization of assessments. *IPRA Papers on Pragmatics* 1, 1–54.

Goodwin, C. & Heritage, J. (1990) Conversation analysis. *Annual Review of Anthropology* 19, 283–307.

Goodwin, M.H. (1990) *He-Said-She-Said: Talk as Social Organization among Black Children.* Bloomington: Indiana University press.

Goodwin, M.H. & Goodwin, C. (1986) Gesture and coparticipation in the activity of searching for a word. *Semiotica* 62, 51–75.

Green, G. (1984) Communication in aphasia therapy: some of the procedures and issues involved. *British Journal of Disorders of Communication* 19, 35–46.

Grodzinsky, Y. (1991) There is an entity called agrammatic aphasia. *Brain and Language* 41, 555–564.

Gumperz, J. (1982) *Discourse strategies.* Cambridge: Cambridge University Press.

Gurland, G., Chwat, S. & Wollner, S. (1982) Establishing a communicative profile in adult aphasia: analysis of communicative acts and conversational sequences. *Clinical Aphasiology Conference Proceedings* (R. Brookshire, ed.), Minnesota: BRK Publishers, 18–25.

Haakana, M. (1993) *Vakavaa ja ei-vakavaa puhetta. Huumorin ja vakavan kategorioista eräässä arkikeskustelussa.* Unpublished M.A. thesis. Department of Finnish. University of Helsinki.

Hadar, U. (1991) Speech-related body movement in aphasia: period analysis of upper arms and head movement. *Brain and Language* 42, 339–366.

Hadar, U. & Clifford Rose, F. (1988) Speech fluency in aphasia. *Aphasia* (F. Clifford Rose, R. Whurr & M.A. Wyke, eds.), London: Whurr Publishers, 302–324.

Hakulinen, A. (1989) Palauteilmauksista. *Kieli 4. Suomalaisen keskustelun keinoja I.* (A. Hakulinen, ed.), Helsinki: Helsingin yliopiston suomen kielen laitos, 98–114.

Hakulinen, A. (1993) The grammar of opening routines. *Suomen kielitieteellisen yhdistyksen vuosikirja 1993* (S. Shore & M. Vilkuna, eds.), Helsinki, 149–170.

Hakulinen, A. & Sorjonen, M.-L. (1986) Palautteen asema diskurssissa. *Kieli 1* (P. Leino & J. Kalliokoski, eds.), Helsinki: Helsingin yliopiston suomen kielen laitos, 39–72.

Hatfield, F.M. & Zangwill, O.L. (1974) Ideation in aphasia. The picture-story method. *Neuropsychology* 12, 389–393.

Heeschen, C. (1985) Agrammatism versus paragrammatism: A fictitious opposition. In: M.-L. Kean (ed.), 207–248.

Heeschen, C. & Kolk, H. (1988) Agrammatism and paragrammatism. *Aphasiology* 2, 299–302.

Heritage, J. (1984) *Garfinkel and ethnomethodology*. Oxford: Polity Press.

Heritage, J. (1989) Current developments in conversation analysis. *Conversation* (D. Roger & P. Bull, eds.) Clevedon, Philadephia: Multilingual Matters, 19–47.

Heritage, J. & Atkinson, M. (1984) Introduction. In: J. M. Atkinson & J. Heritage (eds.), 1–15.

Herrmann, M., Reichle, T., Lucius-Hoene, G., Wallesch C-W. & Johannsen-Horbach H. (1988) Nonverbal communication as a compensative strategy for severe nonfluent aphasics? – A quantitative approach. *Brain and Language* 33, 41–54.

Herrmann, M. & Koch U. & Johannsen-Horbach, H. & Wallesh, C-W. (1989) Communicative skills in chronic and severe nonfluent aphasia. *Brain and Language* 37, 339–352.

Holland, A. (1977) Some practical considerations in aphasia rehabilitation. *Rationale for Adult Aphasia Therapy*. (M. Sullivan & M.S. Kommers, eds.), Omaha: University of Nebraska.

Holland, A. (1980) *Communicative abilities of daily living; Manual.* Baltimore: University Park Press.

Holland, A. (1982) Observing functional communication of aphasic adults. *Journal of Speech and Hearing Disorders* 47, 50–56.

Holland, A. (1991) Pragmatic aspects of intervention in aphasia. *Journal of Neurolinguistics* 6, 197–211.

Holland, A. L. & Forbes, M. M. (1993)(eds.) *Aphasia treatment. Word perspectives.* San Diego: Singular Publishing Group.

Howard, D. (1985) Agrammatism. *Current Perspectives in Dysphasia* (S. Newman & R. Epstein, eds.), Edinburgh: Churchill Livingstone, 1–31.

Howard, D. & Hatfield, F.M. (1987) *Aphasia Therapy. Historical and Contemporary Issues.* Hove: Lawrence Erlbaum Associates.

Hutchins, E. (1993) Learning to navigate. *Understanding Practice. Perspectives on Activity and Context* (S. Chaiklin & J. Lave, eds.). Cambridge: Cambridge University Press, 35–63.

Hymes, D. (1972) On communicative competence. *Sociolinguistics* (J. Pride & J. Holmes, eds.) Harmondsworth: Penguin Books, 269–293.

Jefferson, G. (1972) Side sequences. *Studies in Social Interaction* (D. Sydnow, ed.), New York: The Free Press, 294–338.

Jefferson, G. (1979) A technique for inviting laughter and its subsequent acceptance declination. In: G. Psathas (ed.), 79–96.

Jefferson, G. (1984) On the organization of laughter in talk about troubles. In: M. Atkinson & J. Heritage (eds.), 346–369.

Jefferson, G. (1985) An exercise in the transcription and analysis of laughter. *Handbook of Discourse Analysis*, Vol. 3 (Teun A. Van Dijk, ed.), London: Academic Press, 25–34.

Jefferson, G. (1987) On exposed and embedded correction in conversation. In: G. Button & J.R.H. Lee (eds.), 86–100.

Jefferson, G., Sacks, H. & Schegloff, E. (1987) Notes on laughter in the pursuit of intimacy. In: G. Button & J. Lee (eds.), 152–206.

Joanette, Y. & Brownell H. H. (1990)(eds.) *Discourse Ability and Brain Damage. Theoretical and Empirical Perspectives.* New York: Springer-Verlag.

Johannsen-Horbach, H., Wentz, C., Funfgeld, M., Herrmann, M. & Wallesch, C.-W. (1993) Psychosocial aspects on the treatment of adult aphasics and their families: a group approach in Germany. In: A. Holland & M. Forbes (eds.), 319–334.

Kagan, A. & Gailey, G. (1993) Functional is not enough: training conversational partners for aphasic adults. In: A. Holland & M. Forbes (eds.), 199–227.

Kalin, M. (1995) Coping with Problems of Understanding. Repair Sequences in Conversations between Native and Non-Native Speakers. *Studia Philologica Jyväskyläensia 36.* University of Jyväskylä.

Kann, J. (1950) A translation of Broca's original article on the location of the speech center. *Journal of the Speech and Hearing Disorders* 15, 16–20.

Kaplan, E. & Goodglass, H. (1981) Aphasia-related disorders. In: M. Taylor Sarno (ed.), 303–320.

Karlsson, F. (1987) *Finnish Grammar* (2nd edition). Helsinki: WSOY.

Kean, M.-L. (1985)(ed.) *Agrammatism.* Orlando: Academic Press.

Kearns, K.D. (1986) Group Therapy for aphasia: Theoretical and Practical Considerations. *Language Intervention Strategies in Adult Aphasia.* R. Chapey (ed.). Second edition. Baltimore: Williams & Wilkins, 304–318.

Keller, E. (1994) *Signalyze TM*. Signal Analysis for Speech and Sound. User's manual. Charlestown, MA: Network Technology Corporation.

Kertesz, A. (1982) The Western Aphasia Battery. Test manual. USA: Grune & Stratton.

Klippi, A. & Pyyppönen, V. (1988) Ryhmäterapia – osa afasiaterapiaa (Group therapy – a part of aphasia therapy). *Puheterapeutti* 3, 16–21.

Klippi, A. (1990) *Afasiapotilaiden kommunikatiivisten intentioiden välittyminen ryhmäkeskusteluissa* (The transmission of communicative intentions in aphasic group discussions). The unpublished licentiate thesis of Logopedics. Department of Phonetics. University of Helsinki.

Klippi, A. (1991a) Conversational dynamics between aphasics. *Aphasiology* 5, 373–378.

Klippi, A. (1991b) Variations in Broca's aphasics' communicative behaviour in two different speech contexts. *Proceedings of the 4th Finnish Conference of Neurolinguistics, Turku 1991* (M. Laine, J. Niemi & P. Koivuselkä-Sallinen, eds.), University of Joensuu: Studies in Languages 23, 29–46.

Klippi, A. (1992) Reaching towards mutual understanding in aphasic conversation. Aphasics as contributors in conversation. In: R. Aulanko & M. Lehtihalmes (eds.), 54–67.

Kukkonen, P. (1993) On paragrammatism in Finnish. *Nordic Journal of Linguistics* 16, 123–135.

Kukkonen, P. & Pajunen, A. (1986) Rektio ja agrammatismi. *Virittäjä* 90, 22–45.

Laakso, M. (1992) Interactional features of aphasia therapy conversation. In: R. Aulanko & M. Lehtihalmes (eds.), 69–90.

Laakso, M. (1993a) Sequential repair patterns in aphasic-nonaphasic conversation. Paper presented at the Third Congress of the International Clinical Phonetics and Linguistics Association, Helsinki.

Laakso, M. (1993b) Self-monitoring and self-initiation of repair in conversations of fluent aphasic persons. Poster presented in Academy of Aphasia, Tucson, Arizona October 24–26.

LaPointe, L.L.(1977) Base 10 programmed stimulation: test specification scoring and plotting performances in aphasia therapy. *Journal of Speech and Hearing Disorders* 42, 90–105.

Larkins, P. & Webster, E. (1981) The use of gestures in dyads consisting of an aphasic and a nonaphasic adult. *Clinical Aphasiology Conference Proceedings* (R. Brookshire, ed.), Minneapolis: BRK Publishers, 120–126.

Lebrun, Y. & Buyssens E. (1982) Metalanguage and speech pathology. *British Journal of Disorders of Communication* 17, 21–25.

Lehtihalmes, M. (1984) Use of Bliss-symbolics with adult aphasics. Paper presented at First International Aphasia Rehabilitation Congress, Cracow, Poland.

Lehtihalmes, M., Klippi, A. & Lempinen, M. (1986) Western Aphasia Battery. Unstandardized Finnish version.

Leischner, A. (1969) The agraphias. In: P.J. Vinken & G.W. Bruyn (eds.), 141–180.

Leiwo, A. (1994) Aphasia and communicative aphasia therapy. *Aphasiology* 8, 467–506.

Leiwo, M. & Klippi, A. (Forthcoming) "Agrammatic" utterances in context. Lexical repetition as a conversational resource in Broca's aphasia.

Le May, A., David, R. & Thomas, A. (1988) The use of spontaneous gesture by aphasic patients. *Aphasiology* 2, 137–145.

Lerner, G. (1987) *Collaborative Turn Sequences: Sentence Construction and Social Action.* Unpublished PhD. Thesis. Irvine: University of California.

Lesser, R. (1989) Aphasia: theory based intervention. *Disorders of Communication: The Science of Intervention* (M.M. Leahy, ed.) London: Taylor & Francis, 189–205.

Lesser, R. & Milroy, L. (1993) *Linguistics and Aphasia. Psycholinguistic and Pragmatic Aspects of Intervention.* Harlow: Longman Group UK Limited.

Levinson, S.C. (1983) *Pragmatics.* Cambridge: Cambridge University Press.

Lhermitte, F. & Gautier, J.-C. (1969) Aphasia. In: P.J. Vinken & G.W. Bruyn (eds.), 84–104.

Linebaugh, C., Kryzer, K., Oden, S. & Myers, P. (1982) Reapportionment of communicative burden in aphasia: a study of narrative interactions. *Clinical Aphasiology Conference Proceedings* (R. Brookshire, ed.), Minnesota: BRK Publishers, 4–8.

Linell, P. (1991) Dialogism and the orderliness of conversational disorders. *Methodological Issues in Research in Augmentative and Alternative Communication* (J. Brodin & E. Björck-Åkesson, eds.). Proceedings from the first ISAAC Research Symposium in Augmentative and Alternative Communication, Stockholm. The Swedish Handicap Institute.

Lubinski, R., Dunchan, J. & Weitzner-Lin, B. (1980) Analysis of breakdowns and repairs in aphasic adult communication. *Clinical Aphasiology Conference Proceedings* (R. Brookshire, ed.), Minnesota: BRK Publishers, 111–116.

Luria, A.R. (1970) *Traumatic Aphasia.* The Hague: Mouton.

Luria, A.R. (1976a) *The Working Brain.* Middlesex: Penguin Books.

Luria, A.R. (1976b) *The Basic Problems of Neurolinguistics.* The Hague: Mouton.

Lyon, J. (1995) Drawing: its value as a communication aid for adults with aphasia. *Aphasiology* 9, 33–94.

Marquardt, T.P., Tonkovich J.D. & DeVault, S.M. (1976) Group therapy and stroke club programs for aphasic adults. *Journal of the Tennessee Speech and Hearing Association* 20, 2–20.

Matthews, C. (1987) Discourse before and after the onset of aphasia. *Clinical Aphasiology Conference Proceedings* (R. Brookshire, ed.), Minnesota: BRK Publishers, 221–230.

McNeill, D. (1985) So you think gestures are nonverbal? *Psychological Review* 92, 350–371.

McNeill, D. (1992) *Hand and Mind. What Gestures Reveal about Thought.* Chicago: The University of Chicago Press.

McTear, M.F. (1985) Pragmatic disorders: a question of direction. *British Journal of Disorders of Communication* 20, 119–127.

McTear, M. & Conti-Ramsden, G. (1992) *Pragmatic Disability in Children.* London: Whurr Publishers Ltd.

Miceli, G., Silveri, C., Romani, C. & Caramazza, A. (1989) Variation in the pattern of omissions and substitutions of grammatical morphemes in the spontaneous speech of so-called agrammatic patients. *Brain and Language* 36, 447–492.

Milroy, L. & Perkins, L. (1992) Repair strategies in aphasic discourse; towards a collaborative model. *Clinical Linguistics & Phonetics* 6, 27–40.

Mulkay, M. (1988) *On humour.* Cambridge: Polity Press.

Mäkelä, K. (1990)(ed.) *Kvalitatiivisen aineiston analyysi ja tulkinta.* Helsinki: Gaudeamus.

Nenonen, T. (1987) Afaatikkojen Bliss-symbolikielen oppimisesta. Unpublished M.A. thesis. Department of Phonetics. University of Helsinki.

Nettelbladt, U. (1994) Some reflections on transcribing. *Working Papers in Logopedics and Phoniatrics No 9.* Lund University. Department of Logopedics and Phoniatrics, 53–67.

Nettelbladt, U. & Hansson, K. (1993) Parents, peers and professionals in interaction with language impaired children. *Proceedings of the Child Language Seminar, University of Plymouth.*

Niemi, J., Laine, M., Hänninen, R. & Koivuselkä-Sallinen, P. (1990) Agrammatism in Finnish: Two case studies. *Agrammatic Aphasia – A Cross-Language Narrative Sourcebook* (L. Menn & L. Obler, eds.), Amsterdam: John Benjamins, 1013–1085.

Ochs, E. (1979) Transcription as theory. *Developmental Pragmatics* (E. Ochs & B. Schieffelin, eds.), Orlando: Academic Press, 43–72.

Pachalska, M. (1993) The Concept of Holistic Rehabilitiation of Persons with Aphasia. In A. Holland & M. Forbes (eds.), 145–174.

Penn, C. (1987) Compensation and language recovery in the chronic aphasic patient. *Aphasiology* 1, 235–245.

Penn, C. (1988) The profiling of syntax and pragmatics in aphasia. *Clinical Linguistics & Phonetics* 2, 179–207.

Penn, C. (1993) Aphasia therapy in South Africa: Some pragmatic and personal perspectives. In A. Holland & M. Forbes (eds.), 25–53.

Perkins, L. (1993) *The Impact of Cognitive Neuropsychological Impairments on Conversational Ability an Aphasia.* Unpublished PhD. Thesis. Department of Speech. University of Newcastle-upon-Tyne.

Persson, I.-B. (1991) Semantic processing and agrammatic processing. *Proceedings of the 4th Finnish Conference of Neurolinguistics, Turku 1991.* (M. Laine, J. Niemi & P. Koivuselkä-Sallinen, eds.), University of Joensuu: Studies in Languages 23, 153–168.

Persson, I.-B. (1995) Connectionism, Language Production and Adult Aphasia – Elaboration of a Connectionist Framework for Lexical Processing and a Hypothesis of Agrammatic Aphasia. *Commentationes Humanarum Litterarum 106.* Tammisaari: The Finnish Society of Sciences and Letters.

Pomeranz, A. (1984) Agreeing and disagreeing with assessments: some features of preferred/dispreferred turn shapes. In: J. M. Atkinson & J. Heritage (eds.), 57–101.

Prinz, P. (1980) A note on requesting strategies in adult aphasics. *Journal of Communication Disorders* 13, 65–73.

Prutting, C. (1982) Pragmatics as social competence. *Journal of Speech and Hearing Disorders* 47, 123–134.

Prutting, C. & Kirchner, D. (1983) Applied pragmatics. *Pragmatic Assessment and Intervention Issues in Language* (T. Gallagher & C. Prutting, eds), San Diego: College Hill Press, 26–64.

Psathas, G. (1979)(ed.) *Everyday Language: Studies in Ethnomethodology.* New York: Erlbaum.

Pulvermüller, F. & Roth, V. (1991) Communicative aphasia treatment as a further development of PACE therapy. *Aphasiology* 5, 39–50.

Roberts, J. A. & Wertz, R. T. (1989) Comparison of spontaneous and elicited oral-expressive language in aphasia. *Clinical Aphasiology Vol. 18* (T.E. Prescott, ed.), Boston, Mass.: College Hill Press, 480–484.

Sacks, H. (1972) An initial investigation on the usability of conversational data for doing sociology. *Studies in Social Interaction* (D. Sydnow, ed.) New York: Free Press.

Sacks, H. (1992a) Utterance completion; Co-producing an utterance; Appendor clauses. *Lectures on conversation.* Vol. 1. (G. Jefferson ed.), Cambridge: Basil Blackwell, 647–655.

Sacks, H. (1992b) Adjacency pairs: Scope of operation. *Lectures on conversation.* Vol. 2. (G. Jefferson ed.), Cambridge: Basil Blackwell, 521–532.

Sacks, H. (1992c) Laughing together; Expressions of sorrow and joy. *Lectures on conversation.* Vol. 2. (G. Jefferson ed.), Cambridge: Basil Blackwell, 570–575.

Sacks, H., Schegloff, E. & Jefferson, G. (1974) A simpliest systematics for the organization of turn-taking for conversation. *Language* 50, 696–735.

Saffran, E., Berndt, R. & Schwartz, M. (1989) The qualitative analysis of agrammatic production: Procedures and data. *Brain and Language* 37, 440–479.

Salonen, L. (1989) The language enriched individual therapy program for aphasic patients. *Aphasia: Theory and Treatment* (M. Sarno & O. Höök, eds.), Stockholm: Almqvist & Wiksell.

Sarno, M. T. (1969) *The functional communication profile: manual of directions.* New York: New York University Medical Center – The Institute of Rehabilitation Medicine.

Sarno, M. T. (1983) The functional assessment of verbal impairment. *Scandinavian Journal of Rehabilitation Medicine* 9, 75–80.

Schegloff, E. (1972a) Notes on a conversational practice: Formulating place. In: D. Sydnow (ed.), 75–119.

Schegloff, E. (1972) Sequencing in conversational openings. *Directions in Sosiolinguistics: The Ethnography of Communication* (J. Gumperz & D. Hymes, eds.), New York: Rinehart and Winston, 346–380.

Schegloff, E. (1987) Some sources of misunderstanding in talk-in-interaction. *Linguistics* 25, 201–218.

Schegloff, E. (1992) Repair after next turn: the last structurally provided defense of intersubjectivity in conversation. *American Journal of Sociology* 97, 1295–1345.

Schegloff, E. (1993) Reflections on quantification in the study of conversation. *Research on Language and Social Interaction* 26:99–128.

Schegloff, E. & Sacks, H. (1973) Opening up closings. *Semiotica* 8, 289–327.

Schegloff, E., Jefferson, G. & Sacks, H. (1977) The preference of self-correction in the organisation of repair in conversation. *Language* 53, 361–382.

Scherer, K.R. & Ekman, P. (1982) Methodological issues in studying nonverbal behaviour. *Handbook of Methods in Nonverbal Behaviour Research* (K.R. Scherer & P. Ekman, eds.) Cambridge: Cambridge University Press, 1–40.

Schienberg, S. & Holland, A. (1980) Conversational turn-taking in Wernicke aphasia. *Clinical Aphasiology Conference Proceedings* (R. Brookshire, ed.), Minnesota: BRK Publishers, 106–111.

Schlanger, P. & Schlanger, B. (1970) Adapting role-playing activities with aphasic patients. *Journal of Speech and Hearing Disorders* 35, 229–235.

Schlenck, K.-J., Huber, W. & Willmes, K. (1987) "Prepairs" and repairs: different monitoring functions in aphasic language production. *Brain and Language* 30, 226–244.

Schuell, H., Jenkins, J. & Jiménez-Pabón, E. (1964) *Aphasia in Adults: Diagnosis, Prognosis, and Treatment.* New York: Harper & Row.

Searle, J. (1969) *Speech Acts. An Essay in the Philosophy of Language.* Cambridge: Cambridge University Press.

Shatz, M. & Watson O'Reilly, A. (1990) Conversational or communicative skill? A reassessment of two-year-olds' behaviour in miscommunication episodes. *Journal of Child Language* 17, 131–146.

Shewan, C. M. & Bandur, D. L. (1986) *Treatment of Aphasia. A Language-Oriented Approach.* London: Taylor & Francis.

Skelly, M., Schensky, L., Smith, R.W., Fust, R.S.(1974) American Indian Sign (Amerind) as a facilitator of verbalization for the oral verbal apraxic. *Journal of Speech and Hearing Disorders* 39, 445–456.

Simmons, N.N. & Damico, J.S. (1994) Reformulating the definition of compensatory strategies in aphasia. Manuscript.

Sinclair, J.M. & Coulthard, R.M. (1975) *Towards an analysis of discourse: the English used by teachers and pupils.* London: Oxford University Press.

Smith, L. (1987a) Nonverbal competency in aphasic stroke patients' conversation. *Aphasiology* 1, 127–139.

Smith, L. (1987b) Fluency and severity of aphasia and non-verbal competency. *Aphasiology* 1, 291–295.

Sorjonen, M.-L. (1988) Mm ja joo -taustapalautettako vain? *Isosuinen nainen. Tutkielmia naisesta ja kielestä* (L. Laitinen, ed.), Helsinki: Yliopistopaino, 209–231.

Sorjonen, M.-L. (Forthcoming) On repeats and responses in Finnish conversation. To appear in *Interaction and Grammar* (E. Ochs, E. Schegloff & S. Thompson, eds.), Cambridge: Cambridge University Press.

Springer, L., Willmes, K. & Haag, A. (1993) Training in the use of wh-questions and prepositions in dialogues: a comparison of two different approaches in aphasia therapy. *Aphasiology* 7, 251–270.

Stemberger, J.P. (1985) An interactive activation model of language production. *Progress in the Psychology of Language.* Vol. 1 (A.W. Ellis, ed.), London: Lawrence Erlbaum.

Sydnow, D. (1992)(ed.) *Studies in Social Interaction.* New York: The Free Press.

syncWRITER (1990) *Manual.* Hamburg: med-i-bit EDV-Beratungsgesellschaft mbH.

Tainio, L., Seppänen, E.-L., Raevaara, L. & Purra, P. (1991) "Joku oli sanonut jotain lapsista" – arkikertomukset heijastamassa ja rakentamassa naisten kertomuksia. *Leikkauspiste. Kirjoituksia kielestä ja ihmisestä* (L. Laitinen, P. Nuolijärvi & M. Saari, eds.), Helsinki: Suomalaisen Kirjallisuuden Seura, 17–42.

Taylor, M. (1965) A measurement of functional communication in aphasia. *Archives of Physical Medicine and Rehabilitation* 46, 101–107.

Taylor Sarno, M. (1981)(ed.) *Acquired aphasia*. New York: Academic Press.

Taylor, T. & Cameron, D. (1987) *Analysing Conversation. Rules and Units in the Structure of Talk*. Exeter: Pergamon Press.

Thompson, C.K. & McReynolds, L.V. (1986) Wh-interrogative production in agrammatic aphasia: an experimental analysis of auditory-visual stimulation and direct production treatment. *Journal of Speech and Hearing Research* 29, 193–206.

Ulatowska, H. K., Allard, L. & Chapman, B. (1990) Narrative and procedural discourse in aphasia. *Discourse Ability and Brain Damage. Theoretical and Empirical Perspectives* (Y. Joanette & H.H. Brownell, eds.), New York: Springer-Verlag, 198–198.

Vinken, P.J. & Bruyn, G.V. (1969)(eds.) *Handbook of Clinical Neurology*. Vol. 4: Disorders of Speech, Perception and Symbolic Behaviour. Amsterdam: North Holland Publishing.

Whitehouse, P., Caramazza, A. & Zurif, E. (1978) Naming in aphasia: interacting effects of form and function. *Brain & Language* 6, 63–74.

Wiener, M., Devoe, S., Rubinov, S. & Geller, J. (1972) Nonverbal behaviour and nonverbal communication. *Psychological Review* 79, 185–214.

Wilkinson, R. (1995) Aphasia: conversation analysis of a non-fluent aphasic person. *Case-studies in Clinical Linguistics* (M. Perkins & S. Howard, eds.), London: Whurr Publishers, 271–292.

World Health Organization (1980) *Vaurioiden, toiminnanvajavuuksien ja haittojen kansainvälinen luokitus (International Classification of Impairments, Disabilities, and Handicaps)*, Helsinki: Työterveyslaitos.

Vygotsky, L. (1982) *Ajattelu ja kieli* (Thought and Language). Espoo: Weilin & Göös.

STUDIA FENNICA
1992 -

ETHNOLOGICA

1 M. Räsänen ed.
PIONEERS The history of
Finnish ethnology
2 A. Kirveennummi & al. ed.
EVERYDAY LIFE AND
ETHNICITY Urban families
in Loviisa and Võru
3 T. Korhonen ed.
ENCOUNTERING
ETHNICITIES Ethnological
aspects on ethnicity, identity
and migration

FOLKLORISTICA

1 R. Kvideland & al. ed.
FOLKLORE PROCESSED
in honour of Lauri Honko
2 A-L Siikala & al. ed.
SONGS BEYOND THE KALEVALA
Transformations of oral poetry
3 Matti Kuusi MIND AND FORM IN FOLKLORE
Selected articles

LINGUISTICA

1 U. Nikanne ZONES AND TIERS
A study of thematic structure
2 Heikki Kangasniemi
MODAL EXPRESSIONS IN FINNISH
3 A. Lieko THE DEVELOPMENT OF
COMPLEX SENTENCES A case study of Finnish
4 R. Korhonen BUTS ABOUT
CONJUNCTIONS A syntactic study of
conjunction expressions in Finnish
5 S-L Hahmo GRUNDLEXEM ODER ABLEITUNG?
Die finnischen Nomina der Typen *kämmen* und
pähkinä und ihre Geschichte